Slingsby Sailplanes

Slingsby Sailplanes

A COMPREHENSIVE HISTORY OF ALL DESIGNS

Martin Simons

Airlife
England

Dedication
To my glider pilot daughters, Patricia and Margaret.
Keep in practice!

Copyright © 1996 Martin Simons

First published in the UK in 1996
by Airlife Publishing Ltd

British Library Cataloguing in Publication Data
A catalogue record for this book
is available from the British Library
ISBN 1 85310 732 8

Typeset by Servis Filmsetting Ltd
Printed in England by Livesey Ltd, Shrewsbury

Airlife Publishing Ltd
101 Longden Road, Shrewsbury, SY3 9EB, England

Contents

A photograph of the Derby Club's T-21B by George Thompson. Note the sharp outer corner to the elevator which was changed on subsequent aircraft.

Introduction

This book describes Slingsby sailplanes and gliders from the British Falcon of 1931 to the last motorless aircraft produced, the Vega. Each type is given an accurate three-view drawing, photographs, and text outlining the background to the design and mentioning operational successes or occasional failures. Type numbers were allocated to some design projects which never flew. These and the powered aircraft produced by the company are not included in this volume.[1]

Full sets of working plans for almost all Slingsby aircraft before 1950 were discovered in 1969 by Norman Ellison in the lofts above the offices. They were saved from destruction, and after a long period in storage are now preserved by the Vintage Glider Club. The drawings by the author in this book are based on these originals and on other plans of later types from the company's archives, rather than on previously published outlines or extracts from brochures.

Fred Slingsby first built gliders at his furniture works in Scarborough, but as the business grew and demanded more space he moved for a while into the abandoned tram sheds belonging to the town corporation. A transfer to Kirbymoorside on the northern edge of the Vale of Pickering was made in 1934. (For some reason the town is now spelled Kirkbymoorside on maps and road signs, but to gliding people it will probably always be without the second 'k'.) In 1939 a new factory was built at Ings Lane, south of the village, where it still remains. There were several changes of ownership, and a period of closure when the company was in receivership during 1969. The works reopened later in the same year. Glider design and production at Kirbymoorside then continued until 1982. The modern company, Slingsby Aircraft Ltd, is exclusively concerned with powered aeroplane manufacture.

A full appreciation of the part played by each of the Slingsby sailplane types described in the following pages requires a brief outline of the historical background and technical development of soaring.

The origins of a sport

Before their first powered aeroplane flights, the Wright brothers made many trials with gliders, and on about a dozen occasions achieved soaring flights of more than a minute's duration. The longest of the four famous powered flights on 17 December 1903 was still of less than 60 seconds endurance and another year passed before they exceeded this time.

In 1911 Orville Wright returned to Kill Devil Hills, North Carolina, with a glider. On 23 October he made a soaring flight of 9min and 45sec. Many years afterwards he was asked why he went back to gliding after eight years. His 'official' explanation was that some serious testing of a new control system was to be done, but this was only part of the reason. At the age of 68, Orville admitted that he found soaring to be more fun than flying with an engine.[2] A new sport had been discovered.

---

[1] Two powered aeroplanes begun in 1938 were not completed. Early in the Second World War components were made for Avro Ansons. In the postwar period there were two examples of the Motor Tutor, and a single experimental powered version of the two seat T-49 Capstan sailplane was tested in 1968. Six replica S.E.5As, a Sopwith Camel and two Rumpler C. IV First World War replica fighters were built at this time with some non-flying mock-ups for the film industry. Thirty-two Tipsy Nippers were produced under contract for the Nipper Aircraft Company. Other powered projects were the T-40 Hayhow and the extraordinary Camco V-Liner, neither of which was completed.

The T-61 was a licence-built version of the Scheibe SF35 Falke motor glider, modified and renamed Venture for use by the Air Training Corps. Deliveries began with a batch of 15 T-61Bs in 1977, and 25 T-61Fs with glassfibre mainspars were produced in 1980. There were also sales of the T-61 on the civilian market, bringing the total of all marks to 76.

In June 1980 the Slingsby company reached agreement with the Fournier Aviation Company to build the RF-6B light aeroplane. This soon led to the development of the T-67 Firefly which, completely redesigned for fibre reinforced plastic construction, proved to be a great success and is, at the time of writing, in full production, being used internationally by many flying clubs and air forces including the USAF.

[2] Reported in P. A. Schweizer, *Wings Like Eagles*, p. 6 (Smithsonian Inst Press, 1988).

The first gliding competition also had a serious purpose. The Versailles Treaty of 1919, ending the First World War, banned aeroplanes in Germany. Many pilots, aircraft manufacturers and students of aeronautics saw a bleak future for German aviation, but gliders were not specifically mentioned in the prohibition. Wolfgang Klemperer and his younger friend Erich Meyer, who had experimented with hang gliders in Dresden before the war, saw the loophole. Early in 1920, in an article in the magazine *Flugsport*, they suggested that a glider competition should be held in the Rhön mountains of the Fulda district. The dome-like Wasserkuppe, swampy in places and at that time covered by unfenced pastures, had been successfully used for gliding during several pre-war summers by a group of schoolboys from Darmstadt.

Oscar Ursinus, editor of *Flugsport*, supported the idea of the competition with enthusiasm and agreed to take on the organisation. Under his guidance the two-month-long meeting from mid-July into September was modestly successful despite a fatal accident. Klemperer himself, recently appointed to an academic post in the Aerodynamics Institute of Aachen Technical College, made the best flight in the *Schwarzer Teufel (Black Devil)*, a cantilever monoplane glider which he had designed and built with his students in the Institute. From the beginning, sailplane development in Germany was closely associated with such student flying groups, the *Akafliegs*.

The Rhön contests became annual sporting events, continuing even after the lifting of the ban on powered flight in 1925. A full-time gliding school was established on the Wasserkuppe, and another at Rossitten on the sand dunes of the Baltic coast. Extended slope soaring flights of several hours were achieved in 1922, and thermal upcurrents were discovered in 1925 and used systematically from 1928. Cross-country flights of more than 150km had been achieved by 1930. Sailplane and glider building factories, notably those of Alexander Schleicher at Poppenhausen near the Wasserkuppe, Edmund Schneider at Grunau in Silesia and Gerhard Fieseler at Kassel, were established.

Apart from a brief flurry and one lively meeting at Itford Hill in 1922, very little interest was shown in Britain until the news of the German successes filtered through to the pages of *The Aeroplane* magazine. The British Gliding Association (BGA) was formed late in 1929, and visits by prominent German experts were arranged. In February 1930 Professor Georgii lectured to the Royal Aeronautical Society on soaring meteorology, and Fritz Stamer, who was running the training school on the Wasserkuppe, described the methods used there. The BGA issued its first gliding certificates in March that year. Most influential of all, Robert Kronfeld brought his beautiful Wien sailplane and toured the country, performing a famous slope-soaring cross-country flight from Itford Hill to Bedworth near Portsmouth on 17 June. Carli Magersuppe, sponsored by the *Daily Express* newspaper, joined the tour with a Professor sailplane.

There was an upsurge of enthusiasm. More than 90 gliding clubs were formed all over Britain, and some aero clubs established gliding sections.[3] Fifty clubs responded to a questionnaire distributed at the end of 1930. Every club had at least one glider or was in the process of building one; some possessed two or three. The total active involvement in gliding approached 2,000 persons. The largest group was the London Gliding Club, not yet settled at Dunstable, with 112 members, three club gliders and four privately owned machines.

Slingsby

Frederick Nicholas Slingsby, born on 6 November 1894, had joined the Royal Flying Corps in 1914, and as a flight sergeant gunner/observer earned the Military Medal, when after his pilot had been killed in the air, he regained control and flew the aircraft back to the British side of the trenches. He remained in the service (by this time the Royal Air Force) until 1920, at which time he bought a partnership in a woodworking and furniture factory in Queen Street, Scarborough, on the east coast of Yorkshire. Early in 1930 newspaper reports of the BGA's foundation were brought to his attention by a young dance band leader named Sanders who knew of Slingsby's service experience. With a few friends they founded the Scarborough Gliding Club in February.

The manager of the luxurious Royal Hotel joined and was elected chairman. Members came to meetings in the hotel wearing their best suits for a good meal beforehand. There were lectures and discussions. Flying operations began with a Dagling glider bought from the R. F. Dagnall Company of Guildford, Surrey. They flew at weekends and on Wednesday afternoons, using sites at Flixton Hill, due south of the town, and at Sutton Bank, overlooking the Vale of York. Amy Johnson agreed to become president of the club. This, and the Scarborough Council's support, helped to attract members, especially after the spectacular but rather unsuccessful demonstration by Kronfeld and Magersuppe on Castle Hill above the town in July. Magersuppe's Professor sailplane was damaged when it hit a fence on take-off, and he came down in the sea to be rescued by a fishing boat. Despite this, he was appointed instructor to the gliding club at a salary of £10 per week. By the end of 1930 the club had 40 active flying members, and more than twice that number were paying small subscriptions to become social members and, doubtless, joining the festivities at the Royal Hotel.

Slingsby gained his A and B gliding certificates during the year, becoming the first Scarborough member and only the 30th person to do so according to the BGA register. The A certificate required a straight glide under control lasting 30sec. By the end of the year

---

[3] The information about clubs in 1930 comes from the Dorset Gliding Club's yearbook, *Gliding*, issued in 1931.

the club had trained six members to this standard. Sanders, the band leader, was not one of them. The B Certificate required a flight of 1min and two further flights with safely executed right- and left-hand turns with good landings. Three of the six Scarborough members achieved this. (The training methods used are described in the chapter on Slingsby's Type 3 Primary.)

The Dagling was broken regularly, and Slingsby, the club's ground engineer, found himself and his factory constantly involved in repairs. He was forced to present bills for materials and working hours spent away from his business. Thus he entered the gliding industry as an ancillary to his regular occupation. He had a sound background in aircraft woodwork and rigging, and was an excellent draughtsman. The factory provided tools and machinery. His workmen, he said, began to prefer working on the glider to furniture making. Slingsby had no formal qualifications in aeronautics or engineering but was ready to employ qualified consultants. He had a shrewd business sense and a great enthusiasm for gliding.

The development of soaring technique

In 1930, knowledge of soaring in Britain was almost nil. Gaining height in the upcurrent on the windward side of a hill proved fairly easy. Anyone with a B certificate and a certain confidence could do this. After being bungee launched from the crest the glider was flown steadily along the hill to the end, performing a gentle turn there to come back and fly to the other end of the beat to turn again. Every turn was made away from the slope. As long as the wind blew sufficiently up the gradient a moderately efficient glider, flown well, could soar, possibly rising several hundred feet above the launching point. An extended soaring flight of 5min earned the C certificate. It was quickly learned that to turn or drift behind the hill was to be forced down to a premature landing.

The next important development came more slowly, hampered for the first few years in Britain by the total lack of any instruments in the gliders. To exploit thermal upcurrents to make cross-country flights over level ground seemed almost miraculous at first, and very few understood how it was done. The slope-soaring pilot could judge his rises and falls fairly well by observing the level of the hill, but as soon as a sailplane was more than a few hundred feet up, the lack of a visual reference made it impossible to tell if height was being gained or lost. Turbulence felt in the air might indicate either lift or sink. Airspeed was measured by the force of the airflow on the face and by the humming of the flying wires. Altimeters were not used. The main requirement was a sensitive rate of climb indicator, or variometer. German pilots began using these in 1928.

In 1931 Kronfeld again came to Britain, gliding across the English Channel from a high aero-tow. He made a cross-country flight in thermals over London from Hanworth, south of Richmond, to Chatham, on the Thames estuary. On the following day he returned, passing directly over Croydon on the way to land back at Hanworth. This was one of the first successful goal distance flights. He was observed to circle repeatedly in the narrow cores of the thermals to gain thousands of feet before gliding off in the direction he chose to go. Despite such demonstrations, and subsequent lectures and publications, it was not until 8 January 1933 that a British pilot, Eric Collins, dared to perform a complete 360° turn in a sailplane.[4] In August of that year the first thermal soaring cross-country flights were attempted in Britain, Collins setting a British distance record of just under 50km. By this time, flights of over 270km had been made in Germany.

When good variometers, sensitive altimeters and airspeed indicators became available, British pilots soon learned to use them. The technique was to circle and climb in each thermal and then glide on to find the next one, climb in it to the top and move on again. By 1936 sailplanes were sometimes also fitted with gyro instruments to enable them to fly blind, taking advantage of the strong lift inside cumulus and cumulo-nimbus clouds. Airbrakes, or at least lift spoilers, became essential to allow safe landings in small spaces. The Silver C certificate, requiring a cross country of 50km, a 1,000m gain of height and a duration of 5hr, was instituted internationally in 1931. Collins was the first Briton to achieve this, in 1934. By the end of 1939, 56 British pilots had so qualified.

Before the outbreak of the Second World War, flights over 200km and one over 300km had been achieved in England, the last, together with a height climb in cloud to over 14,000ft, earning the International Gold C badge for Philip Wills.[5] The English Channel was crossed in soaring flight from Dunstable by Geoffrey Stephenson in April 1939, flying a Slingsby sailplane, the Kirby Gull. The Second World War then intervened, bringing a general ban on soaring until 1946.

Penetration

In the post-war period, with mathematical studies pointing the way, the importance of speed was recognised. The length of a good soaring day is limited to a few hours. Some heating of the ground is needed to set off thermals, and this usually meant waiting until about 10 a.m. or later before starting a cross-country flight. The land cools in the evening, so to achieve a worthwhile distance the pilot needed to make a high average speed while the conditions lasted. The sailplane designer was now required to produce an aircraft with a low rate of sink when circling, but which on leaving the lift zone would glide at a high airspeed without losing too much height. Only the best part of each thermal should be used to improve the average rate of

[4] A. E. Slater, *Sailplane and Gliding*, December 1963, p. 452.
[5] Wills was the fourth pilot in the world to achieve this, after Eugen Wagner, Heini Dittmar and Hermann Zitter. Wagner's name was omitted from some earlier published lists.

climb, then in the glides the airspeed must be increased, even at the expense of lost height. This improved the average cross-country speed, always supposing that another strong thermal could be found. If there was sinking air it was proved by calculation and experience that it was essential to fly through it fast, the height lost by putting the glider's nose down to gain airspeed being much less than that wasted by lingering too long in the bad air. The requirements are to a large extent incompatible. To achieve the lowest possible rate of sink at slow airspeed, a low wing loading and a very-high-aspect-ratio wing are necessary.[6] To fly very fast with minimal loss of height in the glide requires a high wing loading, together with wing profile drag and the parasitic drag of tail and fuselage reduced to an absolute minimum.

Low-drag, so-called laminar flow wing profiles developed in the USA were found to be very useful, but required new approaches to glider construction and new materials. The aircraft became heavier with greater and greater spans. To remain safe at high speeds they had to be much stronger and stiffer than before. High-strength metal alloys began to find their way into the structures. To place a check on escalating costs, a simple 15m span Standard Class specification was developed internationally, and proved successful, but the unrestricted 'open class' sailplanes continued to grow in complication and cost.

As aircraft and the pilots improved, gliding competitions changed from simple distance and goal flying to racing round prescribed courses. The need for *penetration*, the ability to glide fast at a shallow angle, became more and more urgent. Given a good glide angle at high airspeed, the racing pilot can sample a large mass of air in a short time, passing through the weaker thermals without circling in them. Only those that yield high rates of climb are selected. The need for low rates of sink in circling remains, still demanding high aspect ratios.

Further researches in aerodynamics produced better wing profiles, but these required even more accurate, wave-free wing surfaces. Careful attention to the form of fuselages and tails yielded worthwhile

savings in drag. Traditional materials such as spruce, pine and plywood, even metal, were no longer good enough. Glassfibre, carbon and aramid fibre-reinforced moulded plastics were widely adopted.

With the new profiles and materials, even higher wing loadings were demanded. Some German sailplanes were fitted with water tanks as early as 1934, but carrying ballast did not become general until the 1970s. Given that the pilot will circle only in the strongest thermals, some loss of climbing ability owing to the extra weight is more than compensated for by the improved glide at high speeds. The water can be jettisoned if the thermals weaken. Some modern single-seat 'open class' sailplanes with spans of about 25m (82 ft) may carry 200 to 250kg (440-550lb) of ballast on take-off.

The most recent development has been the widespread introduction of self-launching. A retractable motor with a propeller is built into the sailplane, dispensing with the need for launching apparatus or aerotowing, and with the business of retrieving sailplanes by road after out-landings. The weight of the propulsion unit becomes unimportant in a sailplane, which will normally be loaded with water ballast anyway. The long-term influence of this development on the traditional gliding club remains to be seen. There is nothing now to prevent a soaring pilot from keeping the sailplane at an ordinary aerodrome, taking off unaided and flying to the open country, where the engine will be shut off for several hours but started up again to fly home in the evening to join the regular landing pattern and taxi in.

The best glide ratio of a sailplane — the measure of how far it can glide in still air from a given height — is a useful indication of all-round aerodynamic efficiency. Slingsby's British Falcon in 1931 probably achieved about 16:1 and weighed about 230kg (506lb) in flight. By 1982 the best open class sailplanes had glide ratios close to 60:1 and weighed 750kg (1,653lb) fully ballasted. Corresponding figures for good 15m sailplanes like the Vega were 42:1 and 508kg (1,120lb). Slingsby's Falcon was used for a 20km (12.4-mile) flight soon after it was completed. In 1982 the world record distance flight for a sailplane stood at 1,460km (907 miles) but, more importantly, the 1,250km (750-mile) triangular flight speed record stood at 133.2kmh (82.76mph). Slingsby sailplanes were produced during the half-century while these advances were taking place, and it was never easy to keep up.

---

[6] Aspect ratio is the relationship of the wing span to the total area. A narrow wing of large span has a high aspect ratio. The ratio may be calculated by dividing the span by the average or mean chord of the wing. The wing loading is the relationship of the total flying weight of the aircraft to the wing area, found by dividing the weight by the area.

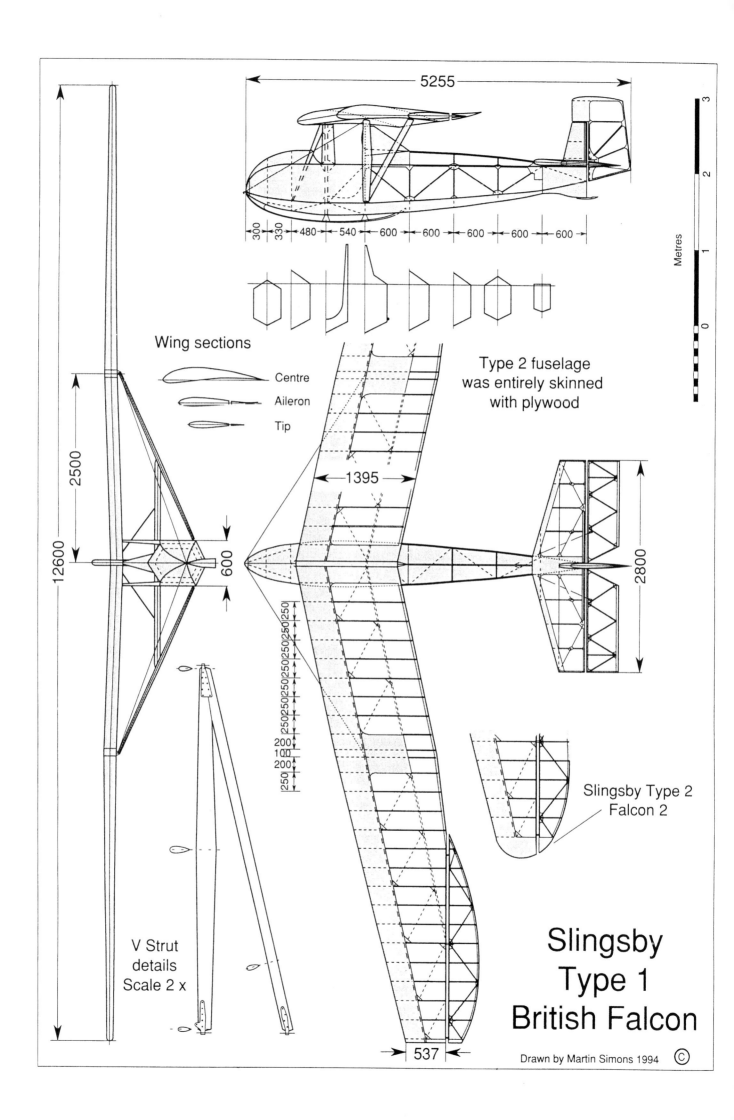

5255

300 330 480 540 600 600 600 600 600

Metres

3
2
1
0

Wing sections

Centre

Aileron

Tip

Type 2 fuselage
was entirely skinned
with plywood

1395

2500

12600

600

2800

250 250 250 250 250 250

200
100
200
250

Slingsby Type 2
Falcon 2

V Strut
details
Scale 2 x

537

Slingsby
Type 1
British Falcon

Drawn by Martin Simons 1994 ©

Types 1 and 2, the British Falcon

Having achieved his A and B gliding certificates, Fred Slingsby was anxious to make progress. For early soaring attempts beginners needed a mild-mannered sailplane that would not respond too sharply to clumsy handling, yet had a sufficiently low rate of sink to allow sustained flight in slope lift. In 1930 there were few intermediate gliders between primary trainers and the advanced sailplanes of the experts. One type used in Germany was the Prüfling, virtually a primary glider wing with a fuselage hung below it on struts. Its performance was poor and it was not very stable. A few had appeared in Britain. Günther Groenhoff, a young German pilot already establishing a high reputation, visited the Scarborough Gliding Club in the winter of 1930, and following Groenhoff's recommendation, Slingsby decided to build for himself, from plans obtainable through the Rhön-Rossitten Gesellschaft (RRG, the controlling body for gliding in Germany), a Falke. He was warned that it was not very easy to build, but he was confident that he could manage it.

The Falke had been designed by Alexander Lippisch in 1929, and it owed almost everything to the experimental tailless sailplanes which Lippisch had been developing since 1925. Flying models with wingspans of about 4m had been flown before the first full-scale Storch was tried in 1927 with limited success. It was followed by improved versions. The Storch 4 which Groenhoff tested in 1929 was entirely satisfactory. Stability was obtained with a back-swept wing having negatively twisted outer panels, or 'washout'. Tip winglets and rudders gave adequate control in yaw. The main improvement distinguishing the Storch 4 was the installation of lobate ailerons, or elevons, with their hinge line at 90° to the line of flight, rather than conforming to the wing sweep. The wing section at the root and for the inner panels was a modified version of the Göttingen 535, but the profile was progressively changed to a strongly reflexed shape at mid-elevon, and thence to a thin symmetrical tip.[1]

Lippisch, who was head of the technical section of the RRG, decided that if a sailplane with no tail could be made stable with a sweptback wing, then a glider with sweepback and an ordinary tail unit as well would be even more stable, and hence exactly what the beginner required. Moreover, with such a layout the pilot would be well protected, sitting under and somewhat behind the centre of the parasol wing. An adequate soaring performance could be ensured by keeping the wing loading down, which could be done by using a large wing area with strut and wire bracing, giving a strong yet light structure. Little attention need be paid to reducing drag. Sailplanes were launched directly into the slope upcurrent by rubber bungee, and there was no need to have a good glide ratio for cross country flights. The Falke was not expected to go anywhere except gently back and forth in front of a hill. It was considered an advantage for an intermediate sailplane that it should not gain much airspeed in a dive. In the inevitable accidents it would not strike the ground so hard.

When Groenhoff met Slingsby the Falke was in production in Germany. There was already one in England; it had been imported for publicity purposes by the J. Lyons tea company.

Gliders at this time were always built of wood. The timber normally used in Germany was pine. Spruce was more expensive and offered only slight advantages. Aircraft-quality birch plywood was readily available. Cold-water casein glues were approved for aircraft construction and, provided the joints were kept dry, were perfectly satisfactory but damp joints could be quickly destroyed by fungus. Accordingly, numerous drainage and ventilation holes were incorporated at all points in the structure where moisture might otherwise accumulate. Mild steel fittings and brackets were bolted to the timbers after painting with zinc chromate. Steel control cables were guided round pulleys and through fibre fairleads where required.

The Falke fuselage, of hexagonal cross-section, was a wooden framework of six curved longerons with cross-frames and diagonal braces, with plywood

---

[1] Lippisch's experiments with tailless aircraft culminated in the Me 163 rocket powered fighter of the Second World War.

skinning in front and fabric covering aft of the cockpit. As usual where wooden members butted together substantial plywood 'biscuits' or solid corner blocks were used to carry the loads through the joint. The undercarriage comprised a rubber-sprung main skid of ash, and a tailskid. An open hook was fitted under the nose for bungee launching. The strut-braced tail unit was simple, but the wing was very complicated. The two spars, swept at 12.5°, were built-up box sections. The upper and lower pine flanges had large 'bird-mouthed' blocks filling in wherever fittings had to go, particularly at the root ends and the strut end points. Both sides of the spars were faced with plywood. The wings had a slight 'gull' kink, enough to complicate construction without having any measurable effect on stability or handling.

To make each wing rib, an outline of 5mm square strip wood was laid in a jig, being steamed where necessary to conform without strain to the aerofoil section outline. Uprights and diagonals were fitted inside this form, and 1mm plywood biscuits and webs were then glued over all the joints, after which a duplicate 5mm square strip outline was laid into the jig with matching uprights and diagonals, and glued. This split-rib structure, which persisted for many years in German sailplane construction, prevented sideways distortions of the ribs when they were under the tension of doped fabric covering. The wing chord was constant over the inner panels, which allowed some saving in work, but for the tapered and reflexed outer wing panels every rib differed from the next.

In the Falke and other training gliders, the plywood covering the front of the wing was little more than an unstressed fairing. Each rib was made in one piece from leading edge to trailing edge and slid into place over the completed spars before gluing. Because the plywood was glued only to the ribs, not to the spar flanges, it added little strength to the wing as a whole. For torsional rigidity a two-spar structure with internal diagonal cross-struts was used. Every third rib was a compression member requiring its own jigging. The wing spars met on the aircraft centreline with simple pin joints, the rear pin also connecting with the pylon behind the cockpit. The front spars had separate connections to the braced vertical cabane struts on either side. The V struts restrained the wings from folding up or down under load, and provided additional bracing against torsion. A detachable plywood fairing covered the gap in the wings at the centre. The aileron control cables ran externally up the side of the fuselage, entering the wing just behind the forward cabane strut. The elevator cables also were external for part of their length. There was a steel bracing cable from the nose to the struts near their outer ends.

Slingsby completed his Falke in the spring of 1931. He stated that roughly 800 man-hours were required. Probably furniture production in his factory was much reduced for the preceding months. On completion the sailplane, in clear-doped finish and glossy varnish, was christened British Falcon. Slingsby made his first brief

flight at Levisham Moors after a bungee launch powered by schoolchildren. Another pilot crashed the Falcon badly on its second flight. After repairs, Slingsby toured the country in search of good soaring sites, gaining his C soaring badge in September at Ingleby Greenhow and competing very successfully in the 1932 National Championships at Ireleth, near Askam-in-Furness, Lancashire. There were seven competing aircraft. The Falcon logged nearly 7hr total flying time during the five day meeting. Mungo Buxton borrowed it to break the British distance record with a 20km slope-soaring flight to Lake Coniston. To put this into perspective, in the German championships that year there were 60 sailplanes. Cross-country flights of 150km (93 miles) were made, but Groenhoff, Slingsby's adviser of 1930, was killed in one of two fatal accidents.

It was remarked that the Falcon flew itself, but handled easily when it was required to manoeuvre and was capable of soaring well. It was a great builder of confidence for nervous pilots. Rigging was rather a struggle, and it suffered from lack of upward view when turning. This became important as the soaring ridges grew more crowded, but for its purpose it had few rivals. Slingsby announced later in the year that he would build a Falcon for anyone for £95.

The second Falcon, which Slingsby later counted as his Type 2, was built to the order of Espin Hardwick, a stockbroker who played an important role in the development of British gliding. Falcon 2 was flying by October 1933, Hardwick obtaining his C soaring badge at a Sutton Bank meeting in that month. The Type 2 had rounded wingtips which improved its performance slightly, and its fuselage was entirely skinned with plywood. Hardwick suffered from a spinal deformity, so most ordinary sailplane cockpits must have been extremely uncomfortable for him. His Falcon had extensive padding and movable elbow rests, and it also possessed instruments, which very few other sailplanes in Britain did in 1933.

Slingsby soon decided that there was a future in glider manufacture, and he began to advertise under the heading, 'Slingsby Sailplanes, Scarborough'. The decision to abandon furniture manufacture altogether came in 1934 with a temporary shift to the disused Scarborough Corporation tram sheds, where there was more space for glider assembly. Eight more Falcons were built during the next few years after the move to Kirbymoorside, making a total of ten including the Falcon 2. One, of which nothing more is known, went to Canada. Three, including Slingsby's original, were written off at various gliding sites before the outbreak of the Second World War. The rest probably survived to be impressed for use by the Air Training Corps (ATC). One of these, piloted by a cadet, met its end in collision with a sheep at Camphill in Derbyshire about 1944. Others doubtless perished at other ATC schools. One was rebuilt with a flying-boat hull for the ATC to fly from Lake Windermere in 1943, and survives at the Windermere Steamboat Museum. Espin Hardwick's

Falcon 2 was ceremonially burned at the Long Mynd following his death in 1955. (In Germany, one Falke survives. It was rescued from a Swiss Alpine mountain railway shed by Klaus Heyn and restored to museum standard by him.)

Mike Russell provided the initial inspiration for the construction during 1984–85 of an entirely new fully airworthy Falcon 1 by Ken Fripp's Southdown Aero Services at Lasham, using the original drawings rescued from Slingsby's loft. There were substantial contributions of work and financial support from John Sproule. The first flight was made in August 1986, with Derek Piggott at the controls. This Falcon, the only extant airworthy example, appears occasionally at vintage glider meetings in its clear-doped and varnished finish like the original Slingsby Type 1.

The British Falcon in flight. (*A. E. Slater*)

Falcon 1 data

Dimensions

Wingspan	12.6m (42ft)
Wing area*	18.48m² (198.9ft²)
Aspect ratio	8.6
Sweepback	12.5°
Length over all	5.26m (17ft 5in)

Wing sections

Root	Göttingen 535 modified
Mid-aileron	Special reflexed
Tip	Symmetrical

Weights (approximate)

Tare	140kg (308lb)
Flying	230kg (506lb)
Wing loading	12.45kg/m² (2.5lb/ft²)

* The wing area given here was estimated from the factory drawings. It differs from figures previously stated, with consequent variations in aspect ratio and wing loading. The German Falke was advertised with tare weight 120kg (265lb).

Slingsby prepares for a bungee launch in his first sailplane, the British Falcon. The steel ring attached to the rubber rope is on the open hook at the nose. Ground crew hold the tail until the rope is stretched sufficiently to launch the sailplane. (*Slingsby collection*)

The last surviving German Falke on exhibition in Friedrichshafen in 1983. The aircraft was taken by its Swiss owners to the summit of a funicular railway to be flown from the mountain. It was abandoned there for many years until discovered and rescued by Klaus Heyn and restored by him. Swiss markings on one side, German on the other. (*M. Simons*).

The Falcon on bungee launch at Dunstable in 1935. Launches were made from the top of the hill directly into the slope upcurrent. (*A. E. Slater*)

Sixty years on, the modern replica of Slingsby's Falcon, built from the original drawings, is seen here at Dunstable in 1991. (*P. Warren.*)

The Falcon I modified for operations on and over Lake Windermere

The Falcon water glider in flight after a successful take off

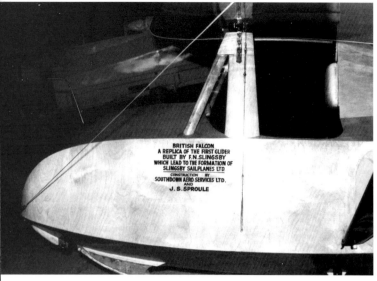

Building the modern replica of the British Falcon at Southdown Air Services. (*K. Fripp*)

The replica Falcon, showing details of the cabane struts, skid and bracing wire. (*M. Simons*)

The British Falcon built in recent times, finished in clear dope and varnish like the original. (*E. A. Hull*)

Details of the replica Falcon's tail unit, showing struts, tailskid and control drive cables. (*M. Simons*)

The cockpit of the modern replica Falcon 1. Instruments were very rarely fitted to the original. Note the external aileron drive cables, rudder pedals and release knob for the modern tow-hook. Instruments, from left to right: airspeed indicator, Cobb-Slater pellet-type variometer and altimeter. (*M. Simons*)

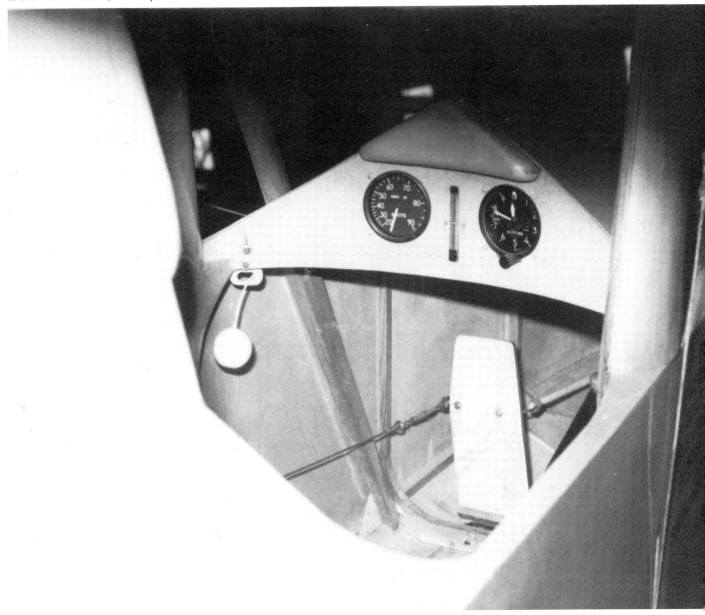

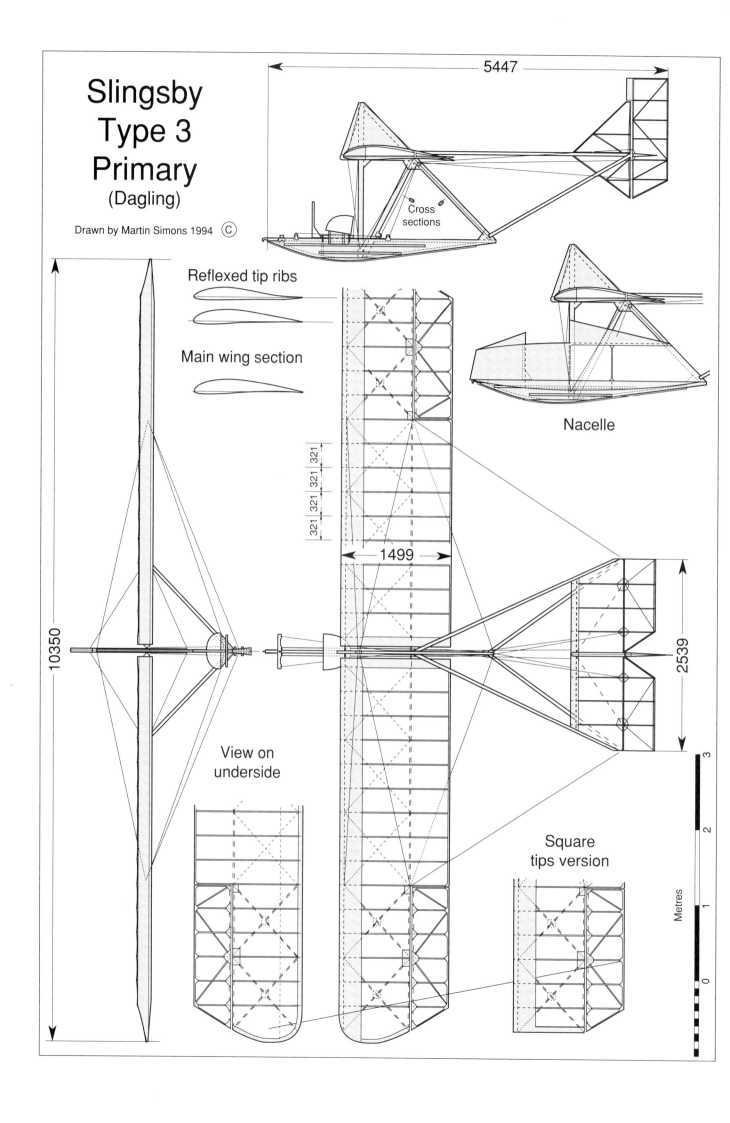

Slingsby
Type 3
Primary
(Dagling)

Drawn by Martin Simons 1994 Ⓒ

5447

Cross sections

Reflexed tip ribs

Main wing section

Nacelle

10350

321 | 321 | 321
321 | 321 | 321

1499

2539

View on underside

Square tips version

Metres

3

2

1

0

Type 3, Primary Glider (Dagling)

The primary glider originated in Germany in the early 1920s, when that country was in economic chaos. To most who wanted to be pilots, powered flying schools were far too costly. There were a few two-seat gliders, but they were not cheap. It was found possible to teach beginners *ab initio* by a careful series of exercises in simple one-seat gliders, and the methods were developed under the auspices of the RRG. Alexander Lippisch designed the Zögling (Pupil), which became the standard primary trainer. It was a monoplane with a rectangular wing spanning 10m. The fuselage, if it could be so called, was an A shaped frame forming a kingpost to carry the wing, with anchorage points for flying and landing wires and a gate-like extension to the tail, which was also wire braced. The seat and controls were mounted on a solid keel. It was common for the open 'primary' to be fitted with a light nacelle around the cockpit which reduced drag slightly and allowed it to be termed a 'secondary'. Slope soaring flights were possible, though when the wind was strong enough to give sufficient lift, the air was also usually too turbulent for the Zögling to be flown safely. Plans were distributed to gliding clubs and manufacturers produced Zöglings, or modified versions, for sale.

A variation of the design was developed at the behest of Wolf Hirth. Instead of the wooden frame aft of the wing, a simpler structure of four steel tubes carried the tail. Drawings for this type found their way to the USA in 1929, where the National Glider Association (NGA) was establishing itself. When the BGA was founded later in the same year, copies of these blueprints were sent back across the Atlantic as an act of goodwill by the NGA. The London Gliding Club obtained a set.

R. F. Dagnall, founder of the RFD Company, already well established in building balloons and with experience in airship construction, offered to build a glider for the London Gliding Club, and he was given these German/American plans of the modified Zögling to work with. Dagnall made some detailed changes, altering all measurements from the metric system to the

Imperial, and produced what he called the Dagling. The prototype was flown by London Gliding Club members on 16 March 1930 at Guildford, and was taken at once to Aldbury, near Tring in Buckinghamshire, for further operations by the club.

About 28 RFD Daglings were produced during the following months, and all similar gliders built in Britain after this were called Daglings, irrespective of their origin. By 1932, however, Dagnall was heavily involved in government contract work, so he handed over the glider business to the British Aircraft Company (BAC), which had its own primary glider design on the market as well as some good intermediate sailplanes and a promising two-seater, the BAC VII. Unfortunately in May 1933 Lowe Wylde, the founder and chief designer, was killed when flying the Planette, a powered version of the BAC VII. Robert Kronfeld, the famous soaring pilot, left his native Austria and took Lowe Wylde's place, and became interested in developing the Drone powered light aeroplane. Glider building by BAC ceased.

The changed directions of RFD and BAC gave Fred Slingsby an opportunity he was quick to seize. Production of primary gliders virtually identical to the Dagling began in Scarborough in 1933 and continued after the move to Kirbymoorside. Sixty-seven were built before the outbreak of the Second World War. (A few more Daglings were built by other companies, some even in post war years.) Slingsby would almost certainly have been unable to continue without the fairly steady sales of this type and the repair business that resulted.

The twin wing spars were solid timber planks set on edge and the ribs, all alike, were threaded over the spars before gluing. The extreme leading edge was covered with a fairing of plywood, the rest with fabric. Torsional resistance was provided by internal diagonal struts and wires. The A frame was made of solid timbers faced with plywood above the wing. The keel, shod with a strip of sheet steel and with no springing whatever, was similar, with strong external longitudinal stiffeners. The seat, a piece of heavy plywood with minimal hip and back support, was rigidly mounted on stout brackets above the keel with space below for the steel torque tube to a bell-crank behind the seat, operating the aileron cables. The tailplane, larger than that of the Zögling, was bolted at the ends directly to the steel tubular supports. The fin, in two separate pieces, was mounted on the centre of the tailplane with more wire bracing to keep it upright. The control surfaces were mounted in the simplest manner, with wide gaps along the hinge lines.

Solo glider training involved a graded series of exercises, closely supervised by an instructor. Fritz Stamer and Lippisch of the RRG outlined the process in lectures and in a book which was published in translation in Britain in 1930. To start, ground slides and low hops would be made. The bungee, a V of rubber rope, was laid out with the steel ring at the apex hooked on to the glider's open hook at the extreme nose. Ropes with large knots at intervals were attached at the ends of the V for the launching crew to hold, and one or more persons would sit under the glider's tail to hold it back. All of the bungee crew would be trainees themselves, and so would learn something from watching others as well as from their own efforts when their turn came. The instructor, after briefing the pilot, gave the orders: 'Walk. . . . Run. . . .', and the rubber stretched. The force of the launch was controlled by judging the right moment to call the final command to the tail crew: 'Let go!' The glider would move forward, the ring falling off the hook as soon as the rubber tension was exhausted. Depending on the force, the glider would either slide along the ground for a short distance or take-off and glide down the gentle incline that was used for such training. After each attempt, instructor and pupil would confer before the next trial. After perhaps three or four such starts, another pupil would take the seat and the last would go to help with the bungee. Payment, in addition to club membership fees, was in pence.

As skill and confidence increased, the launches would be made stronger until hops up to several feet above ground were achieved safely with short, smooth glides and landings, after which the Dagling would be taken to a bigger hill for longer flights until a straight glide of 30sec was achieved for the A certificate. After this, the pilot would learn to make turns in both directions and keep the glider flying for a minute, to gain the B certificate. The C certificate, requiring a 5min soaring flight with a safe landing, could be done in a primary glider, but the pupil usually moved on to something better for this.

With the development of winch launching and automobile towing, a modified system was used. This could be managed with a very small number of people, the instructor, a winch or car driver and two or three pupils to handle the glider on the ground. The Dagling was first given a series of extended ground slides by being pulled along at less than flying speed. This taught the use of ailerons and rudder quite well, though not in a co-ordinated fashion. Some Daglings were modified for this procedure by having most of their wing fabric removed and being fitted with wheels. (The author's own first 'flying' experience was on such a 'Penguin'.)

For the first airborne hops, the tow speed was increased and it was then largely up to the winch or car driver to control the situation. With a complete novice the launch would be very gentle, and power would be cut almost as soon as the glider left the ground. Once this kind of hop was managed safely, the launch would be extended, the glider flying level under tow a few feet off the ground from one side of the flying ground to the other. After this, progress would be made by climbing gently to some height and releasing the cable to glide down. (By now, releasable couplings as well as the open bungee hook were fitted to all gliders.) From this stage it was a matter of doing higher and higher hops with steeper climbs until turns could be managed. The requirement of a 60sec flight to complete the 'B' usually meant that the pupil would take a launch to several hundred feet above the ground and make a full gliding circuit, landing close to the take-off point. The experience of doing a circuit in an open primary was not easily forgotten.

That was the theory. By 1930 Fritz Stamer was the most experienced gliding instructor in the world, running the Wasserkuppe RRG school with an efficient organisation, professionally staffed, with workshop facilities and craftsmen on site to repair damaged aircraft. The pupil was expected to stay for a whole summer season, flying (and working on the bungee) every suitable day. According to Stamer, in 1929 there were 269 such pupils of whom 121 completed the B tests. The success rate after several months under expert guidance was 45 per cent. Those presenting themselves at the school were perhaps not always very talented, but they were keen enough to dedicate a season to the enterprise. The C soaring test was achieved by 30 of the best B pilots who stayed for an extra month; 11 per cent of the hopeful starters.

In the wholly amateur, part-time gliding clubs in Britain and most other countries, and indeed in most small German clubs, the RRG school's modest success rate was not approached.

The structure of the Dagling was simple, though club members found it difficult and frustrating to carry out repairs. Primary gliders were built or bought, broken, repaired, and broken again. A moderately heavy landing could cause the landing wires to snap or stretch, which required careful readjustments. Merely to rig or re-rig a primary could occupy a group of inexperienced people the best part of a morning. Overtightening any of the turnbuckles would cause misalignment. Worn or broken cables required perfect splicing, which few could do. Broken spars and struts and cracked plywood had to be repaired with accurately made scarf joints. The tubular tail supports of the Dagling were not often broken, but they could be bent or torn from their mountings. Selection of materials and quality of workmanship was no less important for these flying machines than for any others.

It is not known how many pupil pilots joined a club,

did a few trial slides or hops and left for ever in sheer frustration. Of the 90 clubs listed as active in Britain in 1930, barely a handful survived for a year. Slingsby's own initially enthusiastic group at Scarborough got a mere handful of student pilots to the A certificate and was in dire straits before 1932. Eventually, amalgamation with the Bradford club, which had itself absorbed the Leeds group and seen the demise of several others in the region, led to the formation of the Yorkshire Gliding Club. With a first-rate soaring site at Sutton Bank, this was one of the very few that survived and flourished.

It is also clear that many potentially good glider pilots were scared off by the solo training system, and some were seriously injured or killed. This continued even into the immediate post-Second World War years, when British clubs persisted with solo training. Despite careful advice by the instructor, almost anything could happen once the glider began to move. With the Dagling's sluggish ailerons and very sensitive elevator, a nervous trainee could pull up from what should have been a modest low hop to 20ft or more, stall, drop a wing and cartwheel, smashing the glider to matchwood.

Trainees airborne for the first time often felt they had been catapulted far higher than they really were. They knew only that the control stick should be moved forward to come down. They often dived back from 10ft to hit the ground hard. The curved keel of the Dagling was just the right shape to throw the nose up again on contact, precipitating a series of violent and very noisy bounces. The unsprung keel and rigid seat transmitted every bump. A good many people left gliding sites with aching backs or necks which continued to give trouble for years afterwards. Shaken and hurt by such experiences or even by seeing them happen to someone else, many decided that gliding was not for them.

More serious and even fatal injuries did happen. When experiencing 'negative g' for the first time, as Derek Piggott has described, an automatic reflex response to the sensation causes some pupil pilots to push the control stick hard forward. The moment of transition from climbing fairly steeply on the winch launch to gliding down in a Dagling, if done rather clumsily, produced exactly this result. Those watching never knew why some pupils dived vertically, or even beyond the vertical, into the ground.

The cheapest possible training method was developed and applied in Germany under the pressure of financial disaster. It seems clear that if, instead of following the RRG system, gliding organisations had stretched their capital a little more and purchased two-seaters with dual controls, the gliding and, more importantly, the soaring movement, even during a great economic depression, would have done a great deal better. Satisfactory two-seater sailplanes did exist, and although they were more costly in the short term they would have been cheaper as well as more effective over a slightly longer period. They would have been less often broken, more pupils would have remained in the clubs and succeeded. Income from flying fees would have been greater. Yet, as remarked above, it is doubtful if Slingsby Sailplanes would have survived had there not been a steady trade in new Daglings, Dagling spares and repairs.

Primary Glider (Dagling) data

Dimensions

Wingspan	10.35m (34ft)
Wing area	15.06m² (162ft²)
Aspect ratio	7.1

Wing section: often stated to be Göttingen 326, but this does not seem to be correct. The Gö 326 was a 1918 Pfalz biplane section, 8.1 per cent thick and quite unlike that of the Dagling or Zögling wing. The section shown on the drawing here is taken from the Slingsby plans.

Length o.a.	5.45m (17ft 10½in)

Weights

Tare	82kg (180lb)
Flying	173kg (380lb)
Wing loading	11.5kg/m² (2.35lb/ft²)

A Dagling-type primary glider in Australia, probably built by the Larkin Aircraft Co of Melbourne in 1930. The design differed in minor details from the RFD product.

An RFD Dagling at Balsdean, near Brighton, in October 1931, when the BGA held a glider meeting on the South Downs. The pupil pilot is Barbara Siever, probably a member of the short-lived Brighton Gliding Club.

Serious accidents did happen. The wreck of a nacelled primary, apparently on the hill at Dunstable. (*Charles E. Brown, RAF Museum, Hendon, neg No. 5835-12*)

Slingsby Type 3 Primary with the Golden Eagle emblem at Dunstable. The Falcon 3 two-seater is approaching to land in the background.

Captain Hope inspects the RFD Dagling at Balsdean in October 1931. The sailplane in the background is Bill Manuel's Crested Wren

Assembling the Primary in the Scarborough tram sheds. The inadequate working conditions are obvious. (*Slingsby collection*)

In the tram shed Slingsby himself works under the wing as one of his workers varnishes the leading edges. The covering fabric was usually madapolam, a lightweight cotton material, doped and varnished. (*Slingsby collection*)

Primary glider in flight. (*A. E. Slater*)

A nacelled primary glider in flight. The shape of the nacelle is slightly different from that of the standard Slingsby design. The glider was built by the Hawkridge Aircraft Co at Dunstable in 1947. (*M. Simons*)

A Slingsby Type 3 primary glider in flight in 1940. It was recognised that cadet pilots could be trained on gliders and the RAF investigated. This led eventually to the Air Training Corps gliding programme.

Slingsby nacelled primary with rounded wingtips at Dunstable. (*A. E. Slater*)

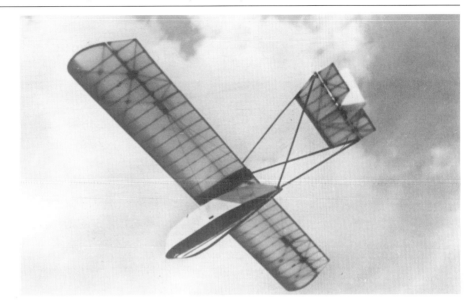

Harold Holdsworth, ground engineer of the Yorkshire Gliding Club from 1934 to 1939, at the controls of a Slingsby Type 3 Primary glider in 1936. (*H. Holdsworth*)

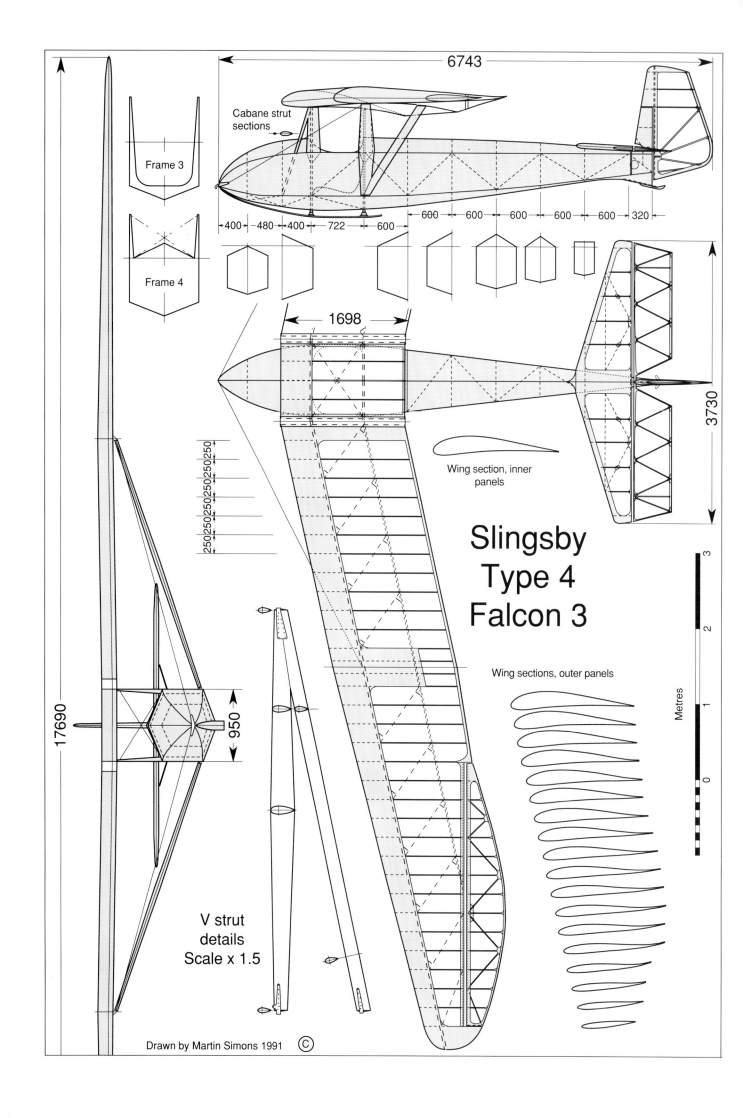

6743

Cabane strut sections

Frame 3

Frame 4

400 480 400 722 600

600 600 600 600 600 320

1698

3730

Wing section, inner panels

Slingsby
Type 4
Falcon 3

Wing sections, outer panels

250 250 250 250 250

17690

950

V strut
details
Scale x 1.5

Metres

0 1 2 3

Drawn by Martin Simons 1991 ©

Type 4, the Falcon 3

Birmingham stockbroker Espin Hardwick was so enthusiastic about his modified Falcon single-seater that in 1934 he persuaded Slingsby, with promises of financial support, to build a two-seat version. It is most unlikely that Slingsby himself would have originated such a project. The structure of the Falcon was not straightforward, and even if he had conceived of a two-seater, which he might have done, there were simpler models that could be built under licence or copied, such as the Kassel SK-3 Hercules, well known in Yorkshire, or even Rex Stedman's homebuilt two-seater TS-1, christened *City of Leeds*, which emerged in July 1934 and soared successfully. But what Hardwick wanted was, so far as either of them knew, the first two-seater sailplane in the world with the seats arranged side by side. Until this time two-seat gliders all had tandem seats. The only exception was a biplane which had been flown in 1922 by Anthony Fokker.

Slingsby admitted that the transformation of the solo Falcon was a formidable job, for he had to work on the drawings single-handedly and had no previous experience of aircraft design. He pored over his drawing board for several months, often late into the night, and sent his plans to the BGA technical committee for stress checking before the end of the year. Unlike the Stedman project, BGA approval was given without the need for any modifications. Work on the Falcon 3 then began in the factory sheds in Kirbymoorside, rented at very low rate from the owner, Major J. E. D. Shaw, who also owned the adjacent agricultural engineering works.

In almost every respect the two-seater was simply an enlargement of the original Lippisch Falke, the wing area and span being increased to retain a wing loading not too much more than that of the single-seater while keeping much the same general proportions. The profiles, sweepback and washout angles, and even the little 'gull' kink in the wing, were all the same as those of the single-seater. The wingtips were rounded like those of Hardwick's Falcon 2, but the prototype fuselage, widened to take two seats under the wing, was fabric covered aft of the cockpit. The only other substantial change in layout was the addition of a rectangular centre-section of wing on a cabane of four vertical struts, cross-braced with wires, with carry-through spars. The main wing panels were attached individually with horizontal pins to this centrepiece. The gaps on either side of the centre section were faired with plywood strips.

Slingsby would probably have seen drawings of the German Falke R Va, an improved version of the Lippisch Falke which had adopted a similar layout and rigging system. Also, in 1933 information was published in the journal *Sailplane and Gliding* about the German single-seat Superfalke, with a stretched wingspan of 16.8m (55.4ft), nearly as much as the Falcon 3 turned out to be. Evidently there was nothing seriously wrong with the idea of an enlarged Falcon, though it cannot have been reassuring to read, a few months later, that the Superfalke had broken up in the air while on aero tow. This, however, was explained by pointing out that the elevator had been of the all-moving or 'pendulum' type, sensitive to clumsy handling by an inexperienced pilot.

There was nothing wrong with the Falcon 3 when Hardwick took delivery of the prototype in May 1935. All the safe stability and handling characteristics of the Falcon 1 were retained, although the big sailplane was heavier on all the controls. The performance was surprisingly good, and Slingsby received orders for more. The later ones had fuselages covered entirely with plywood, and to improve the upward view transparent plastic strips were used instead of plywood to fair the gaps in the wing roots. The centre section, too, was provided with celluloid transparencies, though these did not last long in service and were usually replaced by doped fabric like the rest of the wing. Drop-off dolly wheels were fitted to facilitate ground handling and take-off. After these and some other minor modifications another eight Falcons were produced, seven to orders from all the leading British clubs, and one exported to Belgium. The last of the line was added to the BGA register in December 1938.

Five British sailplanes, including a Falcon 3, went to

Murray (left) and Fox after setting the two-seater duration record in the Falcon 3 at the Wasserkuppe in 1937. The registration letters G-AAAE were allocated only for the overseas trip. The contest number 19 was painted on the nose. (*Slingsby collection*)

Murray (left) and Sproule in the Falcon 3 at Dunstable on the occasion of the 22hr two-seat duration record in 1938. Note the external aileron drive cables, transparent panels in the centre section, and crossed wire bracing behind the cockpit. (*J. S. Sproule*)

the first international championships, held on the Wasserkuppe in July 1937. The Falcon pilots were W. B. Murray and J. S. Fox. The Fédération Aéronautique Internationale (FAI) had only recently instituted a special record category for two-seaters, and Murray and Fox on 12 July made a flight of 9hr 48min which was recognised as the first record in the new category. (A *solo* duration record of more than 36hr had been set by Schmidt in 1933, so no great fuss was made.)

Austrian and German pilots soon reclaimed the record. By the end of June 1938 it exceeded 21hr. Murray broke it again, with J. S. Sproule, during the British national competitions at the London Gliding Club site at Dunstable. The club Falcon 3 was launched by winch just after 4 a.m. on 9 July to soar back and forth in the slope lift all day and into the night. The pilots took turns to fly and were helped by moonlight, the sidelights of spectators' cars along the hill top and a searchlight directed on to the windsock outside the hangar. The landing, aided by car headlights, came after 22hr 13min. A great deal of public interest had been aroused by radio news bulletins during the flight, and Murray and Sproule were welcomed by a crowd and subjected to interrogation by the press. As an international record this, too, did not last long. German pilots raised it to more than 50hr by the end of the year.

By any standards the Falcon 3 was a remarkable sailplane, well liked, spectacular in appearance, yet based on a 1929 original design obsolescent, in German eyes at least, before it was even built. Nonetheless, it is a pity that more were not produced at a time when the British gliding movement could and probably should have used two-seaters much more systematically for *ab initio* pilot training. The regular use of these practical, soarable, safe if rather ponderous two-seat sailplanes would have benefited the British clubs greatly if the solo training system had been less entrenched. Some fortunate trainees did occasionally get some extended soaring experience with an instructor, but the Falcons, though immensely popular for joyriding, were rarely used as they might

have been. It was said that the stability of the type was such that a pupil could not gain as much as might be learned from a less docile aircraft. Even so, most pupils, given the chance, would surely have preferred to fly safely with an instructor alongside rather than beating Daglings to pieces in a seemingly endless series of more or less shattering ground hops.

The Falcons remained in service with the clubs until the Second World War. One was written off in a crash before the rest were impressed, along with many other gliders, for use by the ATC. It is not clear how many survived, but in 1944 the BGA magazine *Sailplane and Glider* reported that four or five remained serviceable. One of the last was severely damaged in a ground-looped landing at Bramcote Royal Naval Air Station, near Nuneaton, Warwickshire, in 1947. This was during the first post-war national championships, although the Falcon was not competing. Rumour has it that two, or parts of two, were burned in South Wales in the early 1960s.

Falcon 3 data

Dimensions

Wingspan	17.69m (58ft)
Wing area*	27.4m^2 (294.8ft^2)
Aspect ratio	11.4
Wing sections:	
Root	Göttingen 535 modified
Mid-aileron	Special reflexed profile
Tip	Symmetrical
Length o.a.	6.74m (22ft 1in)

Weights

Tare	227kg (500lb)
Flying	408kg (899lb)
Wing loading	14.9kg/m^2 (3.05lb/ft^2)

* The wing area given here was estimated from the factory drawings. It differs from figures previously stated, with consequent variations in aspect ratio and wing loading.

Falcon 3 in ATC paint scheme taking a winch launch somewhere in England. Note the apparent gap at the wing root was closed with transparent plastic. Signs of wing damage and repairs may be seen.

Assembling a Falcon 3 in Slingsby's factory in Kirbymoorside village. (*Slingsby collection*)

The Falcon 3 at the hangar door at Dunstable. The building was designed by architect and glider pilot Christopher Nicholson and is now the subject of a preservation order.

The Slingsby Type 4 Falcon 3 at Dunstable in July 1937 prior to competing in the International Championships in Germany. The official registration letters were added for the trip.

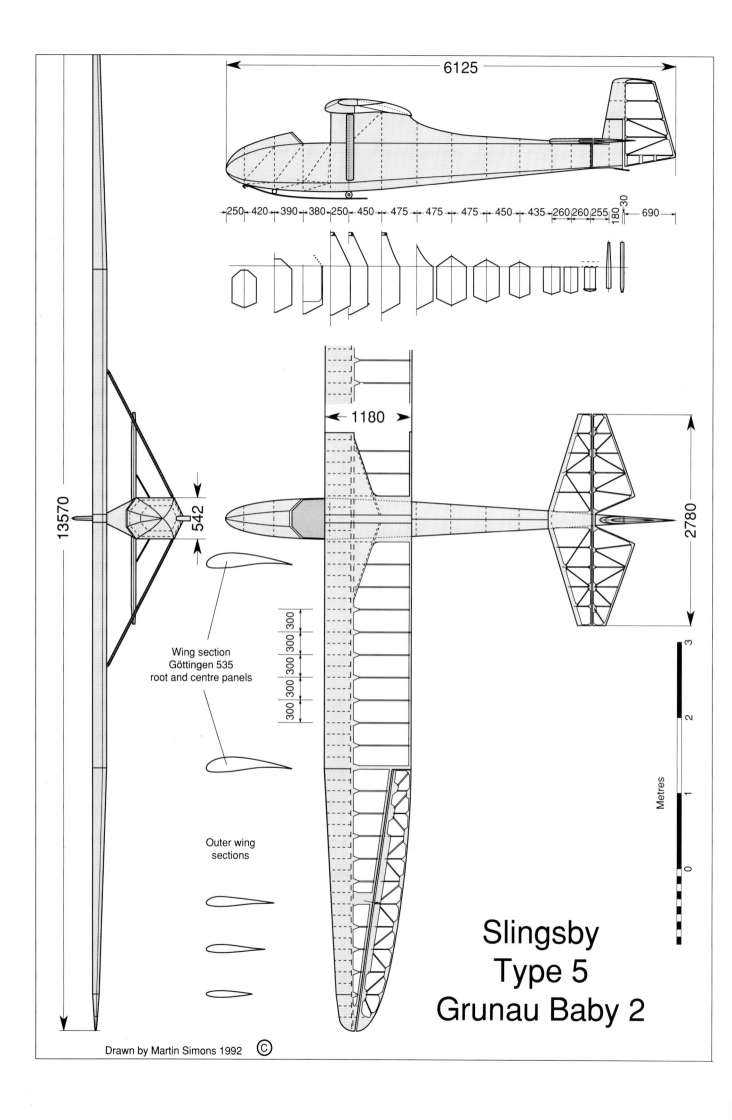

6125

250 420 390 380 250 450 475 475 475 450 435 260 260 255 180 30 690

1180

13570

542

2780

300 300 300 300 300 300

Wing section
Göttingen 535
root and centre panels

Outer wing
sections

Metres
3 2 1 0

Slingsby
Type 5
Grunau Baby 2

Drawn by Martin Simons 1992 ©

Type 5, the Grunau Baby 2

More examples of the Grunau Baby were built than of any other type of sailplane before or since (discounting primary gliders, which were not intended for soaring and so were not strictly termed sailplanes). There was mass production in Germany until 1945, and in other European countries under German occupation during the Second World War. Fairly reliable factory records suggest that at least 4,000 were produced between 1931 and 1945, though more than twice this total has been claimed. Production figures for other outstandingly successful types such as the Ka 6 series, reached nothing like these totals.

The Grunau Baby was also built from plans and kits by amateurs all over the world, and under licence in almost every country where there were any glider manufacturers. Substantial numbers of various marks, sometimes disguised under new names, were produced in Sweden, Switzerland, France, Spain, Yugoslavia, West Germany and Britain in the post-war period.

The Grunau Baby 2 became the Slingsby Type 5. About 15 were built at Kirbymoorside between 1935 and 1939, some for export, and an unknown number of kits was also produced. Others were built in Britain from plans during the same period.

Grunau, renamed Jesow after 1945, is in Silesia, which today remains part of Poland. The village is a *strassendorf*, a simple row of cottages along each side of the country road, typical of the area. Nearby was Hirschberg (Stag mountain), now called Jelenia Gora, on the margins of the Riesengebirge Highlands. In 1923, on the slopes close to the village, Silesian gliding enthusiasts established a gliding school, and they invited Gottlob Espenlaub, a cabinetmaker who had made a reputation as a sailplane builder and pilot, to join them and take charge. He brought with him Edmund Schneider, another qualified craftsman. Espenlaub moved on after three years, but Schneider married a local girl and remained. The glider factory was established in 1928, trading as Edmund Schneider, Grunau, or ESG. At first the chief business was building and repairing Grunau 9 primary gliders, but Schneider designed several successful sailplanes, the

designs being numbered according to the year. Early in 1931 came the ESG 31 Stanavo. This was a relatively simple and inexpensive strut-braced sailplane for the American pilot Jack O'Meara, named after a brand of aviation fuel marketed in Europe by the company O'Meara represented, Standard Oil of New Jersey. The Stanavo attracted favourable attention at the Wasserkuppe competitions, although it was not intended to compete with the very superior and costly sailplanes flown by the recognised champions.

The first Grunau Baby was a smaller version of the Stanavo. Its wing, of only 12.87m (42.2ft) span had a planform similar to that used by the sailplanes of the Akaflieg Darmstadt (Academic Flying Group of the Darmstadt Technical University). A series of advanced soaring craft, the Darmstadt 1, Westpreussen, Lore, Musterle, Schloss Mainberg and others, had emerged from the Darmstadt school. All had fully cantilevered high aspect ratio wings of about 16m (52.5ft) span. A few years previously the advantages of elliptical wings had been proved by Ludwig Prandtl and his staff at Göttingen University, and the Darmstadt sailplanes achieved a very effective compromise with this ideal planform. The inner half of the wing had constant chord, but the outer panels tapered, the trailing edges curving to approximate an ellipse.

Although the Grunau Baby was not expected or intended to perform as well as these more expensive aircraft, and was strut-braced, Schneider followed the fashion. Such wings were not too hard to build, and were more efficient than the plain rectangular form preferred for primary gliders. The profile, Göttingen 535, well tested in Prandtl's wind tunnel and proved in practice on earlier types, extended unchanged from the wing root to the inner end of the ailerons. From there the section changed progressively to a thin symmetrical form. To prevent tip stalling, negative twist, or washout, was introduced. Viewed from the rear, the trailing edge swept upwards gradually towards the tip, the laminated wood trailing edge member being curved in two dimensions. The ailerons required careful jigging during assembly, but this was the only complicating feature of an otherwise simple wing. A small amount of dihedral was built in, because all of the taper in thickness was on the underside.

The monospar wing structure also followed the lead set by the most efficient sailplanes. Baltic pine was used for the spar flanges, with plywood shear webbing between. The entire leading edge was covered with birch plywood glued to the ribs and directly to the upper and lower flanges of the spar to form a complete tube of D cross-section. Sub-ribs ahead of the spar provided additional stiffening for this stressed skin, which resisted all the torsional loads. Aft of the mainspar the unsupported wing ribs of the centre section could sometimes distort under the tension of doped fabric covering. To stiffen them laterally, linen tapes were woven, criss-cross fashion, between the rib booms.

The simple wooden struts allowed the wing to be light and simple yet strong. Up and down loads were transferred by the struts to the base of the main fuselage cross frame, so there was no need to carry massive bending stresses through the wing root itself, which would have required a greatly reinforced mainspar and elaborate steel fittings at the junction. The attachments to the top of the main fuselage frames were simple steel pins, one at the mainspar position, one near the leading edge and one at the end of the short rear diagonal spar. All of the pins, including those holding the struts, were prevented from sliding out by plain washers and safety pins. In 1931 the need for spoilers or airbrakes for sailplanes had not been realised, and the first Grunau Baby had none.

The Baby's fuselage was of hexagonal cross section, and comprised a series of light cross-frames linked by six longerons with a plywood skin forming a box. The cockpit was open, lacking any kind of enclosing canopy or windscreen. At this time it was considered most undesirable for the sailplane pilot to be shielded from the airflow. Airspeed indicators were rarely fitted, so much had to be judged by the feel of the wind on the pilot's face. Little attention was given to comfort. The seating position was bolt upright and the seat itself no more than a flat board.

The landing gear, as usual for the period, was a rubber-sprung skid, laminated in ash. An open hook for bungee launching was mounted on the front skid fitting. The front skid attachment, a single bolt through the keel longeron, proved a source of weakness which persisted through all the later versions of the type. A landing with drift could be relied on to split the skid at the front and bend the attachment bolt or even tear it out of the longeron, necessitating a tricky splicing job on this curved member. Later, when winch and aero towed launches were more common, it was easy to fit the Grunau Baby with a more sophisticated tow release.

The tailplane, fabric covered and with internal diagonal bracing, was held on to the rear fuselage frames by two vertical bolts and braced with simple steel tubular struts. A minimal fin and sternpost provided the attachment for the aerodynamically balanced rudder. All of the controls were operated by stranded steel cables running over pulleys, except for the steel torque tube under the pilot's seat and two vertical pushrods in the fuselage to drive the aileron bellcranks.

Soon after the prototype was completed in 1931 Wolf Hirth, already famous among the gliding community and recently returned from some extraordinary soaring flights in the USA, came to Grunau to manage the training school. (Among his pupils was to be a girl from Hirschberg called Hanna Reitsch.) Schneider showed Hirth the new Baby. Not foreseeing the misunderstanding this was to cause, he obtained permission to use Hirth's name in support of his sales campaign. Although the glider had been completed before he saw it, many subsequent reports wrongly credited Hirth with the design, despite the fact that he was in the USA when Schneider was building the prototype. The association nevertheless did a good deal for the Grunau factory.

The Grunau Baby proved popular, and before long several were being turned out every week for sale to clubs all over Germany. Six were entered for the 1932 Rhön competition, at which one of Schneider's other more ambitious sailplanes suffered structural failure in flight, killing the pilot. Realising that he needed more help with stressing, Schneider persuaded Emile Rolle, a qualified aircraft engineer, to work for the firm.

Rolle undertook a substantial redesign of the Grunau Baby, improving and strengthening it in every respect. The result was the Baby 2, which emerged early in 1933. The span was increased to 13.5m (44.28ft). The fuselage, which previously had a straight back, was given a down-sweeping curve which improved the airflow over the tail, and the tall, angular rudder was reduced in height.

The cockpit of the Grunau Baby 1 was never comfortable, and Rolle did little to improve it. Yet on 3 April 1933 Kurt Schmidt took off in a new Grunau Baby 2 over the East Prussian sand dunes. The stiff breeze sweeping in from the Baltic provided continuous slope lift all day, all night and into the next day. Schmidt remained airborne for a new world duration soaring record of 36hr 36min. Such an event made headline news in those days, and the pilot and his aircraft achieved immediate fame. The order book at Grunau remained full for the next decade.

As a club sailplane the Baby handled well and safely, and it was robust enough to perform simple aerobatics and to withstand occasional heavy landings. It performed quite well enough for inexperienced pilots to attempt their first cross-country thermal soaring, and in the following years many used the Grunau Baby to complete the Silver C badge tests, which had been introduced in 1930: a duration flight of 5hr, a soaring ascent of 1,000m (3,280ft) and a cross-country distance of 50km (30 miles). The 5hr flight was about as much as most pilots could stand in a Baby, even with ample cushions. Admiration for Schmidt's duration record increased as the years went by.

In England, Louis Desoutter, a member of the London Gliding Club now established at Dunstable, began building a Grunau Baby 1 in 1932. In June 1934 Desoutter was fatally injured in an accident to a Dagling primary glider (a flying wire broke) before completing the project, and the Baby was finished by Slingsby in Yorkshire. This was probably Fred Slingsby's first chance to study the design closely, though at least one imported Baby 2 was already flying in Britain at this time. Desoutter's Baby was returned to Dunstable to make its first flights as a club sailplane there on 30 December 1934. Its success was immediate, especially since Desoutter, a superb craftsman, had used ball bearings in place of plain pulleys in the control circuits, making the aircraft extremely pleasant to fly. The London Club asked Slingsby to supply another Grunau Baby and an order also came from Alan Cobham, who incorporated some gliding in his National Aviation Day displays. Slingsby negotiated a licence from Schneider, and production of the Grunau Baby 2 began at Kirbymoorside immediately.

Cobham took the first one, employing Eric Collins, the best sailplane pilot in Britain at the time and the first British Silver C pilot, to fly it. Tragically, in a display at Upwood, Cambridgeshire, on 30 July 1935, Collins unwisely attempted an outside loop. The Grunau Baby had not been designed for inverted manoeuvres of this sort, and the wing collapsed. Although Collins had a parachute he did not use it and was killed.

The London Club took delivery of their Slingsby Grunau Baby 2 soon after this disaster. It was very successful, operating with the club fleet alongside the Desoutter Baby. Other clubs and private owner groups soon followed the Dunstable lead.

The market for sailplanes in Britain was not large. The relatively small total of Grunau Babies coming from Kirbymoorside during the next few years may be explained partly by the fact that Slingsby was very soon offering other types of sailplane in direct competition with the Baby. The first Kirby Kite was already under construction before the London Gliding Club received their Grunau Baby 2. Before long Slingsby was also offering the Type 7 Kadet and Type 8 Tutor, which were, in Britain, destined to take over the Grunau Baby's role and were cheaper.

On 31 July Angus O. Pick set a British duration record of 13hr 27min in a Slingsby Grunau Baby at Sutton Bank during an 'advanced course' held by the Yorkshire Gliding Club. During this flight he witnessed, from above, a mid-air collision between another Grunau Baby and a Scud 2. The Scud, flown by W. R. Horsfield, lost its nose, leaving the pilot's feet dangling in mid-air, but he was able to land in trees and climbed down unhurt. The Grunau 'fluttered down like a piece of paper, for its tail was nearly off', but the pilot, Billy Sharpe, also escaped injury.

Perhaps the most remarkable flight made in a Grunau Baby in England was the climb to 11,140ft (3,398m) by Noel McClean in June 1939 in the Helm Wind wave over Cross Fell. The cold was intense in the open cockpit, and contraction of the cables in the low temperatures caused all the controls to become extremely stiff. Getting the Baby 2 down without any type of spoilers or dive brakes proved extremely difficult. Drifting back to the downward side of the wave would have dumped the sailplane far from home in rough country, as had already happened to another pilot. McClean rightly flew on the upwind side of the cap cloud, but getting down through the upcurrent was almost impossible. Steep sideslipping was the only way the sailplane could be forced to lose height without gaining excessive airspeed. McClean landed safely at last, but held the record for only a few weeks.

In Germany, development continued. A little more span; revised, narrower ailerons; spoilers and an improved cockpit enclosure with canopy and windscreen at last, appeared on the Grunau Baby 2A, and the elevator was redesigned. Subsequently the Grunau Baby 2B became the standard training sailplane adopted by the National Socialist Fliegerkorps to train many thousands of Hitler Youth pilots. It had powerful air brakes of Schempp Hirth 'parallel ruler' type, and a droppable wheeled dolly for take-off. Probably more of this variant were built than of all the rest put together. Derivatives of the Baby 2B were produced in considerable numbers outside Germany after 1945.

Edmund Schneider was forced to flee westwards with his family in 1944, losing his factory. He nevertheless designed the Grunau Baby 3, which had a slightly simplified wing, doing away with the redundant front fuselage attachment fitting, and more washout. A landing wheel was built-in, and the cockpit was improved. The type was built under licence at Poppenhausen by Alexander Schleicher.

Schneider and his two sons, Harry and Edmund Junior, moved to Australia in 1951, and the Grunau 4 and 4B were manufactured in Adelaide. These were really quite new designs, only the name carrying on the old tradition. Harry Schneider continued the business after his father's retirement. Edmund senior died in 1968.

Although the Slingsby factory was responsible for the reconditioning and repair of some Grunau Baby 2Bs, in the immediate post-war period, there was no further production of the type at Kirbymoorside. Elliotts of Newbury stepped in, producing about 50 examples of the EON Baby, with a wheel and enlarged cockpit.

Grunau Baby 2 data

Dimensions

Wingspan	13.5m (44ft 6in)
Wing area	14.5m^2 (156ft^2)
Aspect ratio	11.4
Wing sections:	
Root	Göttingen 535
Tip	Symmetrical
Length o.a.	5.68m (18.6ft)

Weights

Tare	160kg (352lb)
Flying	250kg (550lb)
Wing loading	11.4kg/m^2 (2.34lb/ft^2)

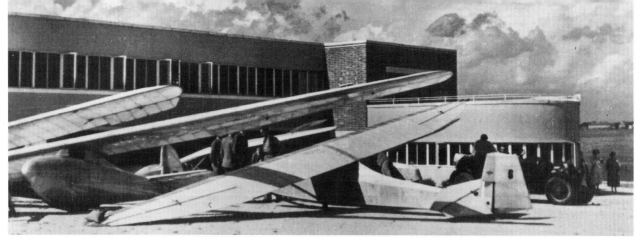

The London Gliding Club's Grunau Baby 2 outside the club-house. It was finished in clear dope and varnish. The competition number 6 and the Slingsby golden eagle trade-mark appear on the rudder. The sailplane behind the Baby is a Rhönbussard. (*A. E. Slater*)

A Grunau Baby 2 bungee launched at the Wasserkuppe in the 1933 competitions. A windscreen has been fitted to this example and some instruments are carried, as indicated by the venturi and pitot tube on the front fuselage decking. Others of the type are visible on the ground. The markings were typical of the year in which Adolf Hitler came to power.

The sailplane was finished in clear dope and varnish, and the registration number 6 indicated the Silesian region. The swastika appeared on the port side of the rudder only. On the starboard side at this time the Imperial German Tricolour appeared. Only after 1937 did the swastika appear on both sides. (*E. Schneider*)

Typically, the Grunau Baby 2 was flown without any wind-screen or cockpit canopy. This example is in Australia. (*The Age,* Melbourne)

A Grunau Baby 2 flying in England in 1938. (*A. E. Slater*)

The Desoutter Grunau Baby 1 flying at Dunstable. Note the straight-backed fuselage and tall rudder. A diagonal bracing wire ran from the strut fitting on the wing to fittings on the front fuselage frame. (*C. Brown*)

A Grunau Baby 2A in Yugoslavian colours. Note the revised form of elevator and cockpit canopy, but the absence of air brakes.

Last of the line. A Grunau Baby 4 on winch launch at Waikerie, South Australia, in 1957. The wing was completely different in both section and plan view, and the fuselage with a fully-enclosed cockpit, bore little relationship to the original Baby. (Courtesy *Adelaide Advertiser*)

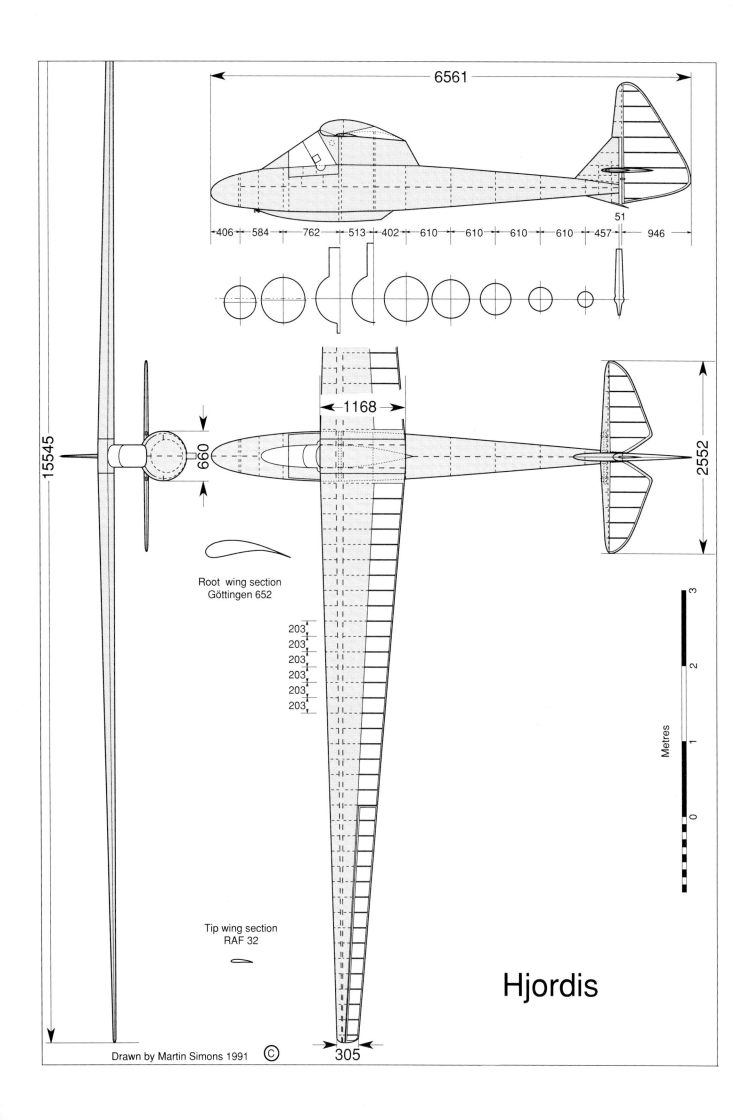

6561

406 | 584 | 762 | 513 | 402 | 610 | 610 | 610 | 610 | 457 | 946

51

15545

1168

660

2552

Root wing section
Göttingen 652

203
203
203
203
203
203

305

Tip wing section
RAF 32

Metres

3
2
1
0

Hjordis

Drawn by Martin Simons 1991 ©

Hjordis

The Hjordis, named after the heroine of a Norse saga, made its first public appearance at the BGA competitions at Sutton Bank in August 1935. This completely new British sailplane had been test flown and made its first soaring flights just before the competition. It was designed by Sqn Ldr Mungo Buxton of the Royal Air Force. Buxton, in partnership with Philip Wills, placed the order for its construction with Slingsby in 1934, but for some reason it never acquired a Slingsby type number. The drawings supplied by Buxton showed all the main features of the proposed aircraft, but most of the details remained to be worked out. A good deal was evidently done in the workshops and never fully committed to paper. Only one of the type was built.

Buxton was well known to British glider pilots through his successful soaring flights and articles, some quite technical, in *Sailplane and Glider*. He used the pen name 'Kentigern'. Wills was Britain's second 'Silver C' soaring pilot, with many outstanding soaring flights to his credit.

The Hjordis was greeted with astonishment. It invited comparison with two other sailplanes well known in Britain but imported from Germany. The Rhönbussard, designed by Hans Jacobs, was small with a rounded but rather dumpy fuselage and an open cockpit under the leading edge of the high-mounted wing. It was rather like a version of the Grunau Baby, but improved with a rounded fuselage and cantilever wing. It had the same wing section. The Rhönadler by the same designer was larger, spanning over 17m (56ft) and having a very strongly tapered cantilever wing mounted on a low pylon above a streamlined fuselage. The cockpit was fully enclosed. Its reputation was already established, since in the expert hands of the late Eric Collins it had broken the British cross-country distance record. The type was known to be very popular with clubs in Germany and, like the Rhönbussard, was in factory production there.

The Hjordis had a cantilever wing of unusually high aspect ratio, strongly cambered and very thick at the root, mounted on a very tall, narrow pylon above an exceptionally refined fuselage. Spanning just over 15.5m (51ft) the wing had a slight anhedral angle. Viewed from the front, the undersurface of the wing was flat from tip to tip. The taper in thickness resulted in the upper side of the wing descending. This very unusual feature was never explained by Buxton, but he may have thought it would improve response to the lateral controls. The cockpit looked unbearably cramped. A cartoon published in *Sailplane and Glider* suggested that Philip Wills, the pilot, 'does not clamber into the cockpit, he just sits down and has Hjordis wrapped round him'. Wills was very tall but, fortunately, slender. The transparent canopy must have seemed almost claustrophobic. There was a small wheel on the control column instead of the familiar stick to operate the ailerons, as there was insufficient room to move a joystick laterally.

Buxton had made a careful study of the latest German high-performance sailplanes, most of which at this period were very large and expensive, with wing spans usually of 19 or 20m (62-66ft), even reaching 30m (98ft) in the case of the *Austria* built for Robert Kronfeld. In straight flight there was no doubt about the superb performance of these large sailplanes, and they were magnificent for hill soaring, gliding from hill to hill at relatively small heights, but there were doubts in some minds about their controllability. Circling in small and feeble thermal upcurrents might be beyond them. Experiments were going on at Akaflieg Darmstadt with the Windspiel, a very small, light sailplane, and in Britain there was the little Scud 2 designed and manufactured by L. E. Baynes. Wills and Buxton had done well with a Scud they had owned.

The German monsters were heavy and cumbersome on the ground, requiring substantial numbers of people to rig them and drag them to the launching point and to de-rig them after an outlanding. Buxton had in mind the needs of private-owner syndicates who would operate with minimal crew. He aimed to achieve the best possible soaring performance with a relatively modest wing span. A tapered planform was necessary, both to cut tip vortex drag and to ensure adequate depth of spar to accommodate bending loads at the inner end of the cantilever wing. This was exemplified by the Rhönadler, which had a taper ratio of more than 5:1, i.e., the tip chord was less than one fifth of the root chord. The taper of the Hjordis wing was fairly pronounced, the ratio being about 4:1, not as extreme as that of the Rhönadler.

Compared with a rectangular wing plan, taper reduces the induced aerodynamic downwash over the outer parts of the lifting surface, so the narrow outer panels meet the airflow at a high aerodynamic angle of attack. The tips tend to stall before the wing root, a common cause of spinning accidents when approaching to land. All sailplane designers were well acquainted with this problem. On the Rhönadler, large amounts of negative wing twist or 'washout' were used to ensure that the tips did not stall early. Hjordis incorporated similar ideas.

The choice of the thick, strongly cambered Göttingen 652 section for the wing root of Hjordis was influenced by the successes of the famous Fafnir sailplane designed by Alexander Lippisch, and by the refined Kakadu of the Austrian Dr Kupper, who also designed the huge *Austria*. All used the Gö 652, and L. E. Baynes had also proved it successfully on the Scud 2. The Rhönadler root section was a modified version of the same profile.The section at the mid semi-span position was one Buxton's own devising, thinner and less strongly cambered than Gö 652. From this position the profile changed gradually to RAF.32 at the extreme tips. The layout was cleverly devised so that, geometrically, the base lines from which the various profiles were plotted remained in alignment. Buxton pointed out that the wing could be built on a flat bench, somewhat like a model aeroplane wing on a simple building board. Each rib would touch the flat surface at two points and would automatically be at the required rigging angle, no complicated blocking up or jigging being needed. Because of the gradual variation of camber and thickness there was 6° of aerodynamic washout, although geometrically there appeared to be none. This stratagem was entirely successful, and tip stalling was never a problem with Hjordis. It was found impossible to make the sailplane spin.

The main wingspar was necessarily massive, the flanges laminated in spruce with plywood shear webbing and hefty steel fittings with horizontal pins to attach the wings separately to the fuselage pylon. A lighter rear spar carried the ailerons. The ribs, with narrow spruce booms and substantial plywood webs to stiffen them, were spaced at a pitch of 8in (203mm). This was less than usual, but obviated the need for intermediate sub-ribs ahead of the main spar. The most unusual feature of the wing was that it was covered with plywood back to the auxiliary spar, when the usual practice at this time was to use ply skin only around the leading edge and cover the rest with doped fabric. The advantages of the extended stressed skin were that the aerofoil section was more accurately preserved and the wing was very much stiffer in torsion. The total weight of the aircraft was considerably

increased, and unlike most sailplanes of the period the plywood covered areas were painted, which added a few more pounds. The colour was light grey, or turquoise grey according to some accounts, rather than white. The extra weight of the paint was not significant. Buxton's calculations suggested, in any case, that a high wing loading was desirable for cross-country flying, providing everything possible was done to reduce drag. The fabric covered areas were clear-doped and varnished, which was orthodox practice. After assembly, the gap between the wings was closed with a light plywood fairing.

The fuselage was a nearly perfect cigar shape with only slight downward droop of the form near the nose. The usual semi-monocoque structure was employed, with four main longerons supported by circular cross-frames and a complete plywood skin. The tall pylon was based on two very robust vertical spars connecting the wing fittings directly to the main skid attachments. Buxton had seen various types of accidents to sailplanes with pylon-mounted wings. In some cases, when a tip dragged on the ground during a landing, the wing could twist completely off the fuselage. In a touchdown with a little sideways drift, the fuselage might be torn off and rolled under the wing. Minor errors of judgement could thus become bad accidents. The Hjordis pylon was stressed to withstand a side load of half a tonne applied at the skid, and 50kg (110lb) dragging force applied at the wingtip.

The tailplane was of the all-moving type, mounted part way up the triangular fin. Buxton again was influenced by German experience. Some sailplanes with tailplanes mounted too low had been damaged with catastrophic results when the elevator touched rough ground on take-off. Günther Groenhoff had been killed at the Wasserkuppe in such an accident in 1932. Hjordis had a large rudder with only a little aerodynamic balancing.

After the end of the 1935 BGA meeting, the editor of *Sailplane and Glider* reported that the new sailplane 'seems to have a simply phenomenal performance'. Wills carried off the de Havilland Cup for height gain and the Manio Cup for a pre-declared out and return cross country flight of 38km (23.5 miles).

All was not entirely well, however. One minor problem was discovered early and easily corrected. The wing itself, though torsionally stiff, was too flexible in bending near the tips. After landing, a sailplane tilts over until the wingtip on one side touches the ground. The flexibility of the outer spars allowed the underside to be pressed down on to the surface for some distance, so any stones readily punctured the thin skin. Re-skinning with heavier plywood was necessary. Philip Wills wrote: 'Quite soon it became apparent that designers have paid too much attention to aerodynamic form and far too little to the shape of the human behind and the needs of the human frame'. He was giving an account of the flight he made in July 1936, which, unpleasant though it was for him, broke the British distance record, 167km (103.5 miles) from

Dunstable to the coast south of Lowestoft. 'The sun beating into the cockpit through the minute talc roof soon gave me a splitting headache. Constant circling and hard work rapidly transformed this into a sick headache. Then came a thirst like the Sahara, closely followed by cramp.' Relief came only when he 'burst thickly out of Hjordis' and sensed 'the fresh, cool smell of the sea.' Additional vents were cut. The cramps were reduced a little by chopping out half-moon shaped pieces on either side of the canopy. From this time Wills flew Hjordis with his shoulders sticking out into the breeze.

Buxton himself admitted that the controls were not good. The elevator was too sensitive, and without a trim tab at high speeds the load on the stick was too great. The ailerons were also unsatisfactory. They lacked diagonal stiffeners and so deflected several degrees at the ends under load, giving poor control. The fin was too small. More directional stability was needed.

Probably most serious of all, the Hjordis had no spoilers or airbrakes. Philip Wills was beginning at this time, as he put it, to nibble nervously at clouds, and he had fitted some gyro instruments. On his first serious attempt to circle up blind inside a cumulus, at an Easter meeting in Derbyshire, he lost control within a minute or two. The airspeed indicator went twice round the dial and he 'burst out of the cloud base in a dive rather over the vertical' with the Hjordis 'bellowing like a bull in considerable pain'. The sailplane did not break up, probably owing to the good torsional resistance of the plywood skinned wings.

It had originally been intended to fit an airbrake. The idea was to make the rudder in two pieces, split like a clamshell along the hinge line. When right or left rudder was applied in the normal way, the two clamshells would move together to the same side. To brake, both of the pilot's feet would be pushed forward and the two shell halves would open out in opposite senses to create high drag. This rudder brake was never fitted. Buxton wrote that among so many new developments this seemed just one too much. In any case a similar notion had been tried, and had failed, on Kronfeld's *Austria*. In a spiral dive in cloud similar to that in which Wills found himself, Kronfeld discovered it was impossible to operate the opposed rudder braking system against the very great loads arising from the high airspeed. The *Austria* broke up and Kronfeld had to bale out.

Apart from the dangers of cloud flying without airbrakes, it was a pity that the Hjordis was without even elementary spoilers for landing. Wills damaged it many times because there was no reliable way of getting safely down within a reasonable space. Sideslipping, turning the entire fuselage at an angle to the airflow, could help during the early phases of a landing approach, but the wings had to be levelled well before touchdown. Skimming a few feet off the ground, some extra drag could be created by fishtailing; using the rudder to yaw the aircraft from side to side. This also

had to stop before landing. On levelling out and straightening up to flare-out, just when high drag was needed, it was reduced because of the proximity of the ground and its restraining effects on the induced downwash. After a cross-country flight Hjordis would float and float and float across a small field until it hit the upwind boundary or until the pilot deliberately ground-looped to prevent hitting it. In one landing Wills turned it over completely. Buxton mentioned another accident which broke one wing in two and severely twisted the pylon. Only his strong vertical members prevented the glider wringing its neck. There were many other occasions when it had to go back to Slingsby for repairs.

Despite the limitations of his aircraft, Wills had many successes. He captured national records for height gain as well as distance. In the 1936 BGA competitions at Camphill in the Peak District he won the cross-country flying prize, reaching Lincoln. It was not customary at this time to total up the scores and declare a National Champion. Separate prizes were awarded for slope soaring duration flights and gains of height as readily as for distance. It was recognised, nonetheless, that Wills and Hjordis were an outstandingly good combination.

The first truly international soaring championships were held in Germany during July 1937. Five British sailplanes were entered. Wills preferred to take Hjordis, with which by now he was thoroughly familiar, rather than one of the new and, as it proved, unreliable King Kites. Wills placed 14th, exactly halfway down the list. He had his usual problems on landing, ending one flight with the sailplane's nose in a stream but he and the rest of the British group learned a great deal by observing how the more experienced German and Polish pilots flew. Doubts about the thermal soaring capabilities of their large aircraft were entirely dispersed.

Soon after the team's return from Germany the British Nationals of 1937 were held in Derbyshire under new rules emphasising distance flying. Wills won outright with three flights over 110km (68.2 miles), two of them ending at North Coates on the Lincolnshire coast. These were not the longest flights of the contest, but Wills became champion by virtue of his consistency over several days.

In August of the same year Wills, on a splendid soaring day, reached the coast of the English Channel, having been launched at Dunstable in the late morning. The coast of France was well in sight as he approached Dover and he calculated, conservatively, that he needed about 1,650m (5,500ft) to get across. A dark cumulus over the town gave him hope of one more good climb, but it let him down and he was forced to land, awkwardly as usual, in a valley with unexpected crosswinds. One more good thermal and he would undoubtedly have made the crossing, and it was early enough in the day for him to have continued for some distance inland on the far side.

After seeing what was now available in Germany,

Wills was planning to buy something more stable, more controllable and more comfortable, a Minimoa.

Advertisements appearing in *Sailplane and Glider* early in 1938 stated:

> For sale, HJORDIS, the outstanding British high efficiency sailplane. It holds the British distance and goal flight record, placed first in the 1937 British competitions; holds most of the British Gliding trophies and awards. It has done over 850 miles of cross-country flying (on purpose), has been dived to 125mph in cloud (by accident), is extremely strong (by gum); won the distance trophy (by Wakefield); is in first class condition (by Slingsby); and is for sale by Philip Wills.

The price was £110. A Scud 2 would have cost £90 and a Slingsby Falcon 1 £60 at this time. Despite the impressive list of achievements, Hjordis was not instantly picked up as a bargain. Perhaps British pilots had been made aware that it was not easy to fly, a claim noticeably absent from the advertisement. It was bought eventually by Messrs Brink & Horrell in Johannesburg. Very little was heard about its exploits after it left Britain, but it was flown in South Africa for some years. A rare photograph shows that, to begin with at least, it retained its British civil registration letters, G-GAAA, and the 1937 Wasserkuppe competition number 15 remained on the nose. Officially it was registered as ZS-23. It was used late in 1939 by E. Dommisse for a record height climb to 3,600m (12,000ft) above ground, which, since the take-off was from Quaggaport 1,740m (5,800ft) above sea level, represented an altitude of 5,340m (17,800ft) without oxygen breathing apparatus. The last 1,200m (4,000ft) of the ascent were in cloud without blind flying instruments, Dommisse relying on his airspeed indicator and a simple cross-level bubble. What finally became of Hjordis is not known. Its remains might still survive in a forgotten corner somewhere.

Hjordis data

Dimensions

Wingspan	15.54m (51ft)
Wing area	11.52m^2 (124ft^2)
Aspect ratio	21
Wing sections:	
Root	Göttingen 652
Tip	RAF.32
Length o.a.	6.58m (21ft 7in)

Weights

Tare	143.8kg (317lb)
Flying	217.2kg (480lb)
Wing loading	18.94kg/m^2 (3.9lb/ft^2)

Philip Wills in the cockpit of Hjordis, with the modifications to accommodate his shoulders. (*Wills collection*)

Hjordis after export to South Africa. Details of the occasion are not known. (*A. J. R. Brink*)

The cockpit canopy of Hjordis before modification. The main fittings on the fuselage frame are also visible. (*Wills collection*)

The start of a winch launch at the BGA competitions at Camphill, Derbyshire, in 1936. Wills won the distance prize for a flight to Lincoln. In the background is the Golden Wren sailplane which pioneered operations on the site. (*Wills collection*)

Philip and Kitty Wills, his indefatigable crew chief for many years, relax while waiting for a launch at the 1937 internationals. (*Wills collection*)

Hjordis at the Wasserkuppe in 1937. The registration was allocated only for the purpose of travelling overseas, but was never removed. (*Wills collection*)

Dragging Hjordis to the launch point during the internationals of 1937. Philip and his brother Bill Wills lead the way, with Gerry Smith helping. Kitty Wills is at the wing-tip.
(*Wills collection*)

The wheeled dolly was used only for ground handling. It was removed before take-off. (*Wills collection*)

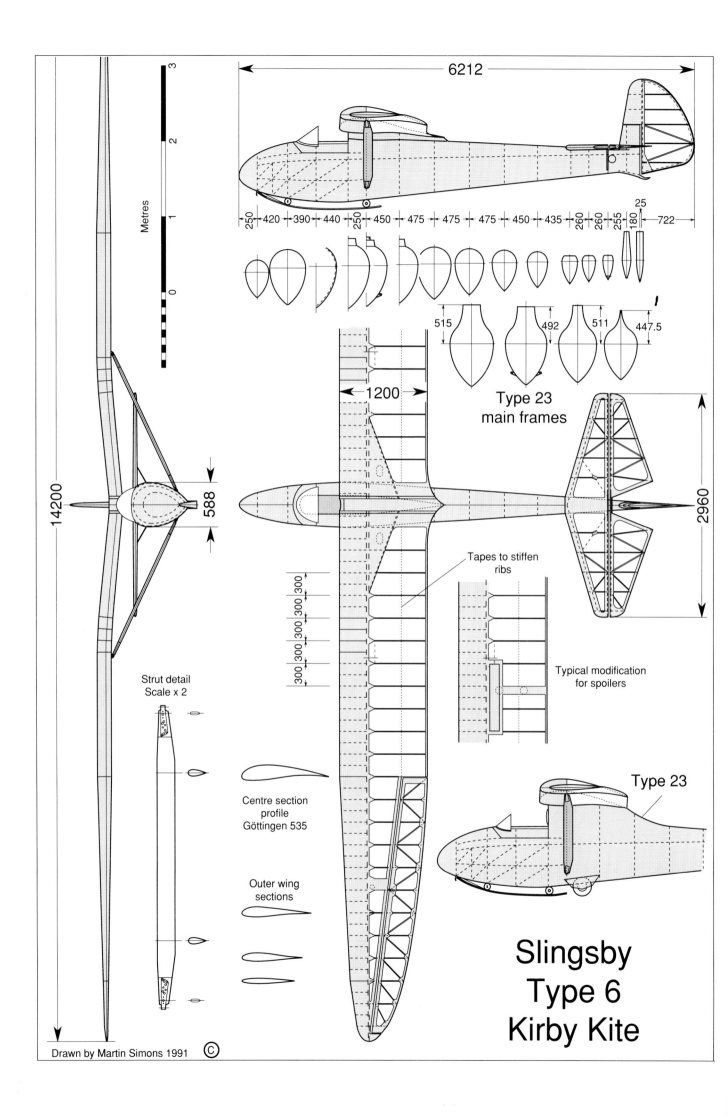

6212

250 420 390 440 250 450 475 475 475 450 435 260 260 255 180 25 722

515 492 511 447.5

Type 23
main frames

1200

14200

588

2960

300 300 300 300

Tapes to stiffen
ribs

Typical modification
for spoilers

Type 23

Strut detail
Scale x 2

Centre section
profile
Göttingen 535

Outer wing
sections

Slingsby
Type 6
Kirby Kite

Metres

Drawn by Martin Simons 1991 ©

Types 6 and 23, Kirby Kite

Slingsby's Type 6 was under construction even before the first Type 5, the Grunau Baby 2, was completed. It seemed to Slingsby that expanding British gliding clubs and private-owner groups would soon be needing something better than the Baby, but he guessed it would be unwise to produce a really advanced sailplane at this stage. He probably looked at the Hjordis and recognised that it was not going to be a sailplane for the average pilot and would never be produced in quantity. He also recognised his own limitations. For stressing and advanced aerodynamic calculations he relied on expert consultants. He felt capable of reworking and developing an existing well-proven design, as he had done when converting the Falcon 1 into the two seater Falcon 3, but he was not ready to begin something totally new from scratch.

There were several obvious ways of improving the Grunau Baby, and with a little cunning it would be possible to use many of the wooden and metal components in the new type, saving on jigging and workshop time. While the wing's main aerodynamic features, including the profiles and the basic planform, could be retained, it could be extended in span to 14.2m (46ft 6in). This would involve only the addition of an extra rib bay on each side, stretching the outer wing panel and so improving the performance at small cost. Gull wings were very fashionable, and improved stability in circling flight compared with wings which had no dihedral at all. They also looked very graceful and had sales appeal. While they cost a little more to build, the spars of a strutted sailplane were not very elaborate, so the extra complication was not likely to cause serious problems. Finally, the fuselage could be given a streamlined form instead of the hexagonal box section of the Grunau type. The Kirby Kite took shape in Slingsby's mind. The prefix, Kirby, came from the village where the factory was now established, Kirbymoorside.

There was some urgency. The BGA was to hold a major competition at Sutton Bank at the end of August 1935. The Hjordis would be there and so would several Grunau Babies from Slingsby's and other factories. If the Kite also could be ready, and made a good impression, orders would come in. Having made the decision, there followed a period of frantic work over a 14-week period. Supervising the workmen building primary gliders, Falcons and Grunau Babies in the factory took most of Slingsby's days, and many details of the Hjordis also had to be elucidated on the shop floor. Design work on the Type 6 was done mostly in the evenings after normal working hours, Slingsby employing a teenager, Thoby Fisher, to help. A general-arrangement layout diagram was completed and construction began, using full-sized lofted templates, long before the detailed drawings were completed. The design was not finalised until some time after the prototype had done what was required of it at Sutton Bank.

Wherever possible, Grunau Baby parts were used in the wing and tail. It was comparatively easy to transfer ideas and components from the older design to the new. The rudder was taken straight from a Grunau Baby. The tailplane and elevator were treated in much the same fashion, but the tips were rounded slightly. The wing, like that of the Baby, had a single mainspar, with a plywood skinned D nose to resist torsion. Aft of the spar the ribs were braced laterally with linen tapes. The ailerons incorporated the nearly elliptical taper of the Baby with change of section and washout, but the additional rib bay near the tips gave the curved outline a slightly more pointed shape. There were very few refinements. The gaps along the hinge line of elevator and ailerons, 30mm wide, were sealed only by strips of doped fabric. The rudder hinge was not shrouded even in this elementary way.

The fuselage was round-backed in cross-section with a pointed keel. The outline of each frame was made up of a semicircle above the datum line. Below, two circular arcs intersected at the keel. The low wing mounting pylon required only small extensions of the three main frames. The whole fuselage was skinned in plywood, forming a monocoque shell over a light framework of longerons and cross-frames. The cockpit was open, but an elementary wooden 'dog collar' type of canopy was fitted, leaving the pilot's head exposed to the airflow without any windscreen. A pad was provided at the junction of the wings as a headrest. As in the Grunau Baby, the seating position was upright.

Everything worked out remarkably well. The Kite underwent its first successful test flights a few days before the BGA competition started, and was entered in Class 1, the 'high performance' category, along with several Grunau Babies (one built by Slingsby), Scud 2s, the Hjordis and the German Rhönbussard. 'Sling', as he was now known, made the first brief flights, but handed over to John C. Neilan for the contest proper. Neilan's first competition flight was a triumph for him and for Slingsby. He was launched over the Sutton Bank slope by winch to 120m (400ft) and quickly found a thermal which took him above the hill lift to 990m (3,300ft). He headed off immediately downwind, eastwards towards the coast. More thermals and glides took him close to Bridlington with plenty of height, so he turned south and, with another thermal to help, eventually landed at Garton. The distance was 87km (54 miles), and it proved to be the longest cross-country flight of the entire competition.

The next day was not so successful. Neilan, without goggles or flying helmet, was sucked into a cloud and soaked with rain. The total lack of windscreen proved a serious matter. On emerging, still finding it hard to see where he was going, he had to land hastily in a small field. To avoid hitting the upwind hedge he ground-looped the sailplane, tearing the skid off and damaging a wingtip on an inconvenient tree. It did not take Slingsby long to put things back in place, and Neilan was in the air again next day. The total flying time recorded by the Kite during the competitions was under ten hours. Neilan carried off the Wakefield Trophy for his flight to the coast.

Slingsby's judgement of the market was correct, and a fairly steady stream of orders came in. The prototype was sold in November, without alteration, to Frank Charles, a champion speedway rider well known at Wembley Stadium. He had never flown before, but to the astonishment of his friends in the Barrow-in-Furness Gliding Club and the rest of the gliding movement in Britain he taught himself to fly within two months. Immediately after taking delivery he made two ground slides and two low hops in the Kite. In January 1936, without any further practice, he had himself bungee launched off the top of the hill above Ireleth, gliding down safely to land 240m (800ft) below on the beach. He retrieved the Kite, which he called *Cutty Sark*, using a trailer he had built himself, and repeated the exercise. On his next flight a few days later, equipped with a variometer, he found himself in a thermal and circled up in it for a flight of nearly half an hour. By the end of January he was making soaring flights of up to an hour's duration, and by February was essaying his first cross-country flights. Whatever else might be said about Charles's exceptional talent, he had certainly demonstrated that the Kirby Kite was not difficult to fly.

The second Kite was built for Dudley Hiscox, a member of the London Gliding Club. The nose was lengthened to create more room for tall pilots. Taking a lead from the later models of the Grunau Baby now appearing in Germany, a better cockpit canopy was designed, incorporating a small and very necessary windscreen. Slingsby did not immediately learn all the lessons of Neilan's field landing incident. The Type 6 lacked spoilers. If owners required these, as most eventually did, a retrospective modification was necessary.

Later models of the Kite had larger rudders of a graceful curved outline. This not only improved the appearance, but gave the controls a more balanced feel. A feature of the Kite which could have been improved was the wing/fuselage junction. By bringing the wing down in the centre to just above the pilot's shoulders and mounting it on a narrow pylon, an awkward constriction between the top of the fuselage and the wing root was created for the airflow. There is little doubt that the performance was reduced slightly by this, but the point was not considered seriously at the time. A rival to the Kite, produced by the small Dunstable firm Dart Aircraft Ltd, was the Cambridge sailplane. This, too used essentially the same, slightly stretched, wing as the Grunau Baby, but without any gull bend. The streamlined fuselage of the Cambridge retained the tall pylon which kept the wing roots out of the disturbed air aft of the cockpit. Only a couple were built. Philip Wills indicated that the control response and harmony of the Cambridge was better than that of the Kite, which he classed as only fair. At the time it was almost impossible to arrive at accurate performance figures without extensive flight tests, but it is probable that the Cambridge would have gained a point or two over the Kite if the comparison had been made.

Early in 1936 a minor controversy arose about the structural weight of the production Kirby Kites. Slingsby claimed 112kg (248lb) empty. In an article Philip Wills quoted 122kg (270lb). Llewellyn Barker stated forcefully that he had weighed a Kite and found it scaled 142kg (313lb). Slingsby responded by taking a new Kite to an official weighbridge which presented him with a certificate reading 114kg (252lb), which included instruments. Barker was unconvinced and prepared to bet £5 on his own figures. Whether Slingsby ever took him up on the wager is not recorded. In much more recent times a carefully restored Kirby Kite was found to weight 127kg (280lb), while another, no less well preserved, scales 163kg (360lb). There is little doubt that quite large variations arise between wooden sailplanes from the same factory, so all the claimed weights and wing loadings, and the associated performance figures, must be regarded with some suspicion. In flight, providing the c.g. with the pilot on board was correct, the total weight probably made very little difference.

Two Kites competed in the 1936 National Competitions at Camphill. The weather was disappointing, and although Hiscox won a prize for the greatest total hours by any individual, there were no especially notable flights by the Kites. By the end of the year, nevertheless, nine had been completed. In 1937 the total reached seventeen, by which time most of the leading British gliding clubs and several private-owner groups possessed one. Among the individual private owners was Amy Johnson. Almost all were finished in clear dope and varnish all over, but one belonging to a syndicate at Dunstable was painted grey, and another at the Midland Gliding Club, on the Long Mynd in Shropshire, had the plywood surfaces yellow with clear-doped fabric.

Kirby Kites were used by many pilots for the Silver C badge flights. Six competed at the Nationals in 1937 although they were no longer classed as high-performance sailplanes. Even so, two of the best flights were made by Kites, 125km (77 miles) by J. E. Simpson to the coast at Withernsea, Yorkshire, and 128km (79 miles) by K. Lingford to Easington. Production continued until 1939, by which time 25 had been completed.

An interesting variation, about which nothing more is known, was the Kite built with the NACA 4416 wing profile, tapering at the tip to NACA 2412. Apparently flown in 1937 or early 1938, it might have been a trial of NACA sections before applying them to the Type 12 Gull, which flew in April 1938.

One early production Kite was shipped to South Africa, where Philip Wills, during a business visit to that country, demonstrated it and where it remained after he left. Others were exported to Canada and Rhodesia, another went to South Africa, and one or two found their way to the USA. One, registered NC28800, was built from plans, with a very neat fully enclosed cockpit, by Herman Kursawe in the USA and flown there successfully.

In 1940 most gliders and sailplanes in Britain were impressed into service with the RAF. To find out if wooden aircraft could be detected by radar, sailplanes of several types were flown over the English Channel from Christchurch, Hampshire, in 1940. They were towed out to sea by Avro 504 tugs, released at 3,000m (10,000ft) and flown back towards the land while the radar operators at Worth Matravers near Swanage attempted to detect them. It was established that they did show up on the screens. They all had steel pushrods and cables operating the controls. After these early tests, a Kirby Kite was stripped of its covering and all of its control drives were replaced with wooden pushrods wherever possible. Further tests showed that it could be detected, though not easily. By this time, the danger of a glider-borne invasion of England had receded, and attention was turning in the other direction. A large programme was launched to work out operational methods and to train military glider pilots. A small fleet of sailplanes, mostly Kirby Kites, was assembled at Ringway aerodrome, Manchester.

One of the first exercises from this base, described by Lawrence Wright, who was there as an observer,

was a simulated attack on a railway viaduct near Macclesfield in Cheshire. A Kite and a Rhönbussard played the role of military troop-carrying gliders. Painted in the standard camouflage of dark green and dark earth, they floated to the objective silently and landed safely, after which imaginary airborne troops stormed out of them and destroyed the objective. The local Home Guard never noticed.

After some doubt about a suitable airfield for further work, the Number 1 Glider Training Squadron (GTS) moved to Haddenham in Buckinghamshire, where five Kirby Kites, duly camouflaged, arrived on 1 Jan 1941. Others came later, a total of 14 being on the squadron's books. Experiments and demonstrations for high-ranking officers were organised with Tiger Moth tugs. A Hurricane fighter was used to discover if gliders were easy to shoot down. They proved to be sitting targets while on tow, but in free flight they were hard to catch in the gunsights. If he was unable to see the fighter approaching, the glider pilot could hear it and take evasive action. Time trials were made to see how rapidly a large fleet of troop carriers could be launched. The Kites were supposed to be towed off in rapid sequence, released, and then to land quickly so that they could be launched again without delay, simulating a continuous stream of larger craft. A similar trick is used in the theatre sometimes, when a few 'extras' are made to simulate an army, marching on at stage left and off stage right, running round behind the scenery to re-emerge stage left. This went wrong at Haddenham when some of the undisciplined pilots, former gliding club members, found thermals and refused to come down.

Inevitably, in the slightly longer run, not many of the 1 GTS Kites survived. Those that did were mostly allocated to the ATC, though they were little used since soaring was not permitted in wartime.

As the war drew to a close, Slingsby looked again at the Type 6, and decided that a modernised version would be worth developing. It was allocated the type number 23. The wing was unchanged except that spoilers were fitted as standard. The fuselage was redesigned with a landing wheel and a taller pylon to eliminate the aerodynamic trap under the wing root. The pilot's headrest now was lower than the leading edge. The new sailplane flew in December 1945, but did not enter production. The gain in performance over the old Type 6 was insufficient to justify the additional cost, and Slingsby was sure something better could be achieved. The eventual outcome was the Type 26 Kite 2. The Type 23 was sold to the Cambridge Gliding Club in 1946, but soon thereafter was resold to the USA. Its final fate is unknown.

Some six or seven Kirby Kites still survive. The prototype, owned once by Frank Charles, is still extant, though at the time of writing it is in a very sad condition at Dunstable and awaiting restoration. It was flying regularly until the late 1960s. The remainder are highly prized by their owners, maintained in excellent condition and flown whenever possible. All have been fitted with spoilers, and some have enclosed transparent canopies improvised by their owners at some time. One, painted again in wartime camouflage, is displayed at the Museum of Army Flying at Middle Wallop in Hampshire. Another has been restored by Michael and Tony Maufe to its original clear varnish and dope condition.

Kirby Kite data

Dimensions
Wingspan	14.2m (46ft 6in)
Wing area	14.49m² (156ft²)
Aspect ratio	13.8
Wing sections:	
Root	Göttingen 535
Tip	Symmetrical
Length o.a.	6.21m (20.37ft)

Weights
Tare	137.8kg (304lb)
Flying	230.8kg (509lb)
Wing loading	15.9kg/m² (3.26lb/ft²)

The prototype Kite with the angular Grunau Baby type of rudder. (*Wills collection*)

Frank Charles, with children, in the cockpit of the prototype Kite 1. His experience of speedway racing caused him to wear a crash helmet. Note the absence of windscreen. (*Slingsby collection*)

In production the Kite was provided with a windscreen, but a persistent draught blew down the pilot's neck. The clear-varnished finish was typical for all sailplanes of the period. (*Slingsby collection*)

BGA registration number 291, known as *Gracias* (pronunciation left to the imagination) was a Kirby Kite based at the Midland Gliding Club in pre-war times, which remained in service until 1964. The Air Ministry registration letters G-ALNI, were required for a short period during 1949-50. (*J. Grantham*)

BGA 310 has been restored by A. and M. Maufe to the clear-varnish and clear-doped finish it would have had on leaving Slingsby's factory when new. Note the spoilers, a retrospective modification. (*A. Maufe and E. A. Hull*)

BGA 394 in its present colour scheme, on winch launch at Dunstable in recent times. (M. Simons)

The Kirby Kite as painted for use during the Second World War. (P. Warren)

A Kirby Kite recently restored to its wartime camouflaged colour scheme, as it appeared at the time of the radar trials during the Second World War. (P. Warren)

One of nine Kirby Kites flying in the 1938 BGA National Competitions at Dunstable, The pilots of this Midland Gliding Club example were F. J. Davies, R. F. James and B. T. Oliver. Note the absence of any seal for the elevator hinges. (*C. Brown*)

Another photograph of the Midland Gliding Club Kirby Kite, possibly BGA 251, at Dunstable in 1938. The contest number 20 was on paper, pasted on the wings and rudder for the duration of the competition only. If the identification is correct, this aircraft still survives in modified form, with a landing wheel. (*C. Brown*)

A rare photograph of the only Slingsby Type 23 Kite 1A in flight over Sutton Bank. The large sailplane below is the T-14 Gull 2, another prototype which did not go into production. (*Slingsby collection*)

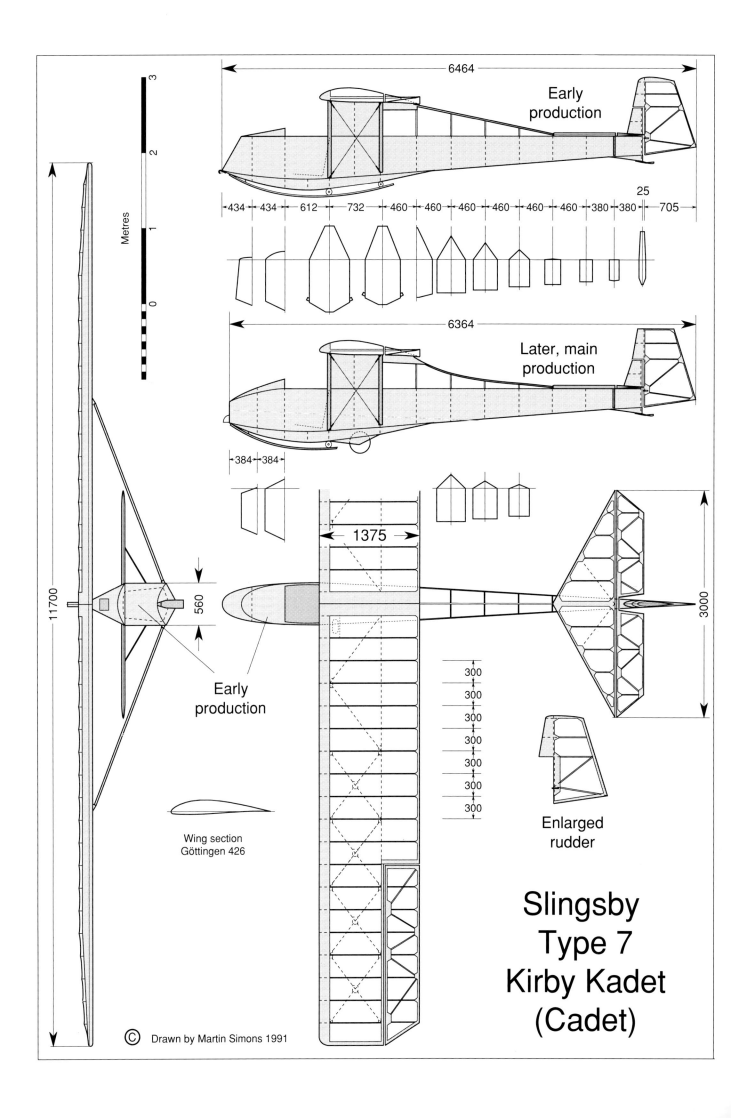

6464

Early
production

434 | 434 | 612 | 732 | 460 | 460 | 460 | 460 | 460 | 460 | 380 | 380 | 705

25

6364

Later, main
production

384 | 384

3

2

Metres

1

0

11700

560

Early
production

1375

300
300
300
300
300
300
300

Wing section
Göttingen 426

Enlarged
rudder

3000

Slingsby
Type 7
Kirby Kadet
(Cadet)

© Drawn by Martin Simons 1991

Type 7, Kirby Kadet (Cadet TX Mark 1)

The Kirby Kadet, which subsequently suffered a change of name to become the Cadet TX Mk. 1, made its first test flights on 11 January 1936. With various modifications it remained in quantity production for ten years, and a few were still being produced in the early 1950s. The Slingsby factory built 254, which does not include some kits sold to amateur construction groups and sets of spare parts which may have been made up into complete aircraft some time later. Sets of plans were also distributed, which might have resulted in some additional unrecorded amateur building. Other manufacturers produced the type under licence, the chief of these being Fox & Davies Ltd in East London, Papworth Industries, Enham Industries, Martin Hearn Ltd and Ottley Motors in Wood Green, Middlesex. The recorded total of all Type 7 Kadets and Cadets when production finally ceased at Ottley Motors in 1954 was 431. A few were exported either complete or in kit form to Canada, Eire, Palestine and South Africa. One at least was built as the UT-1 in the USA, and one was built from a kit in Australia in 1939. Probably the true total is more than the published records suggest.

The designer was John Stanley Sproule, who began working for Slingsby during 1935. Sproule had been a member of the group of Yorkshire lads who had toured Yorkshire with Slingsby in 1930–31, looking for soaring sites. When he left school he joined Vickers in Weybridge, Surrey, as an apprentice. He gained experience helping to build the Manuel Wren sailplanes at Dunstable, and had done more flying there. Now, as a qualified draughtsman and also a capable metal fitter, he came to Kirbymoorside with ideas.

At this time British pilots who had survived their first efforts in primary gliders and wanted to progress to soaring flight were put into one of two types of 'secondary' aircraft. The Prüfling, designed in 1926 by Alexander Lippisch in Germany, handled fairly well but had a higher wing loading than the primary gliders without being much more efficient. Accurate control of airspeed and well co-ordinated turns were required if it was to be kept aloft above a soaring slope. Few beginners were able to use it for their 5 min soaring flight for the C badge. Sproule felt that it was quite unsuitable for its purpose, and suspected that German clubs had discarded it long before. The other well-known secondary sailplane was the Hols der Teufel (Devil take it). This, too, originated with Lippisch, and an enlarged version was in production at the Schleicher factory near the Wasserkuppe. A set of plans for an almost identical sailplane were contained in a pocket in the back of a small book on building gliders, produced by Hans Jacobs, Lippisch's assistant. It looked in most respects like an enlarged nacelled primary glider. It had a lighter wing loading than the Prüfling, with a plywood and fabric covered fairing around the pilot. The wings were of large area, braced with struts rather than wires. The tail unit was mounted on an open 'gate'-type fuselage. Schleicher's prototype had appeared in 1927, and the Jacobs book in 1928.

In 1935 a few examples of the Hols were flying in England; one built in 1932–3 by Harold Holdsworth of the Bradford Gliding Club from the Jacobs drawings, others imported as kits or complete from Schleicher. This type, too, Sproule found unsatisfactory for beginners. The controls were sluggish and, although it had the reputation of soaring well in light breezes, it did not give inexperienced pilots much confidence in turbulent air. Accordingly, soon after arriving at Kirbymoorside, Sproule persuaded Slingsby to let him design a more satisfactory training sailplane. It had to be robust, easy to fly and capable of soaring, but cheap to build and repair. Slingsby evidently did not need much convincing, for Sproule was given an almost free hand and set to work. Drawing and construction of the prototype went ahead at great speed during the autumn and winter of 1935.

The wing was based on that of other training gliders, with a rectangular planform and parallel twin spars diagonally braced internally against torsion. Sproule did not have available any ordinates for suitable wing sections, so he designed his own profile. It was quite satisfactory. The leading edge was covered with plywood, but this was not intended to carry any stresses, being merely a fairing to form a good entry to the airflow. Fabric covered the rest of the wing. The ailerons were of the simplest type, with a little reflexing of the section towards the tips. The gap along the hinge line was sealed with strips of doped fabric above and below, but was sometimes left open in service. Twin lift struts with diagonal wire bracing, attached to the wings quite near their mid points, obviated the need for expensive and heavy wing root fittings. The first Kadet had slight dihedral, but this was removed before the type entered production. The wings at the centre butted closely, root rib to root rib, and were connected to the fuselage with two long steel rods, one for each wing being pushed in from the front when the holes in the steel fittings were aligned. To lock these rods in place a strap was clipped over the handles where they rested on either side of the pilot's headrest.

The main fuselage cross-frames extended upwards to carry the wing, forming a pylon which was skinned with plywood. The tubular steel struts attached to the lower corners of these frames. Behind the pylon the rear fuselage was a box of square cross-section, skinned on all four faces with plywood. This was not obvious on external inspection, because on top of the box a light fairing was built with a straight upper longeron supported by triangular cross-frames, running from the trailing edge of the wing down to the leading edge of the tailplane. This relatively flimsy structure was covered with fabric, hiding the top skin of the inner box from view. The front of the fuselage was modelled after the Prüfling and Hols der Teufel. The nose, rounded in plan view, was raked back. The very elementary cockpit was immediately ahead of the main fuselage frame, which supported the pilot's back and headrest. There was no windscreen. It was still considered important to leave the pilot's face fully exposed so that the airspeed could be sensed and any slipping or skidding more easily detected. An elementary seat, control column and rudder pedals were provided but there was no trimmer, no airbrake lever, and at this stage, no instrumentation of any kind.

A rubber-sprung landing skid laminated in ash and shod with a thin steel plate, extended from the extreme nose to the rear main frame. At the extreme front an open bungee launching hook was fitted, but at first it lacked a releasable coupling for winch launching.

The tailplane, of triangular plan, was also based on existing types of glider, and was mounted on the fuselage box with two vertical bolts and castellated nuts. Two small steel struts underneath provided additional stiffening. The elevator was hinged to the tailplane spar with a gap between, sometimes closed by strips of fabric, as with the ailerons. The rudder, mounted on a plywood covered fin, was quite tall on the prototype and aerodynamically balanced. The hinge gap was not sealed. A spring-steel tailskid completed the undercarriage.

Early flights revealed some teething troubles, though there is some disagreement about their sever-

ity. The outer wings of the prototype Kadet were not sufficiently stiff in torsion, aileron reversal was experienced. This was not very unusual in the lightly-built sailplanes of this time. Some, notably the German Professor type, would readily continue to circle one way at moderate airspeeds with the stick fully over for turning in the opposite direction. The forces on the control surfaces were great enough to cause the wing itself to twist. With left aileron applied, the leading edge on the port side twisted up and the starboard side twisted leading-edge down, and the sailplane would bank to the right. To recover from this situation the airspeed had to be reduced, which usually restored normal control response. On the first Kirby Kadet, aileron reversal was cured by doubling the internal diagonal cross-members in the wing outboard of the struts.

Another minor problem was apparently caused by separation of airflow over the fuselage, which resulted in buffeting of the tailplane. At certain airspeeds this could set up a harmonic vibration with the whole fuselage structure which was sufficient to alarm the pilot. Some were convinced that something had broken, or feared that something was about to do so.

The wing section was changed on the second prototype to the Göttingen 426. In April 1936 the first two Kadets were being tried out by members of the Midland Gliding Club at the Long Mynd, one of whom reported: 'These machines exactly suit our requirements. They are responsive to control without being tricky; they have no vices and immediately imbue confidence in the downy class of "B" candidates. Kadet I (the original of the species) has a lower-lift wing section than Kadet II, and is consequently faster and more pleasant to handle. The unrestricted outlook and nippyness of Kadet I is refreshing after the cloistered complacency of the Falcons – in spite of the better performance of the latter.' Tail buffeting was not noticed. Despite these comments about handling, presumably the slower stalling speed of the Gö 426 version was in the end thought more important for 'downy' pilots than the slightly better controllability of the prototype. The Gö 426 profile became standard in production.

According to Harold Holdsworth, who was ground engineer for the Yorkshire Gliding Club at this time, the prototype Kadet was bought by the club at Sutton Bank and was frequently damaged by inexperienced pilots. It met its demise in a spectacular accident. A visitor, misjudging the altitude badly, turned downwind from the soaring slope and struck the top wire of the fence which ran along the summit at that time. The wire scraped along the steel-shod skid and then cut the rear fuselage horizontally in half. After the dust settled, only the port wing remained more or less intact. The Kadet was never rebuilt. The pilot escaped with bruises. If the wire had been a little higher it would have sliced into the cockpit.

A cure for the tail buffeting was suggested by changes that had been made to the fuselage of Edmund Schneider's well known Grunau Baby design. On the

Kadet, the straight spine of the fairing behind the wing was redesigned with a curved sweep down, and the fuselage nose was improved to give a slightly smoother entry. After this there were no more complaints, and the basic outline of the Kadet was settled. How many Kadets or kits were sold before the fuselage modifications were introduced is not recorded, but it seems that the type entered production in the straight-backed form. In April 1937 a drawing showing this was published in the BGA magazine *Sailplane and Glider*. However, some of those sold before the outbreak of the Second World War had the modified fuselage.

The height of the rudder was also altered, but exactly when this was standardised in production is not clear. The American example (which survives) was of the straight-backed type, and it had a tall rudder. The Australian Kadet of 1939 had the curved fuselage spine and revised nose, but this example (which also still exists) had a tall rudder. Yet some photographs show that straight-backed Kadets sometimes had small rudders with only one rib bay above the height of the small fin. The 1937 drawing also shows this. Slingsby and Sproule probably experimented with various ideas before the final configuration was established. In any case, Kadet sales to British gliding clubs reached about 20, not counting kits, before production ended at the outbreak of war. No one could have anticipated that a few years later, The Slingsby Type 7 would enter mass production.

The Air Ministry became convinced that a gliding programme for the ATC would be worthwhile. The first ATC gliding school was opened at Kirbymoorside, early in 1942 using gliders built by Slingsby, and further courses for instructors were arranged there. Slingsby supplied a set of small-scale plans for the Kadet to the ATC upon request, and Jim Ford, an officer of the 85 Squadron ATC at Southgate in Middlesex, undertook the task of redrawing these and working out the necessary system of jigs to enable the aircraft to be constructed by cadets under supervision. The squadron itself began work on a Kadet while this was being done, using one of the outbuildings of the old house, Ashridge, which served as the headquarters of the squadron opposite what is now Oakwood station on the Piccadilly Line of the London underground railway. Copies of Ford's plans were distributed to other squadrons. Within ten months the Kadet was completed, and it was assembled and shown off in Trent Park early in 1943. This was the first glider to be built by ATC cadets. Newspaper photographs published at the time show that it was of the older design with straight back, tall rudder and no wheel. Others were built by other squadrons though how many is not known.

The Kadet design was now reviewed by Royal Aircraft Establishment (RAE) engineers at Farnborough and modified. Sproule, who by this time was serving in the Royal Navy, was not impressed. In his opinion most of the alterations were unnecessary, adding weight without really doing much to make the aircraft more practical. For instance, the light rudder cables he had specified were replaced by cables which, he remarked, would be almost strong enough to operate the rudder of the *Queen Mary*. The most substantial changes were to the fuselage. Instead of the enclosed square-section plywood tube aft of the wing, only the bottom and sides were ply-skinned. The three-sided box then required diagonal strutting on the fourth, upper, side to provide the torsional stiffness needed in the rear fuselage. The advantage was that, during construction, the inside of the fuselage could be more easily treated with preservatives. Access for inspection and maintenance in service was easier, too. The fabric covered enclosure above the box remained. A wheel was added between the main fuselage frames, the skid being shortened to make room for this. This alteration certainly was worthwhile, making the glider much easier to handle on the ground.

Winch launching now being the norm, an Ottfur releasable coupling was mounted externally on the extreme nose. (The Ottfur hook, produced by Ottley Motors was designed to release the winch cable automatically if it reached an unsafe angle during a launch.) Otherwise there was some minor strengthening all round and the entire aircraft was painted to wartime Air Ministry requirements, with RAF roundels. The name was changed from the slightly Germanic Kadet, to TX Mk. 1 Cadet. There was a 13 per cent gain in weight. In 1937 the production Kadet was advertised at 118kg (260lb) empty. The Cadet TX Mk. 1 weighed 134.5kg (295lb).

More ATC schools were opened. Jim Ford went to command No. 124 ATC Gliding School at Elstree, Hertfordshire. Winches, adapted from barrage balloon winches, were used to give ground slides and low and high hops, and eventually a successful a trainee would be launched to full height for a circuit or two, gaining the B gliding certificate. That was usually as far as it went. An order for 200 Cadets was placed with Slingsby, and before long the other companies mentioned above were brought into the system. In addition, a steady stream of repair work was generated and there was constant demand for spare parts. The solo training system was quite productive of broken gliders.

The ATC programme continued after the war's end, though it tended to taper off gradually. A good many Mk 1 Cadets were written off. Many had their wings replaced by those of the Type 8 Tutor, so there was a surplus of old Cadet wings stored at various places. No complete aircraft were released on to the civilian market; gliding clubs requiring them ordered them new from the factories. Some kits were supplied. Cadets were again used for their original purpose, the gaining of the 'C' soaring badge.

For a few years British gliding clubs persisted with solo training methods and still relied largely on the Dagling primary glider or the improved German SG 38 type. There were now plenty of experienced instructors who had worked with the ATC, using the Cadet, so it is not surprising that dissatisfaction with the old ways was expressed. In February 1947, G. E. P. Green penned an article in *Sailplane and Glider* entitled 'Let's have done with the Dagling'. He wrote:

> Training methods in most clubs today are right where they were ten years ago. Starting with those horrible ground slides on the 'elementary' which teach one nothing about flying and everything about the roughness of the earth's surface, via the low hop that frightens the instructor even more than the pupil, to the high hop that is frequently involuntary and ends with a smashed wingtip.

Green recommended the adoption of the Cadet for everything from low hops to soaring. With care, he argued, young beginners like the ATC cadets he had trained could be flying circuits after about 30 launches. The idea was not taken up. By the end of 1947, after some serious accidents with Daglings, clubs in Britain at last began to look round for simple two-seat training gliders which, though more expensive to buy in the first place, would last longer, earn more revenue and train more pilots than any kind of solo glider. The Cadet's time had passed.

There was a swan song. A surviving Cadet was operated at Dunstable by its owner, Peter Fletcher, for years. He modified it, rounding off the wingtips, and some attention was given to sealing aerodynamic gaps and fairing the worst protuberances. With this aircraft in June 1960 John Jeffries made a cross-country thermal soaring flight of 212km (131.4 miles) from Dunstable via Stratford upon Avon to land at Cranwell. No one had ever flown a Cadet to such effect previously, and nothing like it has been achieved since.

Kadet data

Dimensions

Wingspan	11.7m (38ft 6 in)
Wing area	15.8m² (170ft²)
Aspect ratio	8.67
Wing sections:	
Root	Göttingen 426
Length o.a.	6.36m (20ft 10½in)

Weights

Tare	134.5kg (295lb)
Flying	232.7kg (513lb)
Wing loading	14.7kg/m² (3.01lb/ft²)

The prototype Kadet, showing the straight-backed fuselage with raked nose and tall rudder. The finish was clear dope and varnish over all. (*Slingsby collection*)

A Kadet with a small rudder parked behind a nacelled Dagling, which is about to take off, and a Slingsby Grunau Baby 2 in the background. (*Slingsby collection*)

Building Cadets for the ATC in the Ings Lane factory during
the Second World War. (*Slingsby collection*)

The Australian Kadet, imported as a kit in 1939 by members of the Gliding Club of Victoria. It first flew in January 1941. The aircraft still survives and is complete in Adelaide, although not now airworthy. Note the tall rudder, the absence of a landing wheel and the later type of fuselage.

A Cadet at Dunstable in the post-war period. (*M. Eacock*)

The UT-1, a Kadet built by Miller and Dawydoff in the USA. It was used for appraising the type as a trainer for military glider pilots. This aircraft, which still exists, has a straight-backed fuselage and tall rudder and no landing wheel, but the nose is of the later form. (*R. Smith*)

The cockpit of the UT-1, showing the handles of the wing mounting rods behind and above the pilot's head. A windscreen was fitted.(*R. Smith*)

A Kadet flying at Dunstable in 1939. (*A. E. Slater*)

An early Kadet taking a winch launch. (*Slingsby collection*)

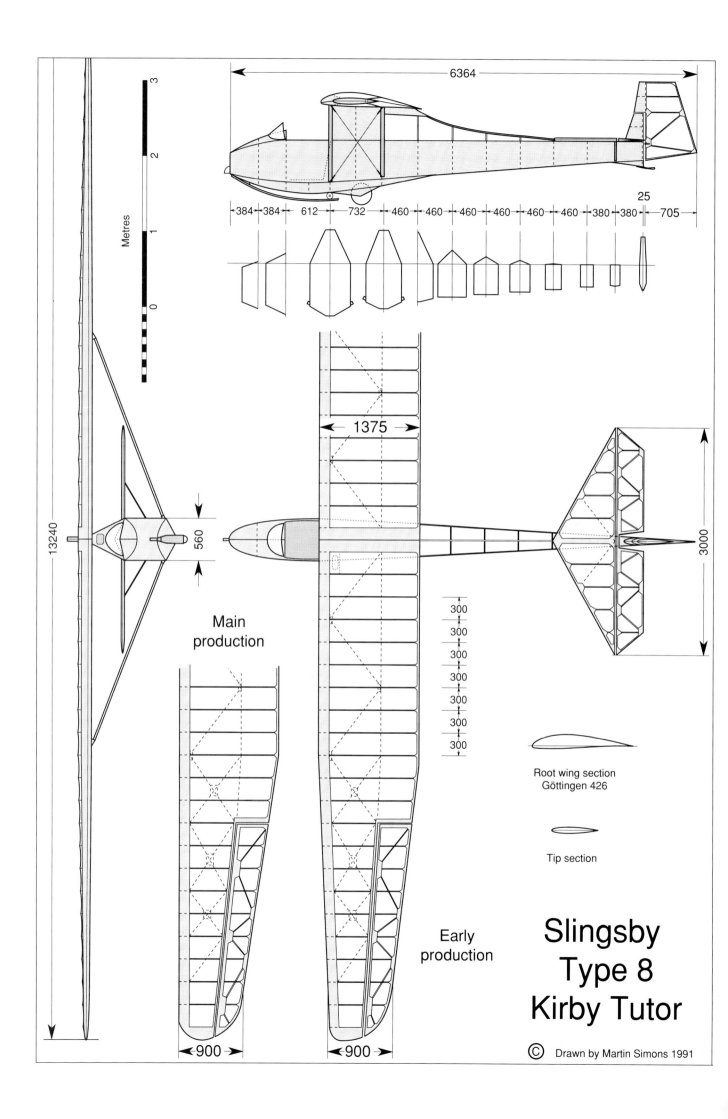

6364

384 384 612 732 460 460 460 460 460 460 380 380 25 705

Metres

3

2

1

0

13240

560

1375

300
300
300
300
300
300
300

3000

Main
production

Early
production

Root wing section
Göttingen 426

Tip section

900

900

Slingsby
Type 8
Kirby Tutor

© Drawn by Martin Simons 1991

Type 8, Kirby Tutor and Motor Tutor

The stimulus for the production of the Slingsby Type 8 Kirby Tutor came early in 1937 from the Midland Gliding Club, based on the Long Mynd in Shropshire with branches at several other sites. The club possessed ten aircraft. Having accumulated some soaring experience, the pilots of the Type 7 Kadets needed to progress to something better, and Slingsby was asked to produce a set of alternative, higher-performance wings to fit the Kadet fuselage to improve its soaring capacities. The idea was to rig whichever wings were appropriate for the prevailing conditions, getting almost two aircraft for the price of not much more than one.

Slingsby's chief and only draughtsman designer at that time was John Sproule, barely out of his teens, who had designed the Kadet. In the workshops for repair was a BAC VII two-seater, a few of which had been built to Lowe Wylde's design by the British Aircraft Company at Maidstone, Kent, some years previously. The BAC VII had a two-spar, twin-strutted wing, the outer panels being tapered and the tips rounded. Its span was just under 12.5m (41ft). Sproule, in his own words 'ran the rule over the uncovered wings thereof' and devised the new wings 'in somewhat similar style'. Slingsby sent the drawings to a consulting engineer to have the stressing checked.

The wings of the Taper-wing Kadet, as it was known, incorporated a moderate taper from the position where the struts joined. Sproule remarked that he copied the reflexed profiles for the outer panels from those of the Falcon 1, building in washout and changing the section to a symmetrical form at the tip. The required interchangeability of the components prevented any alterations being made to the fuselage, struts or root fittings. The span was now 13.2m (43.3ft) for the same total area as the Kadet, giving a higher aspect ratio which promised a measurable improvement in performance with very little increase in weight or cost. Sproule himself, in July 1937, did the test flight which was a great success.

The Midland Gliding Club took delivery of their new wings and the Type 8 slipped into the gliding club scene without fuss. It was hardly acknowledged as a new type at all. In January 1938, the London Gliding Club reported the first flights at Dunstable of what was still described as a Taper-wing Kadet. The club did not immediately buy it. By the time the Surrey Gliding Club took delivery of one towards the end of the year, the name Tutor was in use. Seven complete aircraft were sold by Slingsby before the outbreak of war in 1939, but kits of parts, spares and sets of wings were also produced. One of the kits was sent to New Zealand and successfully completed and flown there. Probably, once tapered wings had been rigged on a Kadet fuselage, the reasons to change back were not compelling. Despite the lack of spoilers for approach and landing control, the Tutor was almost as easy for beginners to fly as the Kadet, and in more experienced hands it could stay up longer and so earn more revenue for a club.

As with the Kadet, the T-8, modified and renamed TX Mk. 2 Cadet, was ordered for the ATC gliding programme in 1944. The only externally visible difference between the Mk. 2 wing and that of the Taper-wing Kadet was that the leading edge was straightened, creating a very slight sweep forward. This made little aerodynamic difference, but marred the appearance of the aircraft slightly. No spoilers were fitted even now, but there was a simple windscreen for the pilot. Strengthening, the addition of a landing wheel, and layers of dark camouflage paint made the Cadet Mk. 2 heavier than the civilian version. A total of 62 were built at Kirbymoorside for the ATC.

After the wartime bans soaring was permitted in 1946, and the production of sailplanes for civilian use began again. Slingsby entered into a subcontracting agreement with Martin Hearn Ltd of Hooton Park, and a production run of 25 Tutors and a similar number of Cadets was undertaken by Hearn during 1946 and 1947. No changes were made to the Tutor design, except that the proffered paint schemes were brighter. A report in *Sailplane and Glider* in September 1946 suggested that the 'new' Tutor was able to maintain height over the Sutton Bank slopes with Slingsby's

Type 23, a version of the pre-war Kirby Kite which was flying on the same occasion. The Tutor stalled at 22kt, flew efficiently under full control at 25kt and retained a useful glide ratio at 35–40kt.

After the subcontracting agreement terminated, about a dozen more Tutors were built at Kirbymoorside, along with some kits and partly assembled components, the orders being spread over the next few years. Some were exported. This brought the total number of Tutors to more than 100 including the ATC aircraft. Others were built by clubs and amateur groups. Some of the ATC machines were subsequently sold on the civilian market, often requiring repairs or reconditioning.

A curious combination was found at the Long Mynd in the immediate post-war period. According to the published records, BGA No. 657 was built by an amateur, D. C. Burgoyne, and was first registered as a Type 7 Cadet. Aft of the wing it had one of the very early, pre-1939 Kadet fuselages with the straight spine and tall rudder, but it also possessed a landing wheel and an Ottfur tow coupling on the nose, bringing the front end to the standard of the ATC Cadet. The cockpit was partly enclosed with a neat canopy and small windscreen. In 1950, registered G-ALTU, it was flying with Tutor wings. (For a short time during 1949–50 all gliders were required to display full registration letters.) It seems likely that the aircraft was assembled from several damaged sailplanes, including at least one old-style, pre war Kadet, a more recent Cadet TX Mk. 1, and a set of Tutor wings. Burgoyne is also on record as having built, or perhaps rebuilt, another Tutor, BGA 709, in 1954.

Many aircraft originally registered as Cadets became Tutors by cannibalism. The practice of interchanging wings seems to have ceased altogether, leaving a large number of old Cadet wings in storage at various places.

The absence of spoilers on the Tutor was by now considered a defect, so a kit for conversion was marketed and almost all of the aircraft were so modified.

The Avro Gliding Club undertook a more extensive programme of improvements on their Tutor in 1956. The upper side of the wing was sheeted with lightweight, low-density gaboon plywood back to one-third of the chord, improving the accuracy of the wing profile. Control surface hinge gaps were reduced and sealed, ball bearings were introduced to the control circuits, and many other details were cleaned up. A fully enclosed cockpit was devised, requiring a widening of the wing mounting pylon to give the pilot adequate headroom inside the transparent canopy. The rudder area was greatly increased. This Super Tutor delighted the club members, who reported much improved handling and performance. The idea of improving the Tutor did not appeal to many clubs, as the amount of work involved was considerable and the aircraft was out of action for a long time during the conversion. Better training sailplanes were now readily available.

In 1947, against his better judgement, Slingsby was prevailed upon to produce the Motor Tutor, which became his Type 29. The wings, struts and tail unit were retained, but a new fuselage was constructed with the pilot's seat under the wing, a motor in the nose and a wheeled undercarriage. After early test flights resonant vibration in the front struts was cured by the addition of a small stiffening auxiliary strut a short distance inboard of the main strut fitting on the wing, running vertically upwards to the spar. This modification was found desirable for all Tutors when they were aero-towed and they were modified retrospectively. The Motor Tutor type met considerable difficulties with the Air Registration Board and did not go into production, only two being built. The T-29 A, with a 25 h.p. Scott Squirrel motor, was exported. The T-29 B, powered by a 40 h.p. Aeronca JAP J.99, flew successfully for some years but was eventually crashed, without injury to the pilot, during an air display at Dunstable in June 1964.

Tutors continued in regular service until the early 1960s. By this time dual training had been universally adopted, but some clubs were reluctant to risk their two-seaters, which were relatively large and costly, in the hands of early solo pilots. It was usual, at Dunstable for instance, for a pupil trained on the Slingsby T-21 with side-by-side seating, to be sent off for first solo flights in a Tutor after thorough briefing. The first solo flight was also a conversion to a new type quite unfamiliar to the trainee, with a different cockpit, different handling characteristics and a performance certainly inferior to that of the T-21. The system seemed to work well enough, and the Tutor earned its place in the affection of many pilots. It was nonetheless recognised as obsolescent.

At this late date an unexpected problem appeared. Tutors and Cadets and other types of glider of similar construction had given good service. They were practical and strong, but there was a potential weakness. Routine inspections during major servicing of some hard-used ATC aircraft revealed that the spars in both wings were liable to damage. Compression shakes, caused by crushing and collapsing of the cellular structures of the timber, were found in the spar flanges, possibly initiated by long-forgotten heavy landings, or several of them. Once started the shakes worsened gradually over several years, and eventually one of the weakened spar flanges might fail in tension during a normal flight.

A contributory cause could be traced back to the very beginning of gliding in the 1920s. Almost all of the early two-spar gliders and training sailplanes, on which the original Tutor wing was based, were constructed in a similar way. The spars were continuous beams, and on primary trainers often consisted merely of solid planks of wood set on edge or spindled out slightly to reduce weight. On secondary gliders they were built-up with spruce or pine flanges and vertical plywood webbing between to give an I or [section. Their calculated strength and stiffness was normally quite adequate. Internal diagonal bracing, between the two spars, resisted torsional forces. The spars did not occupy the full depth of the wing, but passed through the ribs. Each main wing rib was a single sub-assembly, a light girder built-up from thin strips of spruce or pine with plywood gussets or 'biscuits' glued over every joint. Rectangular openings of appropriate dimensions were left so that when the spars had been made and aligned in their jigs, the ribs could be threaded on to them and glued at the required spacing. The rib outline members bridged over the spars and diagonals above and below, keeping the wing covering clear of them. The leading edge was partly covered with plywood, but the skin, like the fabric over the rest of the wing, was not regarded as a part of the primary structure and was not stressed. It could be glued to the ribs only, and need not come into contact with the spars at all.

It was tempting, however, to attach the rear edge of the plywood nose skin indirectly to the spars. This was done on the Cadet, Tutor and many other gliders. Between each pair of ribs a narrow packing strip of wood was cut and glued to the top and bottom flanges of the spar, planed and sanded level with the ribs. The plywood skin was wrapped over the leading-edge ribs and glued to them and also to the packing strips. The packing pieces, ending abruptly at each rib station, created an abrupt change of stiffness in the spar. When the wing flexed under load, concentrations of stress occurred in the spar at every rib.

By 1965 most Tutors were old. Some had been in continuous use for more than 20 years, and had survived hard times. Over such a long career, with occasional bad landings and clumsy handling by inexperienced pilots, the stress concentrations caused by the apparently insignificant packing strips encouraged the development of compression shakes. Repeated rough handling over years of service would produce no external sign. Wherever the small compressive crushing might develop, the plywood skin and the ribs covered the place. The invisible damage tended to accumulate.

Once the problem was recognised, modification schedules were issued not only for Tutors but for all those sailplanes, including some much more advanced types, which incorporated similar structures. The ply and fabric covering was opened up and the packing pieces removed over a substantial part of the wing where the bending loads were severe, exposing the spars for meticulous examination and repair. The ribs had to be cut where they crossed the spars, and a continuous strip of wood, in essence an auxiliary spar flange, was glued in place before the ply and fabric skin could be replaced. If the work was done professionally its cost tended to exceed the cash value of the aircraft, and some of the remaining Tutors were scrapped.

Duly modified and carefully restored, a few Tutors survive in airworthy condition. In skilled hands they have proved themselves capable of very good cross-country flights. A Tutor owned by a Dunstable group has made excellent cross-country flights and participates regularly in Vintage Glider Club rallies. Another, flown by Norman James, accumulated a total of 920km (570 miles) distance flying during 1989. James came second in the informal British National Ladder competition which was narrowly won that year by a modern fibre-reinforced plastic sailplane. Among his flights was one of 200km (124 miles), in which he crossed the Solent and landed on the Isle of Wight. At least equally impressive were Keith Nurcombe's Tutor flights, which included a highly adventurous excursion from Husbands Bosworth into Wales, landing in Snowdonia after 6hr in the air. Nurcombe won the 'Weekend Ladder' competition in 1990.

Tutors, in various states of disrepair are still offered for sale occasionally, and some are almost given away. As an indication of the life of a typical Tutor, one was advertised in 1990 as having done 5,629 launches for a flying time of 584 hr. The average flight was 6.22min. Also, a completely new BAC VII has been completed from old drawings by Michael and Tony Maufe. It would be possible once again to 'run the rule over the wings thereof'.

Tutor data

Dimensions

Wingspan	13.24m (43ft 3¾in)
Wing area	15.8m² (170ft²)
Aspect ratio	11.0
Wing sections:	
Root	Göttingen 426
Length o.a.	6.36m (20.9ft)

Weights

Tare	159.5kg (350.9lb)
Flying	258.5kg (568.7lb)
Wing loading	16.4kg/m² (3.36lb/ft²)

Performance

Max L/D 16:1 (claimed)

ZK-GAG was a Tutor built from a kit by the Napier Aero Club in New Zealand about 1939, to the earliest Slingsby plans. It had no landing wheel or windscreen and retained the original wing taper. The object mounted under the port wing was a crude airspeed indicator: a pressure plate on a pivoted arm tensioned with a spring blown back by the air pressure against a graduated quadrant. The photograph was taken in 1955 and shows a pitot and static tube on the nose, suggesting that by this time another ASI had been fitted. (*J. Deans.*)

A new Tutor built post-war by Martin Hearn Ltd, at Camphill, the site of the Derbyshire and Lancashire Gliding Club. Blue stripes on the rudder and the figure 1 on the nose were club insignia. Number 2 was a similar Tutor.

A Tutor flying at Sutton Bank. (*P. Selinger*)

G -ALTU, a composite flown in 1950 at the Long Mynd. The rear fuselage and tail unit are those of an original T-7 Kadet, but the front fuselage with wheel and Ottfur coupling on the nose evidently came from a later Cadet, while the wings were those of a Tutor. The semi-enclosed cockpit canopy was also a non-standard feature. (*Wills collection*)

G-ALNK was a Tutor built by Martin Hearn Ltd. For a short period in 1949-50 gliders in Britain were required to carry registration letters, but the regulation was soon rescinded. (*Wills collection*)

TS 291 was originally registered as an ATC Cadet Mk 1, but with new wings became a Tutor or Cadet Mk 2.

The 'Taper-wing Kadet' flown at Dunstable in 1938 by Philip Wills. (*A. E. Slater*)

A brightly painted Tutor, restored to fly at the Vintage Glider Rally at Terlet in 1992. (*M. Simons*)

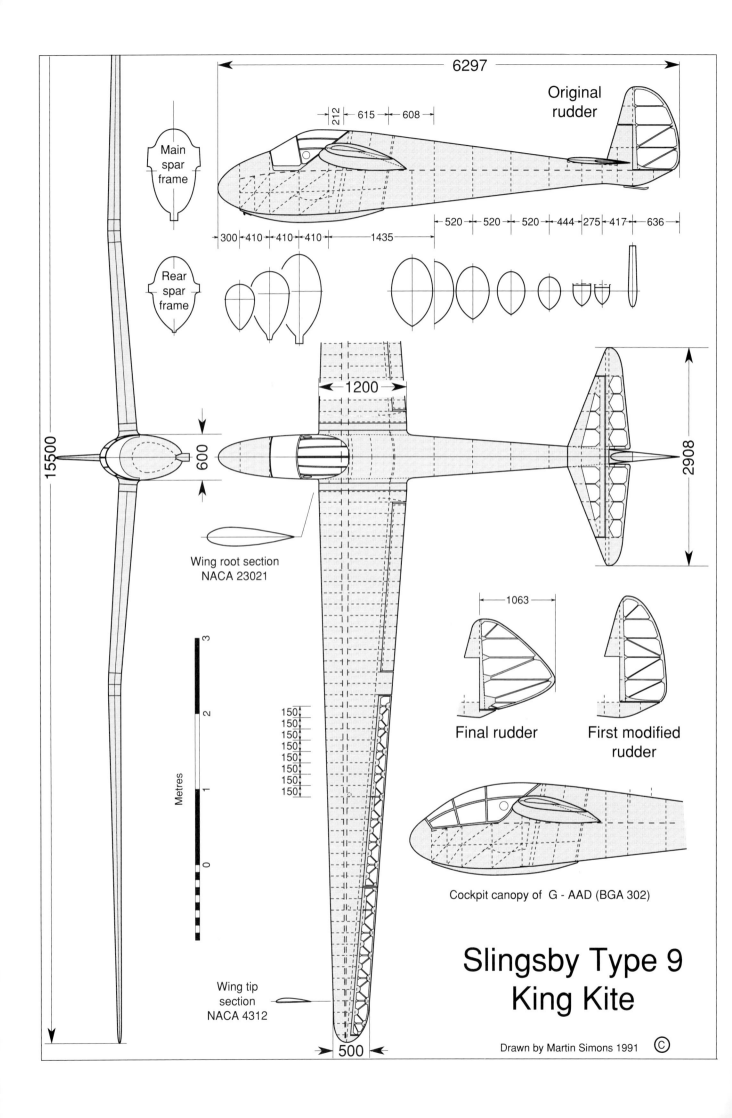

6297

Original rudder

Main spar frame

212 615 608

300 410 410 410 1435

520 520 520 444 275 417 636

Rear spar frame

1200

15500

600

2908

Wing root section
NACA 23021

Metres

3
2
1
0

150
150
150
150
150
150
150
150

500

1063

Final rudder

First modified rudder

Cockpit canopy of G - AAD (BGA 302)

Wing tip section
NACA 4312

Slingsby Type 9 King Kite

Drawn by Martin Simons 1991 Ⓒ

Type 9, King Kite

In connection with the Berlin Olympic Games in 1936, there were gliding displays and a successful cross-country soaring meeting. The international commission for the study of motorless flight, the ISTUS, headed by Walter Georgii, launched a campaign for soaring to be included as a sport in the next Olympics, due in 1940. It was decided to hold a big international championships at the Wasserkuppe in Germany from 4–17 July 1937 as a way of publicising the Olympics proposal and demonstrating its feasibility. News of the forthcoming competition was published in *Sailplane and Glider* in January 1937. Each national team was limited to five sailplanes and a maximum of ten pilots. At first it was not certain that the British could enter. Although a small subsidy had been granted to the gliding movement, there was no government support for participation in such international meetings, but the BGA decided to make the effort. Where the money was coming from was not explained. After some rather private deliberations a team of eight was chosen .

Few British pilots had attained the Silver C badge. None had achieved 200hr soaring. Joan Price, who flew for Cobham's National Aviation Day displays, had more glider time than any of the others, 183hr including many air display flights, plus 167hr of powered flying. She had not completed her Silver C. (She was one of three women competitors.) Gerry Smith had 95hr flying, all in gliders, Dudley Hiscox 100hr gliding and 20hr under power and John Neilan 85hr and 600hr respectively. Philip Wills with 110hr gliding and 510hr power flying, was probably regarded as the most talented soaring pilot of the group. Flight Lieutenant P. M. 'Willy' Watt had only 20hr in gliders, but 2,600hr flying in the RAF.

The BGA were reluctant for their team to fly aircraft of foreign design, but although Slingsby's Kirby Kite was produced in sufficient numbers it was quite uncompetitive. Only the solitary Hjordis designed by Mungo Buxton looked remotely suitable. However, Buxton had a new design in mind. A few drawings had already been done with the name Hjordis 2 in the corner. There was nothing else in prospect. If there had

been no hurry a prototype would have been built and thoroughly tested, any changes found necessary would have been made, and only then might further examples be built. Under pressure the BGA committed themselves to Buxton's proposal. Slingsby agreed to build three for the team.

Buxton, a serving RAF officer, had limited time to devote to the project. When it came to stressing calculations and preparation of drawings for the workshops, a young Cambridge engineering graduate, Peter Shaw, was employed to work with Buxton and Slingsby. John Sproule and Shaw set up their drawing boards side by side in the small office. Just how the effort was divided between the four is uncertain. It appears that Buxton himself was wholly responsible for the basic dimensions and layout, including the choice of aerofoil sections and the main structural features. Shaw, who had never worked on aircraft previously, although he was a pilot, did the required calculations and probably also worked out most of the detailed design with Sproule's assistance. The BGA's usual consultant engineer, H. C. Smith of the Supermarine Company (not Joe Smith of Spitfire fame, as has been thought) checked the figures. Buxton presumably visited the factory as often as possible for consultations.

Sailplane and Glider reported at Easter:

> There was a lively discussion as to what the new machine is to be called when it has a name of its own. Kirby Kittiwake and Kirby Koodoo were suggested (the latter with an eye to business prospects in South Africa). But Slingsby has now settled the matter by sending the *Sailplane* a General Arrangement drawing, with the name King Kite in indelible ink.

Learning from the best European flights made during the preceding year or two, Buxton described accurately what the new soaring techniques would be. To achieve large distances in the few hours of a typical soaring day demanded a high average speed. Pilots would have to select only the stronger thermals. Loitering at the top of a climb to extract the last few feet of altitude wasted time which should be converted to distance, and the search for another strong thermal. Penetrating quickly through sinking air without losing too much height was just as important as climbing fast. In good conditions progress could be made without circling by flying slowly through lift and fast through downcurrents (what is now termed 'dolphin' soaring). To use the strong lift in cumulus and even cumulonimbus clouds would require blind flying with gyro instruments and oxygen apparatus. Navigational calculations would be required. Everything Buxton foresaw came to pass eventually, though in 1937 British pilots were not ready for such developments.

Turning to the kind of sailplane that would be required, Buxton emphasised the need for gliding at high speeds. A high wing loading would be necessary. A fast basic aerofoil section with only a slight camber would be preferable, providing flaps were fitted to assist circling in narrow thermals at low airspeeds. The flaps would also permit landings in small fields, which had proved a serious problem with the Hjordis. Stability and a strong basic structure would be essential for cloud flying. Also, after experience with Hjordis Buxton now recognised that the pilot must be comfortable in the cockpit. If this meant sacrificing a little in terms of fuselage cross-sectional area and hence drag, the advantages of having a good seating position and good view would outweigh this.

The shape that appeared was a gull-winged sailplane with the moderate span of 15.5m (50.85ft), a high aspect ratio of 18 and a wing loading about 20kg/m^2 (4lbs/ft^2). The fuselage was rather plump but not out of proportion. Buxton's choice of wing sections, which aroused astonishment, was inspired by recent results from wind tunnels in the USA. A new range of sections in the NACA five-digit series had been developed. The point of maximum camber on all of these was much further forward than had been usual. In the case of the 23021 section used for the King Kite the camber maximum, less than 2 per cent, occurred at 15 per cent of the chord from the leading edge. A more typical sailplane profile at this period would have had 4 per cent camber at about 35 per cent. The pitching moment of such strongly cambered profiles was large, which caused wings to twist at high speeds and also threw large loads on to the tailplane. The advantage of the five-digit, forward-camber section was that the twisting forces were very small. At the same time the maximum lift coefficient was high so the stalling speed of the aircraft would be moderate, despite the high wing loading. With flaps down, tight turns would be possible without increasing the rate of sink.

Knowing the danger of wingtip stalling with loss of control at low flight speeds, Buxton tapered the profile gradually to the conservative NACA 4312 at the tips. This section, as the four digits show, had 4 per cent camber at 3/10ths of the chord, and was 12 per cent thick. Buxton specified 3.5° of progressive washout; negative wing twist. The usual technique to avoid tip stalling on a tapered wing was to change gradually from a strongly cambered profile at the wing root to a symmetrical profile at the tip, combining this with a very large washout of seven or eight degrees. This ensured low-speed controllability, but at high speeds the outer parts of the wing were forced to operate at negative angles of attack, 'lifting' downwards. From the cockpit in such a situation the pilot could see the outer wings bending down, more severely as the airspeed rose. Drag increased and the sailplane lost height rapidly, the reverse of what was needed for penetration through sinking air. The torsional flexibility of the wing tended to multiply these bad effects. By using a more cambered section at the tip and a comparatively small washout angle, Buxton hoped to obtain good low-speed control without the serious loss of efficiency at high speeds. Here once again he was ahead of his time, even ahead of most German designers. Modern sailplanes use his method of combining safe handling at the stall with good high speed glide.

The King Kite wing was thick enough at the root for a very strong and deep laminated timber mainspar to be used. The ribs were spaced at half the usual pitch, and the whole was skinned with plywood. Buxton was concerned to retain full aileron control at high speeds, which requires a wing stiff in torsion. The closely spaced ribs supported the skin against buckling and also helped to preserve an accurate profile. Almost all other sailplanes at this time had fabric covering aft of the main spar, usually clear doped and hence translucent, with the fabric sagging slightly between the ribs. The King Kite looked very solid and smooth in comparison. The flaps, confined to the inboard section of the wing, were also plywood covered, and could be lowered to a large angle for landing. Only the ailerons, suitably braced diagonally, were covered with fabric.

Buxton gave some thought to reducing interference drag, but in the absence of wind tunnel tests decided to mount the wing as simply as possible at shoulder level on the fuselage without any elaborate fairings. The spars were attached to the main cross-frames on each side with the necessary strong steel fittings and heavy structure to carry the bending loads through the fuselage. The gaps at the wing junctions on each side were closed by simple plywood strips clamped in place after rigging.

The fuselage was of the usual plywood skinned semi-monocoque type, with a large and comfortable cockpit. The rudder pedals were adjustable, which pilots found wholly admirable. A neat transparent canopy, built-up from curved sheets of plastic screwed to a light wooden frame, was fitted. Although it spoiled the smooth outline of the nose to some extent, it cost very little in terms of drag and gave the pilot a clear view ahead and, in turns, to the sides and above. A bungee hook was fitted at the nose, along with an aero tow and winch launch coupling. There was the usual rubber-sprung laminated ash skid for landing and a steel spring tailskid. When landing on a skid, the tail of a sailplane cannot be lowered as much as can be done if there is a wheeled undercarriage. A large rigging angle of wing to fuselage is required so that the touchdown can be close to the stalling angle of attack. On the King Kite 10° incidence was used. This necessitated setting the main fuselage frames, which carried the wing fittings, at this angle to the datum. The tail unit was straightforward, mostly fabric covered, with small horn balances on the elevators.

The prototype was completed and test flown on 17 April 1937, at first with no problems. Philip Wills wrote in glowing terms of the King Kite, which he still called Hjordis 2, in *Sailplane and Glider*. He had done some brief soaring flights in it and anticipated no trouble.

Came the day of the spin test, about a month after the first flight. Wills was aero-towed to 1370m (4,500ft) and did a one-turn spin to the left from which he recovered easily. The next, a fully developed spin to the right, almost killed him. The King Kite would not recover, even with the flaps in different positions. Height was disappearing very quickly. Wills jettisoned the cockpit canopy, undid his straps and jumped. He was thrown violently back into the cockpit. Again he heaved himself out against the centrifugal force and was forced back. In desperation he flung himself even more violently out and was dumped back again. Fortunately his latest strenuous action had somehow brought the King Kite out of the spin. It emerged half inverted, without the canopy, the pilot without his spectacles but with just enough height and presence of mind to recover, make a shaky circuit and land.

Explanations were not immediately forthcoming. The competition was six weeks away. Hastily, a new, taller rudder was made and fitted. Further tests established that it was possible now to recover from a spin, though it was still very easy to get into one. The prototype was taken to York aerodrome for aero-towed launches and to be flown by the team members during the last few days of May. An even larger rudder was fitted. All three King Kites, with giant rudders, were delivered and shipped to Germany late in June. The team was made up to five aircraft by including the Hjordis, which Wills decided to fly in preference to the King Kite, and the Falcon III two-seater, to be flown by Murray and Fox.

The first take-off by a British sailplane on the first day of the first International Championships was also Willy Watt's first bungee launch. As soon as the rope fell away he attempted a turn. The King Kite instantly spun and hit the ground 50m (165ft) down the slope. The worst fears of the British team were confirmed. Fortunately Watt emerged from the wreckage unhurt, having, he declared, landed on his toes.

Watt continued to compete, taking over one of the other King Kites, and achieved three distance flights without further accident. On one day he flew in cloud for a total of 90min. His extensive powered flying experience undoubtedly helped him in this. John Neilan damaged the other King Kite in an unsuccessful bungee launch, and it was repaired overnight by the German workshops. A few days later, immediately over the Wasserkuppe, he too discovered the King Kite's propensity to spin. To the relief of his friends he

recovered safely, though very low down, and continued undaunted on a cross-country flight. When her turn came, Joan Price also made a good flight of 92km (57 miles) without incident. Of the British pilots, Willy Watt did the best in the final tally, totalling 460km (286 miles) in the ten days and placing twelfth out of 22 individual entries, two places above Wills in the Hjordis. The team returned thoughtfully to England. The National Competitions were held in Derbyshire, starting in late August. The King Kites had been expected to enter, but they did not turn up. Wills, in Hjordis, won.

In 1938 Slingsby, who had the two remaining King Kites on his hands, invited Watt to fly one in the National Competitions at Dunstable. It now had a new type of cockpit canopy, faired to a smoother contour than the original. On the second contest day Watt flew 140km (87 miles) to Wymondham, near Norwich. Later in the week another flight found him working his way carefully round the west side of London via Brooklands and Woking to a landing in Kent for a projected distance of 122km (75 miles). Three others, Christopher Nicholson, Philip Wills and Joan Price, landed in Kent on this day but had flown east of London. Watt came second to Nicholson in the final results. The King Kites apparently did very little further flying, if any, before the outbreak of the Second World War. In the 1939 competitions Watt flew a Slingsby Type 13, Petrel.

What was wrong with the King Kite?

According to an article, probably written in Slingsby's own publicity office, 'the rush to complete the machine resulted in wing jigging errors which were repeated in all these prototypes' and the error was not discovered for some considerable time. In 1965 Slingsby himself wrote 'Many years later I was making an incidence check on a King Kite wing and discovered to my surprise that instead of the three degrees "washout" we had specified, the wings had two degrees "wash in"—hence the tendency to drop a wing and spin at low speeds'. How such an error could occur has never been explained. The original blueprints, which survive, show 3.5° washout correctly.

It was once suggested by Philip Wills in conversation that the wings had been built-upside down. This could not have been literally true. Possibly the unusual shape of the NACA 23021 wing profile caused some confusion. It undoubtedly puzzled ordinary glider pilots. *Sailplane* published a photograph with the caption: 'The wing root of Hjordis II, showing the bi-convex wing section. By looking along it from one end, the reader will see that it is not symmetrical.' To some it might have seemed that, in the desperate hurry to get the aircraft ready, wing ribs of the nearly symmetrical section might have been put in the wrong way up, perhaps as far out along the wing as the 'gull' bend in the main spar. This could have caused the wing to exhibit some very peculiar stalling behaviour. That the profile was not actually symmetrical was visible in the photograph, but because of the character of the NACA five-digit camber it is not very easy to tell from a casual glance whether the root rib was the right way up. Comparison of the photograph with a computer plot of the 23021 section, however, indicates quite clearly that it was not inverted. Moreover, the section changed towards the tips progressively to an orthodox four-digit cambered section which could not be, and was not, mistaken. Another photograph of the wing assembly shows clearly that the ribs were correct over the outer panels at least. It is almost impossible to believe that ribs could have been put into the wing upside down. It is not much easier to accept that the main wing jig was set up with the carefully designed change of angles the wrong way round.

The mystery remains. Slingsby admitted that a fundamental mistake was made in his workshops, but never said exactly how it happened. A highly promising prototype sailplane was doomed before it left the factory, and two more were built with the same fault.

During the Second World War the remaining King Kites were impressed and occasionally flown by ATC Officers at various stations. In 1946 one broke up in the air, killing the pilot. The accident was attributed to glue failure, probably as a result of storage in damp conditions. The last King Kite, the one with the new-style canopy flown by Watt in 1938, was seen de-rigged in a hangar at Bramcote Naval Air Station during the first post-war British National Competitions in 1947. It became the property of the RAF Gliding and Soaring Association, but was scrapped at Detling in 1950.

The story does not quite end there. The blueprints were rescued from their damp storage place in the loft at the factory in 1978. David Jones, an enthusiastic builder and restorer of sailplanes, was determined to bring the King Kite back to life. With advice from Prof Wortmann in Stuttgart, modern low-drag wing profiles were chosen. Thoby Fisher, who as a teenager had worked for Slingsby and who had done some of the design work on the original Kirby Kite of 1935, helped with restressing to modern requirements. A moulded cockpit canopy was fitted, but otherwise, only minimal changes were made. The new King Kite, not looking much out of place at a modern gliding site, flew magnificently and safely in 1983, 46 years late.

King Kite data

Dimensions

Wingspan	15.5m (51ft)
Wing area	13.6m² (166.8ft²)
Aspect ratio	18
Wing sections:	
Root	NACA 23021
Tip	NACA 4312
Length o.a.	6.297m (20ft 8in)

Weights

Tare	195kg (429lb)
Flying	282kg (620lb)
Wing loading	20.7kg/m² (4.24lb/ft²)

Performance
Best glide ratio (estimate) 1:25

The King Kite being moved to the launch point at the Wasserkuppe in 1937. Behind is the Falcon 3. (*Wills collection*)

Neilan chats with his crew on the Wasserkuppe landing
ground. (*Wills collection*)

Neilan in the cockpit of the King Kite. Note the old form of the
Slingsby logo; a golden eagle on a blue background with a
wreath. (*Wills collection*)

The prototype King Kite before the test flights. (*Wills collection*)

The first modification to the rudder. (*Wills collection*)

Moving a King Kite to the launch point at the Wasserkuppe. (*Wills collection*)

King Kite in flight. (*Wills collection*)

David Jones's new King Kite in 1983, with entirely new wing profiles but otherwise as close as possible to the original. Behind are a Slingsby T-31 and other vintage sailplanes of various types. (*E. A.Hull*)

Wills (right) and Watt (left) rigging the King Kite with its new canopy at Dunstable in 1938. (*Wills collection*)

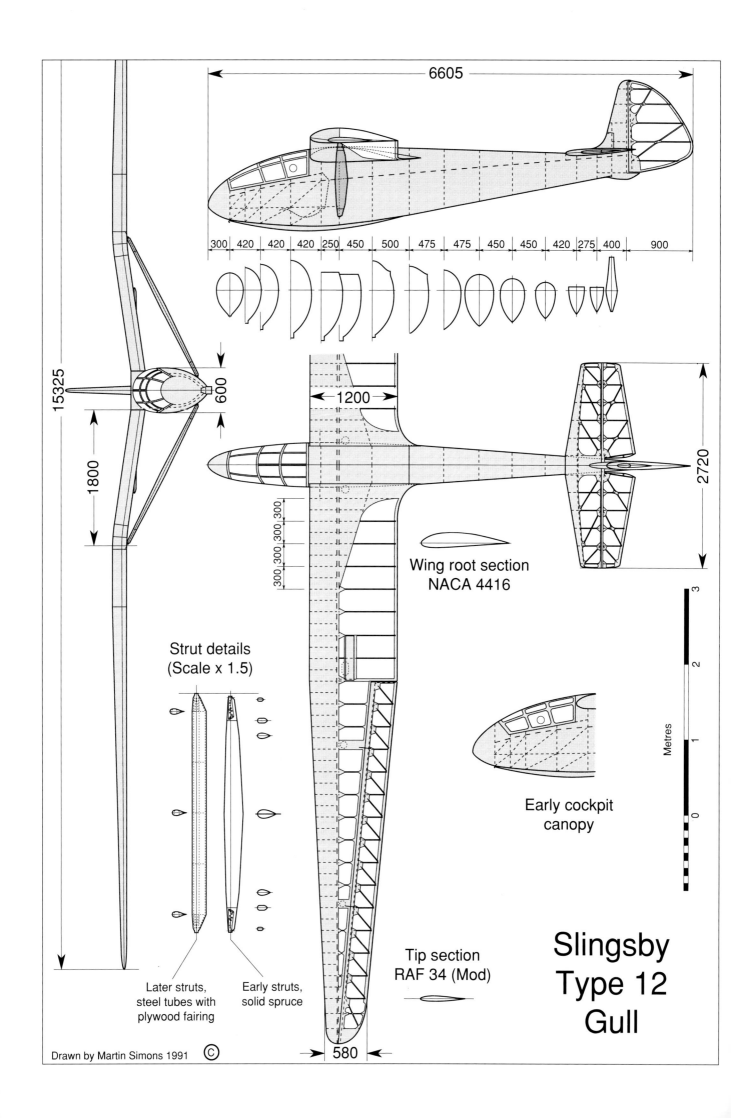

6605

300 | 420 | 420 | 420 | 250 | 450 | 500 | 475 | 475 | 450 | 450 | 420 | 275 | 400 | 900

15325

600

1800

1200

300 300 300 300

Wing root section
NACA 4416

2720

Strut details
(Scale x 1.5)

Early cockpit
canopy

Later struts,
steel tubes with
plywood fairing

Early struts,
solid spruce

Tip section
RAF 34 (Mod)

Metres

3

2

1

0

580

Slingsby
Type 12
Gull

Drawn by Martin Simons 1991 ©

Type 12 and 15, Kirby Gull

The Slingsby Type 10 Kirby Kitten and Type 11 Kirby Twin were small powered aeroplanes which Fred Slingsby designed with the help of John Sproule and Mungo Buxton. A good deal of work was done on the airframes, but neither was completed. Sproule then left to work for Airspeeds, and Slingsby, alone again in his drawing office, laid out a new sailplane, his Type 12, which he named Kirby Gull.

Without the kind of government support that gliding received in several European countries, it was vital that any new product from the Yorkshire factory should be inexpensive. It also had to cater for the needs of the ordinary club glider pilot, whose experience was very limited and who could not be expected to handle any very large, fast and heavy aircraft. The market was not ready for anything comparable to the 19m and 20m sailplanes which dominated the international record breaking and competition scene, yet something better than the old Kirby Kite was needed now. The ability to stay up in the lightest of slope lift and climb in weak thermals remained important, but the need to fly fast through sink, to 'penetrate' without losing height too rapidly, was becoming equally significant.

The Kirby Gull was a little over 15.33m (50ft) in span, with a strut-braced gull wing mounted high on the fuse-lage. The aspect ratio was 15.8. The most radical depar-ture from Slingsby's previous practice was the adoption of an American wing section, the NACA 4416, which was tapered over the outboard panels to a version of the RAF. 34 at the tip. Slingsby cautiously tried out the NACA profile by having a special Kirby Kite built with this section. (It was flying at Sutton Bank early in March 1938, and stayed there all summer.) Having established that the section behaved as the wind tunnel tests from the USA indicated, he felt confident that it would be suitable for the Gull. With 4 per cent camber it would be faster than the old Göttingen 535 but not as extreme as the NACA five-digit profiles used for the King Kite.

Not yet understanding why the King Kite had behaved so badly (the errors in construction had not been detected), Slingsby reverted to an older policy for preventing tip stalling. The RAF. 34 section had a slightly reflexed camber, 2 per cent at its maximum, compared with the 4 per cent of the 4416. In Germany it would have been normal to give such a wing six or eight degrees of negative twist. The amount of washout incorporated in the original Kirby Gull is uncertain, since drawings exist which conflict slightly but it was quite small, probably 2°. Slingsby was trying to prevent the serious loss of efficiency at high speeds associated with large washout angles, the outer wing bending down as the angle of attack there became neg-ative. It is possible that Slingsby changed this feature after experience with the first two or three Gulls, increasing the washout geometrically from the original 2° to 3.5° which became the advertised figure.

Structurally, the wing was entirely orthodox, with a laminated spruce mainspar curved gently to produce the gull shape and a stressed-skin plywood leading edge, stiffened with extra riblets to withstand torsion. The spar was a box section over the inner part of the wing, but changed to a C, with only one plywood web further out. A diagonal member transferred the tor-sional loads to the rear wing root fitting. Since the single streamlined strut reduced the bending loads to zero at the wing root, the fittings were of the simplest and lightest kind. The leading edge, mainspar and rear diagonal spar were each joined to the fuselage frames with a single horizontal steel pin. The port and star-board wings were not directly attached to one another, the gap between them being closed by a rather elabo-rate built-up plywood fairing after the controls had been connected. A light spar attached to the rear of the outer wing ribs carried the ailerons. There was no sec-ondary spar inboard. Tapes were used to stiffen the ribs laterally. The control surface hinges on the Gull were much neater than those of the Kite. The aileron spar was faired and stiffened with a D-section leading edge of plywood, and the hinge line was shrouded, though not totally sealed against air leakage through the wing.

The fuselage was also orthodox, being a semi-mono-coque shell supported by light longerons and cross-frames with stouter mainframes to take wing, strut and landing loads. The cross-section was round backed with a pointed keel. The cockpit was comfortable with a well shaped seat and space for a back-type parachute. A small instrument panel, the rear of which was accessible for making and inspecting connections, was large enough for four instruments.

Having seen the latest German techniques during his visit to the international competitions in 1937, Slingsby developed a contoured cockpit canopy. At this time, small sheets of transparent plastic could be moulded individually by hand into three-dimensional curves, but the pulling or blowing of entire canopies was not yet practicable. To build the canopy a wooden frame had to be laminated on a form. Into this, 11 separate trapezoidal segments of plastic were fitted. Aerodynamically the shape was excellent, with only small ridges at the edges of the panels to disturb the airflow, but the view from inside the cockpit was not good, being obstructed in every direction by the rather wide wooden hoops. Because of reflections on the front panel, which was at a very oblique angle to the pilot's line of sight, and the distortions caused by the moulding process, the view directly ahead was very poor. There was only a small round porthole at each side to allow clearer vision. The view directly ahead became most important when approaching to land, a lower standard of visibility at this time was accepted by expert pilots for the sake of improved performance. The main danger for them was that of collision with another sailplane when circling together in a thermal. When turning it was most necessary to look out to the sides and above, and the Gull canopy was not bad in this respect.

There was no wheel, landings being made on a rubber-sprung skid. A coupling for aero-tow and winch launching was fitted just above the front skid mounting, and there was an open bungee hook on the skid plate itself. It was not usual at this time to mount a winch launch release under the belly of a sailplane. The tail unit followed usual practice, being constructed from wood and covered with fabric. It was not strut-braced. The most serious and surprising omission from the original Kirby Gull was any form of landing approach control. There were no spoilers, flaps, or airbrakes.

The prototype made its first flight in March 1938. Satisfied with its behaviour by the end of the month, Slingsby was allowing prospective customers to fly it at Sutton Bank. One of the first to try it was Frank Charles, who had bought the prototype Kite, but he did not place an order for a Gull. (Probably at this time he discussed with Slingsby the type of sailplane he would really like; the result was the Type 13 Petrel.) Slingsby took the Gull to an Easter aero-towing meeting at Ratcliffe aerodrome, Leicester. This, the first meeting of its kind in Britain, was arranged jointly by the London and the Derby & Lancashire gliding clubs. P. M. Watt demonstrated the Gull, releasing from tow at 1,800m (6,000ft) and putting it through an aerobatic routine including spins and recoveries on the way down. It was bought on the spot by Dudley Hiscox,

who completed a cross-country flight of 93km (58 miles) on the following day.

The Gull was greeted with enthusiasm, and in the preliminary lists for the forthcoming national competitions four were entered. Three were completed in time, one going to the Derby & Lancs Club, one to the Yorkshire Club, and one to the Midland Club. In the event only one, from Derby & Lancs, appeared in the competition in July. It did well, though it made only two cross-country flights.

It was soon clear to all the new owners that some improvements were necessary. After the first three or four production Gulls, by the end of July 1938 spoilers were introduced. At the same time the cockpit canopy was redesigned. The wooden hoops holding the transparent panels were reduced in width to make them less obtrusive, and the front of the canopy was extended forward as far as possible and the foremost central segment was hinged at the leading edge so that the pilot could lower it and obtain a direct, if rather restricted, view ahead. An alternative type of strut was introduced, a circular-section steel tube faired with a built-up plywood case. In this form production continued. Five more were completed before the end of the year. In the USA, Herman Kursawe built a Gull from plans in 1942. This brought the total to ten.

On 30 May 1939 the Yorkshire Club's Gull was involved in a double fatal accident. On aero-tow at Welburn, it got out of position soon after take-off and rose too high. Probably the poor view ahead was partly responsible, causing the glider pilot to lose sight of the tug. The tow aeroplane was pulled tail-up into the ground and the Gull's starboard wing broke. Both pilots were killed.

The Gull also acquired a reputation for spinning easily, though it was as quick to recover as it was to enter the spin. One pilot at the Derby & Lancs Club suffered a broken winch cable in mid-launch, stalled and spun, but recovered to land safely, all within the space of about 120m (400ft).

Providing the pilot was aware of the characteristics of the Gull it proved easy to fly, responsive to the controls and there was no doubt that its performance at high speeds was a considerable advance on that of the Kite.

It had been an ambition among British glider pilots for some years to soar across the Channel. There had been crossings during 1931 by Lissant Beardmore, who was aero-towed from Lympne, and by Robert Kronfeld, who was twice launched to 3,000m (10,000ft) to glide across in each direction. Neither had attempted any soaring on these occasions. A prize offered in 1938 for the first person to soar across had not been claimed. Philip Wills and Christopher Nicholson on separate occasions had come into sight of the opposite shore and contemplated it, but had insufficient height to glide over when they reached the coast.

The opportunity came on 22 April 1939. Geoffrey Stephenson in the *Blue Gull* was winch launched quite late in the afternoon at Dunstable, in a strong northwesterly wind. Not at first thinking of the Channel, he made rapid progress, crossed the Thames, reached the Medway at 900m (3,000ft) and arrived at Hawkinge, near Folkestone, below 300m(1,000ft), expecting to land. A strong thermal over the aerodrome changed his mind. He climbed swiftly to cloud base and continued into the cumulus, gaining height at 360m/min (1,200ft/min) to 1,800m (6,000ft), and from there set course. Emerging from the cloud, Stephenson was already offshore, and he flew on through sinking air to arrive over the French coast a little east of Cap Gris-Nez. He found no more thermals and landed at Le Wast, 16km (10 miles) inland, at 5.35 p.m., less than 3hr after take-off. The distance was 204km (126 miles). The flight was rightly greeted in the the press as an epic achievement. It was 11 years before the feat was repeated by two pilots on the same day in April 1950. The exercise of getting the glider and its pilot back home was almost equally meritorious, since authorities on both sides required documents which did not exist. Anne Edmonds (later Welch), having a valid passport, deserted her engagement party to join the retrieving crew.

In the National Competitions of July 1939 at Camphill, three Kirby Gulls competed. The *Blue Gull*, now sporting English and French flags painted on the fuselage just below the leading edge of the wing, was flown alternately by Stephenson and Donald Greig. They were placed third in the final score sheet, beaten only by Christopher Nicholson and Philip Wills, both flying German aircraft.

To those who had bought Gulls in the early days, Slingsby offered a retrospective modification scheme, but in the case of his first buyer, Dudley Hiscox, he offered to exchange the aircraft for a new one. Late in 1938 Hiscox accepted the replacement. Adjacent photographs published subsequently in *Sailplane and Glider* showed the two aircraft. The new arrival was now named Gull 1, because the Gull 2 (a two-seater) was on the drawing board at Kirbymoorside. It also bore Slingsby's new transfers instead of the old golden eagle emblem.

The prototype Kirby Gull was bought by the Sydney Soaring Club, whose representative visited Dunstable late in 1938. It was returned to the factory and brought up to the new standard, with spoilers and an improved canopy, and freshly painted light blue but with clear doped fabric. The old golden eagle insignia was replaced by the more modern Slingsby transfers. It is probably not a coincidence that the Sydney Gull was re-finished in the same colour as the cross-Channel Gull. There was plenty of blue paint available.

Gliding in Australia at this time was underdeveloped, with scattered clubs surviving almost in isolation from one another. There was no doubt that the potential for cross-country flights was great, but little had been achieved. The Sydney Soaring Club would now be called a private-owner syndicate rather than a club, as it had only four members. Its base was at Camden, south of the city. The Gull arrived there in April 1939

complete with trailer. It was the most advanced sailplane so far seen in Australia. The Gull attended the first national gliding meeting ever held in Australia, at Belmont in Victoria, during the last nine days of 1939. From flat ground with launches by winch it made several good local soaring flights in the hands of Martin Warner and Norman Hyde, and a great many more brief circuits. In 1940 soaring was forbidden in Britain, but no such restriction applied in Australia. Back at Camden, again from a winch launch, the Gull, flown by Stephen Newbigin, broke the Australian Height record on 27 January with a 2,370m (7,900ft) climb.

Cross-country flying from Camden was greatly restricted, because mountains and bush country enclose Sydney on three sides, with the Pacific Ocean on the fourth. At Easter 1940 the Sydney group decided to explore the vast interior. An area of relatively flat wheat and sheep farming country, exceeding Western Europe in area, was available beyond the Great Dividing Range. The sailplane was taken to Narromine, beyond the Blue Mountains, 460km (285 miles) by road from Sydney. A de Havilland Moth tow aeroplane owned by Dr G. A. M. Heydon, a central figure in the club, flew there to await the ground party's arrival. There followed what was probably the world's first soaring tour. Each day the sailplane was launched and flew across-country as far as possible in any direction the pilot found suitable. He would land in a large paddock (field) or at an aerodrome. From there he telephoned the others to announce his position. The Moth and the trailer followed. On the next day another pilot would be launched to land as far away as he could, and the others would follow. In the four days of the Easter weekend a total of 550km (340 miles) cross-country soaring was done, and the height record was raised to over 3,300m (11,000ft). With the outbreak of war in the Pacific, soaring was suspended.

In 1945 the Sydney Gull required re-covering with new fabric. After this the group set off for a second sailplane safari, starting at the Royal Australian Air Force (RAAF) base at Parkes. Heydon's tow aeroplane was now a Tiger Moth. After a day's practice flying, on 24 December Martin Warner flew 317km(197 miles) to Jerilderie and reached 3,510m (11,700ft) on the way. The flight would have qualified for the international Gold C badge, but the barograph carried did not read above 3,000m (10,000ft) so the claim was disallowed. The next day, the Tiger Moth having arrived early in the morning, Harry Ryan was launched in a hot northerly wind, and to the astonishment of the air traffic controllers landed shortly after 2 p.m. at Essendon, which at that time was Melbourne's main airport. Ryan had seen an airliner take-off shortly before he made his own approach into a wind that almost equalled his flying speed. The distance was 271km(168 miles), and the newspapers made much of it. The Gull was returned to Parkes by road and the tour continued, with further flights by all the members of the club investigating large areas of the plains north of Parkes. The return to Sydney was made on 9 January 1946. A total of 925km (573 miles) cross-country soaring had been achieved. Another tour with the Gull was undertaken at the turn of the years 1947-48. Early in the week, the Tiger Moth and also a de Havilland Dragon airliner, tied down on the aerodrome, were blown over and written off during a sudden storm. Fortunately a substitute Tiger Moth was made available by the RAAF. Successful experiments were made with a radio in the glider, but this excursion was only partly successful, the Gull being damaged after a few days in a ground-looping incident on take-off.

In Britain, soaring was permitted again only in 1946, although there was an illegal meeting at Sutton Bank during 1945. Most Gulls were impressed into military service during the war, but those that survived re-emerged to serve with clubs and private owners.

Also among the Gulls flying post-war was the Slingsby Type 15 Gull 3, often called the Cantilever Gull. The strut had been eliminated, and the main wing-spars were suitably strengthened and the root fittings redesigned to join the two main spars directly together to carry the bending loads. The Type 15 had been under construction at the outbreak of war and was completed and test flown during 1940. At this stage it was finished in the usual clear dope and varnish but sported RAF roundels. It gained a certificate of airworthiness in 1941 and was then stored until 1944, when it was bought by the famous racing driver Prince Bira of Siam. Bira worked as an ATC gliding instructor, and had opportunities to fly his Gull which were denied to civilian pilots at this time. He flew it illegally during a 1945 Sutton Bank meeting. He had a special window fitted behind the cockpit where there was a small space between the wings. In this compartment he took his Highland terrier dog Tichiboo, or Titch, who accompanied him happily on all his flights.

According to contemporary reports the Gull 3, which Bira himself seems to have christened *Kittiwake*, was at least equal in performance to the Olympia sailplanes which, from 1947, came to dominate the British soaring movement. In terms of aerodynamic form, aspect ratio and wing profiles this was probably the case, though no serious comparative flight testing was ever done. The Gull 3 did not handle quite so well as the Olympia, but it was felt by many that Slingsby should have carried out his plans, announced in January 1945, to market the type with a revised cockpit canopy and landing wheel. If airbrakes had been added too, it would certainly have been a genuine competitor for the Olympia and could have been on the market at least a year sooner.

Apparently Bira crashed the Gull 3 badly, though the circumstances are obscure. Possibly this was the accident which occurred when he was caught by unexpectedly rough air when landing in an awkward spot on Dartmoor not far from his home at Bodmin. (By June 1946 he, in company with Titch, was flying the Minimoa which had belonged to Philip Wills. Bira eventually replaced this with a Weihe.) The wreck of the Gull 3 was bought by Hawkridge Aircraft Ltd at Dunstable

and rebuilt, emerging in dark blue with a moulded cockpit canopy. It was then bought by members of the Oxford Gliding Club at Weston-on-the-Green, but fell out of use and was stored after 1971. After nearly 20 years it was rescued by Mike Beach and totally restored, repainted in 'Bira Blue' to match the prince's racing colours and, except when being flown resides now at the Brooklands Museum, Weybridge, Surrey.

Only one Type 12 Gull of the original ten remains in service. This aircraft, BGA 378, was owned originally by W. Coleman of the mustard manufacturing family, but after his death in a wartime Hawker Hurricane accident it passed to A. Binfield and was then sold to the Derby & Lancs Gliding Club in 1949. It was flown in the National Competitions that year, as was the cross-Channel Gull, and BGA 378 flew also in the 1950 contest. Following an incident in flight, when the cockpit canopy began to shed panels, this component was rebuilt with a more orthodox transparent bubble adapted from a General Aircraft Hotspur troop-transport glider, which spoiled the lines of the fuselage but gave the pilot a very much better view. The aircraft changed hands several times subsequently, but was never out of service for long. It has performed outstandingly well in the Competition Enterprise series, begun in 1974.

A Gull 1 is on display in the Royal Scottish Museum, Edinburgh, and the prototype, after serving with various groups in Australia, is in a museum in Perth, Western Australia. The American Gull is also still extant and may be restored to flying condition. Finally, a completely new Gull 3 has been built from the original drawings. The project was begun by Mike Garnett, and after his unexpected death it was taken over by a small group at the Blackpool and Fylde Gliding Club. With a moulded canopy and landing wheel, it was completed in 1992, after more than ten years' part-time work.

Kirby Gull data

Dimensions

Wingspan	15.33m (50ft 3¾in)
Wing area	14.86m^2 (160ft^2)
Aspect ratio	15.8
Wing sections:	
Root	NACA 4416
Tip	RAF. 34 (modified)
Length o.a.	6.61m (21ft 7in)

Weights

Tare	172.5kg (384lb)
Flying	283.5kg (624lb)
Wing loading	19.1kg/m^2 (3.91lb/ft^2)

Performance

Best glide ratio (estimate) 1:24

Gull 3: Similar, but tare weight approx.190kg (418lb), wing loading 20kg/m^2 (4.1lb/ft^2).

BGA 378, with wheel, at the Derbyshire and Lancashire Club site at Camphill in 1949, showing the club's blue and white stripes on the rudder and the registration letters. Otherwise the finish was clear dope and varnish. This Gull, with modified cockpit canopy, still flies regularly. (*M. Simons*).

Gerard O. Smith with the Derby and Lancs Club Gull, receiving the Air League prize in 1938. The original form of cockpit canopy is visible. (*C. Brown*)

The Derbyshire and Lancashire Gliding Club's Kirby Gull, BGA 378, flying at the 1938 National Gliding Competitions at Dunstable. This was the second Gull built. No spoilers were fitted at this time. (*C. Brown*)

The prototype Gull flying at Gawler, the base of the Adelaide Soaring Club, in South Australia, 1957. (Courtesy *Adelaide Advertiser*)

The modified prototype Gull soon after its arrival in Australia in 1939. The cockpit canopy and spoilers were brought up to the new standard before export. (*M. Waghorn*)

The London Gliding Club's Gull being manhandled outside the hangar in 1950. It was withdrawn from use after 1964. (*M. Eacock*)

Prince Bira with the fuselage of the only Gull 3, which was named *Kittiwake* when he owned it. (*Wills collection*)

The restored Gull 3 on winch launch at Camphill, Derbyshire. (*M. Simons*)

The Gull 3 wing root fittings, showing how the main spars were joined on the centreline with horizontal steel pins. (*M. Simons*)

The prototype Kirby Gull in its museum shelter in Perth, West Australia. After several accidents, the front fuselage of the Australian Gull was rebuilt, without drawings, by Harry Schneider. (*N. Wynne*)

The cross-Channel Gull, BGA 380, at the National Gliding Championships at Camphill in August 1949. The tailplane has not yet been rigged. (*G. Stephenson*)

The cross-Channel Gull at Dunstable in 1949 with its registration letters added by law, to the disgust of the owners. (*M. Eacock*)

The restored Gull 3 at Booker (High Wycombe). Note the small window between the wings for Titch's aerial kennel. (*M. Beach*)

Dudley Hiscox flying the prototype Kirby Gull at Dunstable (*C. Brown*)

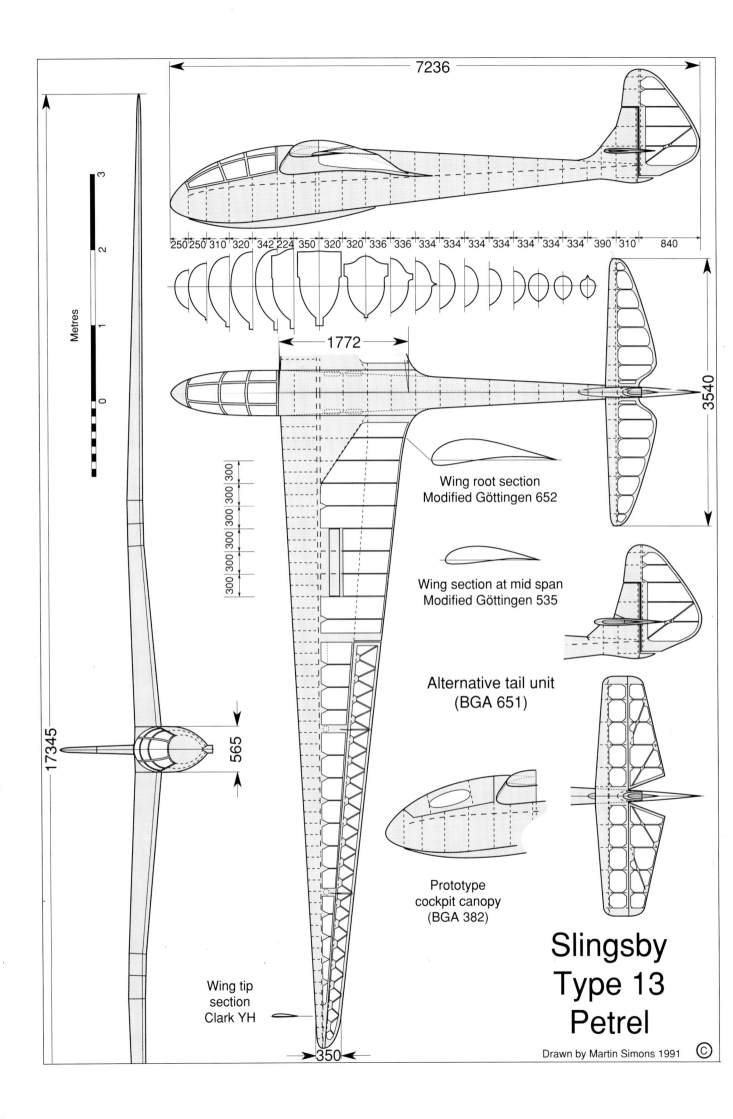

7236

3540

17345

1772

300 | 300 | 300 | 300 | 300

565

350

250 250 310 320 342 224 350 320 320 336 336 334 334 334 334 334 334 334 390 310 840

Metres

3

2

1

0

Wing root section
Modified Göttingen 652

Wing section at mid span
Modified Göttingen 535

Alternative tail unit
(BGA 651)

Prototype
cockpit canopy
(BGA 382)

Wing tip
section
Clark YH

Slingsby
Type 13
Petrel

Drawn by Martin Simons 1991 ©

Type 13, Petrel

One of the first people to fly Slingsby's Type 12 Kirby Gull in 1938 was Frank Charles, the speedway champion, who had surprised the gliding movement a few years earlier by teaching himself to fly his Kirby Kite. What Charles thought of the Gull was not recorded, but he did not order one. Instead, he asked Slingsby to build him a modernised version of the Rhönadler, a sailplane produced by the German firm of Alexander Schleicher. Designed by Hans Jacobs, the Rhönadler was the first high-performance sailplane ever to be mass-produced in a factory. The prototype made its first competition flights at the Wasserkuppe in 1932, with Peter Riedel as the pilot. The Rhönadler was smaller than the very special advanced sailplanes custom-built for the few ace pilots. It was light, easy to handle in the air and on the ground, and relatively inexpensive, being designed from the outset for easy production. It soon became very popular, but by 1938 it was regarded by the more experienced pilots as outmoded.

The Rhönadler embodied the lessons learned from the previous generation of sailplanes, which were designed mainly for slope soaring. It was known that thermals existed, but not many pilots in 1932 understood how they should be used. The need for manoeuvrability, to turn tightly in small areas of upcurrent, was accepted. The desirability of flying at high speeds when penetrating sinking air on cross-country flights was just beginning to be appreciated, but it was still thought that a very light wing loading and minimal rate of sink were essential.

The Rhönadler had a strongly tapered cantilever wing with an unusually deep root, allowing a very light mainspar to be used. Plywood stressed skin covered the leading edge to the mainspar, with fabric behind. Long, narrow ailerons extended over more than half the semi-span. The aerofoil section at the wing root seems to have been a special design by Hans Jacobs himself. It was based on the extraordinary Göttingen 652, a very thick teardrop shape with extremely pronounced camber. This profile had been used successfully on the famous Fafnir sailplane, and in England on

the little Scud 2. For the Rhönadler Jacobs reduced the camber but the basic thickness form was retained. At the mid semi-span the section blended into the familiar Göttingen 535 used on the Grunau Baby and then to a thin reflexed tip, probably the Clark YH. Very pronounced washout was incorporated to preserve lateral control near the stall.

The fuselage, a semi-monocoque structure of a style that was becoming normal, was round backed with pointed keel, and the wing was mounted on a low pylon. The usual type of skid undercarriage was fitted. The earliest Rhönadlers had cockpit canopies of wood with small portholes cut to provide the pilot with a restricted view. Before long the factory was fitting simple transparent enclosures. An all-moving tailplane and an aerodynamically balanced rudder were used; very orthodox for the period.

In 1934 a Rhönadler was imported into Britain and, flown by Eric Collins, earned a great reputation. It handled well, and Collins demonstrated that it could soar in a wide variety of conditions. After Collins's death (performing aerobatics in a Grunau Baby for Cobham's National Aviation Day displays), his Rhönadler was taken over by a private syndicate and continued to make impressive cross-country flights in England. There was really not much competition for it until the arrival, from Germany, of Jacobs's later design, the Rhönsperber, and the Schempp-Hirth Minimoa.

Frank Charles apparently could see no advantage in these newer types or in Slingsby's products, the King Kite and Gull, and believed that an improved Rhönadler would suit him best. Slingsby, for whom definite orders backed by adequate cash were always vitally important, was in no mood to disagree. Work on his new two-seater design, the Gull 2, was shelved in order to produce the Type 13. Charles himself gave it the name Petrel.

Slingsby described the Petrel as 'merely a gull winged version of the Rhönadler', and so it was. The same wing was used except for the gull dihedral. This brought the centre section down to fair directly to the fuselage without any pylon. Spoilers were fitted. The fuselage was redesigned with a smoother, more generous line ahead of the wing allowing for a contoured canopy similar to that of the Gull. The cockpit was more comfortable than the German type, with room for the shoulders. The tail unit and almost everything else was transferred as directly as possible from the Rhönadler. (Drawings for the Rhönadler '32 were found in the Slingsby archives.)

Harking back even further into the past, Frank Charles required Slingsby to give him a wooden cockpit canopy with only two elliptical portholes, one on each side, to allow him to look out. Cockpit canopies at this time were usually built-up, transparent panels set in a wooden framework, but Charles evidently preferred to have direct access to the air, even at the cost of restricted vision. He may have felt that the inescapable small irregularities of the panelled canopy created more drag than a smooth wooden structure with portholes.

The first flight took place in December 1938. Details of the new sailplane were published in January 1939, when it was stated that Charles had already taken delivery, but he did not fly the aircraft until 19 February at his club's site near Barrow-in-Furness, a good local soaring flight and a short cross-country being made on this day. Crude calculations suggested that the Petrel had a minimum sinking speed of 0.33m/sec (1.08ft/sec). Charles reported that it stalled at 46kmh (28mph) and showed no signs of dropping a wing at low speeds. He dived it to 128kmh (79mph) with no ill effects. One who observed it remarked that the Petrel was very like the Rhönadler when seen from below, which should have been no surprise. Because of the slightly tidier wing root and fuselage junction the Petrel might have been a little superior to the Rhönadler, but the difference cannot possibly have been very great. Charles flew the Petrel again a few days later at Sutton Bank, where it excited much admiration, and he made some more cross-country flights in March and April.

Presumably feeling that the numerous jigs made for the Type 13 should not be allowed to stand idle, Slingsby decided that it should go into production, but with a more orthodox cockpit canopy. A fixed tailplane instead of the 'pendulum' elevator could be ordered if preferred. In advertisements the Petrel was described as 'The latest development in high performance sailplane design, with a large speed range, low sinking speed and remarkable gliding angle'. Slingsby asked P. M. Watt to fly the second Petrel in the BGA competitions due to take place in July at Camphill, Derbyshire. New advertisements read: 'Two machines of this type will be competing with German sailplanes of the same class. These two machines are the first of a batch of eight now on order for various parts of the Empire.' The third, which had the fixed tailplane, was ordered by members of the Newcastle-upon-Tyne Soaring Syndicate, but was evidently not ready in time for the contest.

Watt flew well in the contest, completing several good cross-country flights including one by a very roundabout route via Nottingham and Boston to Skegness on the coast, using the sea breeze convergence to get him over the last 20km (12 miles). He arrived to discover Stephenson's cross-channel *Blue Gull* on the ground there already. In the final tally of scores Watt placed fifth, but any sense of satisfaction, even for the winners, was overwhelmed by sadness. There had been a fatal accident earlier in the week, the first ever at Camphill, when W. E. Godson spun into the hill in his Kestrel, a small sailplane designed by Bill Manuel which Godson had built from plans.

The Camphill flying ground is about 390m (1,300ft) above sea level. On the final Saturday there was a damp, overcast sky with a southerly wind, and the clouds were only a few hundred feet above the take-off point. Frank Charles in his Petrel was launched by winch in a rain shower. Towards the top of the climb the Petrel entered the cloud and vanished. The winch driver cut the power, expecting Charles to release the cable. When the Petrel emerged from the overcast it was heading downwind, as if to complete a normal circuit and landing, but the winch cable was still on, sagging in a loop. At about 60m (200ft) the slack ran out and the cable tightened, bringing the Petrel to a halt in the air and pulling it vertically into the ground. Charles was killed.

No completely satisfactory explanation was ever forthcoming. Why Charles did not release the cable when he felt the power fail is not known. The tow coupling was found to be in good working order. He may have assumed that the cable had broken. The winch driver was provided with an axe (there was no built-in guillotine), but it was said he could not see that the cable was attached to the sailplane because of the rain. In any case, he had very little time to get out of the driving seat and race round to the chopping block. There was even talk of a loose dog getting in the way. The wreckage of the sailplane was carried off the field. The author as a child saw this accident, and remembers the sailplane passing along the western side of the field with the cable dangling, and then its fall and total collapse, apparently into a heap of tiny pieces, on the airfield. I also remember later looking at the broken remnants of the wings, the varnish still glistening as they lay against a dry stone wall behind the hangar. Flying continued.

It was not the first time an accident had been caused by failure to release from a winch tow. The axe was provided to allow the cable to be chopped if the release jammed, which was not a very rare thing. After cutting, a sailplane with several hundred feet of loose steel cable dangling below could still be brought down sharply if the wire caught on some obstruction, and at least one pilot had lost both feet in an accident from this cause. The accident to the Petrel brought matters to a head. Letters in *Sailplane and Glider* suggested possible precautions, including the use of weak links in the cable so that it would snap under any unusual strain. This eventually became standard practice. A design for a simple type of automatic release was published, and though it was not adopted it was certainly on the right lines. The outcome before long was the invention by John Furlong and Leonard Ottley of the Ottfur release. This device, if properly used with two rings of correct size on the end of the cable, let go immediately if the angle of the line relative to the aircraft approached too nearly to the vertical. If Frank Charles's Petrel had been equipped in this way, the release would have operated automatically as soon as the winch stopped. From 1944, when large production orders for gliders for the ATC were issued, no sailplane in Britain was built without an Ottfur hook.

Yet old sailplanes were still permitted to fly with old types of release for several years more. Furlong wrote as late as June 1948 to warn of the dangers of these, or of burying the release inside a tunnel where the rings could stick. Rings which could jam in the release were used sometimes. There was danger in relying on a mechanical guillotine on the winch which might become rusted and ineffective through lack of use. The old axe, Furlong said, was still the most reliable cable-chopper. It was not very unusual, even at this time, to see a sailplane trailing cable over trees, fences, parked vehicles and even people in order to make a landing after a cable break or chop. Safety releases equivalent to the original Ottfur are now mandatory on all motorless aircraft.

Within a very few weeks after this, sport flying in Britain ended for the duration of the Second World War. Slingsby never completed any more Petrels after the third, and customers around the Empire, mentioned in his advertisements, waited in vain. Most sailplanes were impressed for various kinds of military uses. In the case of the Petrel, John Neilan gave an account of how he flew one over some unspecified part of northern England for a few happy days during 1940. It was an exercise for anti-aircraft gun crews and the Royal Observer Corps in a part of the country where they were not getting much practice, even during the Battle of Britain. The idea was to take a tow behind a Gipsy Moth, to 3,000m (10,000ft) some distance away from base and then glide back by a circuitous route, Neilan taking note of heights and distance while the gun crews and observers on the ground attempted to keep track and estimate ranges and altitudes. It is probably no surprise that the officer who thought of this was himself a pre-war gliding enthusiast. The lack of any engine noise prevented alarm among the public and compelled the ground observers to scan the skies in all directions most assiduously. Perhaps accidentally, or perhaps not, the tow rope sometimes broke and Neilan was obliged to proceed by soaring. He praised the Petrel warmly.

In late 1944 and on into 1945 Slingsby was advertising the Petrel 2, a development which would have become his Type 22. The new Petrel was to have had a landing wheel, and the canopy would have been redesigned with a simple stepped shape with windscreen, instead of the original fully contoured nose. A fixed tailplane would have been standard. It was described as 'A high performance sailplane most suitable for British conditions', but there was no concealing the fact that the Petrel 2 had a Rhönadler wing, unchanged in any important respect. The basic design dated back to 1932. The Petrel 2 would have been no advance aerodynamically on the pre-war Petrels, which had in any case been only marginally better than the original Hans Jacobs design. With the prospect of several much more advanced types about to come on to the market, no interest was shown by customers. Construction of the Petrel 2 was never even started.

The second and third Petrels both came through the war and still survive. They have done much more flying since 1945 than they ever did before, and are to be seen from time to time at vintage glider rallies. They are graceful, safe, easy to fly, can soar in the feeblest of lift and will float gently around all afternoon on almost any sunny day. But if the pilot wishes to fly across-country, they seem very slow.

Petrel data

Dimensions

Wingspan	17.3m (56ft 11in)
Wing area	16.72m^2 (180ft^2)
Aspect ratio	17.9
Wing sections:	
Göttingen	652 modified
Mid span	Göttingen 535
Tip	Clark YH
Length o.a.	7.24m (23ft 9in)

Weights

Tare	199.5kg (438lb)
Flying	289.5kg (640lb)
Wing loading	17.3kg/m^2 (3.54lb/ft^2)

Performance
Best glide ratio (estimate) 1:27

The cockpit canopy with port-holes of the prototype Petrel, as ordered by Frank Charles (*Slingsby collection*)

A post-war photograph of Slingsby Petrel BGA 418 in flight. (*C. Brown*)

A characteristic view of the Petrel on approach to landing. The very thick wing root and pronounced taper, with the gull wing, give it a highly distinctive appearance. (*M. Simons*)

Possibly the last photograph of Charles in the cockpit before his fatal accident in the Petrel. (*Wills collection*)

The instrument panel of BGA 418. The knob on the left is the tow release. (*M. Simons*)

BGA 651 for a few years was restored partly to its original clear-doped and varnished finish. It is seen here at a vintage rally at Sutton Bank. It has since been repainted. (*M. Simons*)

The instrument panel of BGA 651. The tuft of wool on the pitot tube is the most sensitive slip indicator available, and the cheapest. (*M. Simons*)

A Petrel being rigged at the Long Mynd in 1978. The wing section at the root is clearly shown. It was taken directly from the Rhönadler, and is a greatly modified form of the Göttingen 652. This is the aircraft flown by Watt in 1939. (*M. Simons*)

The contest number 19 and the transparent canopy identify this Petrel as that flown by P .M. Watt, taking a winch launch at the 1939 National Competitions. (*A. E. Slater*)

The only Petrel built with a fixed tailplane, BGA 651 flew in Eire for many years and was retired to a museum. It was returned in 1973 to England. The wheeled dolly is dropped after take-off. (*M. Russell*)

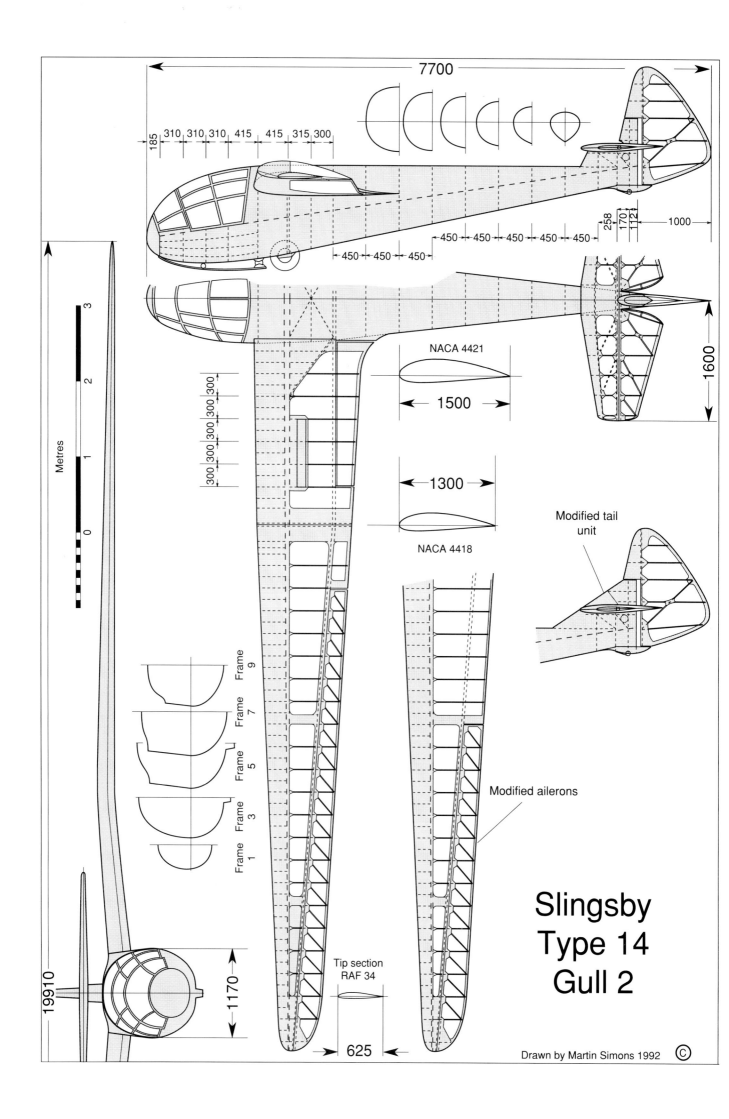

7700

185 310 310 310 415 415 315 300

450 450 450

450 450 450 450 450

258 170 112

1000

1600

Metres

3

2

1

0

300 300 300 300

NACA 4421

1500

1300

NACA 4418

Modified tail unit

Modified ailerons

Frame 9

Frame 7

Frame 5

Frame 3

Frame 1

19910

1170

Tip section RAF 34

625

Slingsby
Type 14
Gull 2

Drawn by Martin Simons 1992 ©

Type 14, Gull 2

The Type 14 Gull 2 was unlucky in the hour of its birth. Fred Slingsby began on this large high-performance two-seater in 1938, but shelved it temporarily to work on the Petrel. *Sailplane and Glider* carried a general-arrangement drawing and a brief description of the projected aircraft in January 1939. It was expected to be ready for test flying in April, but Slingsby was short of staff. In July the Gull 2 was again advertised as nearing completion, but was not actually ready for test flying until October, by which time Britain was at war.

It was by far the largest and most complex aircraft Slingsby had undertaken, and it was expensive, representing a large investment for his small company. What prompted him to produce it is not clear. With the British gliding movement still relatively small and the demand for advanced cross-country two-seaters limited, he cannot have expected many sales. According to statements published years later, Slingsby recognised the need for students to be trained in cross-country soaring, to increase the number of 'Silver C' pilots in Britain. In the long run this would have increased the market for all of his aircraft. If he thought like this in 1938 he was well ahead of the British gliding clubs, among whom such ideas had hardly begun to dawn. Probably he hoped to satisfy a few relatively wealthy private customers, one or two of whom might have been interested in such an aircraft. He would also have had an eye open for the export market.

To assist with design work, stressing and drawing he employed Thoby Fisher, now a well qualified young engineer. Even with this help, much of the construction was done in advance of drawings. Using the general-arrangement and basic layout plans, full-scale lofting was carried out on the shop floor, the results being transferred to paper later. The Gull was unusual in having the seats arranged side-by-side. This increased the frontal area of the fuselage compared with contemporary two-seaters such as the German Kranich but Slingsby, with the experience of his Falcon 3 behind him, believed that many pilots preferred this arrangement. The performance would not suffer much because the general aerodynamic shape was good.

The alternative of tandem seats led to various difficulties. The Kranich, for example, placed the second pilot behind the mainspar with his head emerging between the wings. He was surrounded by structure, able to see upwards but not forward or downwards except through very inadequate transparent panels in the wing root, nor even directly sideways because the gull dihedral cut off most of the view in that direction. Other designs had placed the second pilot entirely under the wing, which gave excellent view downwards, but not forwards or upwards and sideways into the direction of a banked turn in a thermal. The solution of a forward-swept wing had been adopted for the magnificent Kim-3 Stakhanovetz which set world records in the USSR, but this raised structural problems and would have required some unfamiliar stressing and stiffness calculations. A side-by-side arrangement simplified every aspect of design and construction. The only disadvantage, apart from the small drag penalty, was that if the aircraft was ever flown solo it would require ballast to compensate for the absent pilot, to bring the c.g. within safe limits. Slingsby was not the first designer to adopt this seating arrangement, but there were only one or two precedents in the high-performance class of sailplane.

The Original Gull 2 sketches showed a wingspan of 18.3m (60ft). As work progressed the weight and wing loading estimates were revised. The span was extended to nearly 20m (65½ft), with an aspect ratio over 18. A tapered planform was adopted, with a very slight change of taper on the leading edge outboard of the gull dihedral bend. The wing sections, from the NACA four-digit series, were almost the same as those on the Kirby Gull single-seater, but at the extreme root the 21 per cent thick 4421 was used to give plenty of spar depth. Washout and a progressive change of aerofoil section to RAF. 34 at the tips was expected to ensure adequate lateral control at low speeds and prevent dangerous wing dropping at the stall. To prevent negative angles of attack over the outer panels at high speeds, the washout angle was kept to the minimum necessary.

The Gull 2 was stressed for a normal load factor of 8*g* and inverted 6*g*. The stalling speed was about 56kmh (35mph), and the estimated best glide ratio was 1:29.5, which was probably optimistic. Nevertheless, the performance would have been extremely good by the standards of the day. With the higher aspect ratio and up-to-date wing profiles the Gull 2 must have been superior, in terms of sheer gliding performance, to the successful Kranich which dated back to 1935. There had certainly never been anything as good available in Britain.

To rig and de-rig such a large aircraft and to carry it by road on a trailer made it necessary to construct the wing in more than two segments. Slingsby decided on three, a centre section and two outer panels. The three components of the wing were of fairly similar weights, the centre section weighing 196kg (431lb) and the outer panels 176kg (387lb) each. This made it feasible for a relatively small ground crew to assemble or de-rig the Gull 2. Even so, without special equipment five able-bodied persons were necessary. The rudder could easily be removed for transport, so the trailer to carry the Gull 2 needed to be very little longer than the outer wing sections, 7m (23ft).

The mainspar of the centre section was continuous across the fuselage, the flanges being laminated in spruce and incorporating the gull dihedral form. A diagonal sub-spar was used to transfer the torsional loads from the plywood covered 'D' wing nose to the rear root connection. The plywood stressed skin of the leading edges of the whole wing ahead of the mainspar was laid with the grain diagonal, increasing its torsional resistance. Behind the mainspar, as usual, the wing was covered with fabric. In the original schematic sketch of 1938 only flaps were shown. These were intended not only for landing but to aid turning tight circles in thermals. It was soon, very sensibly, decided to include spoilers on the upper surface as well. The flaps were confined to the inboard panels, clear of the bend in the wing, and the spoilers too were built into the centre section. The fuselage was hung on to this very strong unit with four plain steel pins locked with wire. Much weight and cost was saved by obviating the need for massive metal fittings to accommodate the powerful bending loads in the middle. The ailerons, with diagonal bracing, extended over most of the outer wing, carried on an auxiliary spar which, inboard, connected with the flap supporting spar.

The fuselage was of standard semi-monocoque type. The cross-section changed progressively from a nearly circular form at the front to a pear or heart shape with a pointed keel at the rear. There were two large and comfortable seats under a large panelled Plexiglas canopy which had butterfly-type doors, and a large landing wheel, essential on a sailplane of this size and weight, with a skid forward. When fully rigged, a large built-up plywood fairing covered the junction of wing to fuselage. The tail unit was orthodox but the tailplane was mounted high on a sub-fin. This provided additional area clear of any blanketing effects to help spin

recovery, and also kept the tail clear of the ground when landing in rough fields.

Completed at last, the Gull 2 was ready for flight, but all civilian sport flying was now banned. It was not allowed to take-off, even for testing, until in April 1940 two brief circuits were permitted, after which it was immediately grounded again by official decree. A very brief film clip exists, in colour, showing Slingsby with several helpers moving the pristine new aircraft out of a hangar, probably at Welburn, and trying out the cockpit seating. It was at this time finished in the usual clear dope and varnish. This film might have been made on the occasion of the first, all too brief, flights.

Eventually the Gull 2 was requisitioned for the ATC, ostensibly to be employed for demonstrations and publicity. It was not considered suitable for use as a basic trainer. It is not clear how much flying it did during the next few years, but at least it was not smashed or allowed to deteriorate too much, as many other requisitioned aircraft were. In May 1945 a rather bitter comment, accompanying a description of the sailplane, appeared in *Sailplane and Glider*. 'Tucked away in a hangar somewhere in the North,' the article began, 'sits a high performance sailplane gathering dust but otherwise well-preserved.' The writer, who may have been Slingsby himself, ended: 'Last year the designer was given permission to make two soaring flights at Sutton Bank, but further test flights were not permitted and, apart from showing its excellent soaring qualities, speed range, and low sinking speed on the two flights at Sutton Bank, we are denied the valuable data which can only be obtained from flight tests by a qualified test pilot.'

The Gull 2 made another brief appearance, but did not compete, in the first post-war British National Championships, held at Bramcote Naval Air Station in 1947. *Sailplane and Glider*, reporting the meeting, described it and another ATC aircraft, a Falcon 3, as 'battle scarred', though the Gull 2, still clear varnished, appeared to be fully airworthy. (The Falcon did not remain airworthy long; it was broken on the airfield on the same day.)

At about this time there was a half-formed plan to take the Gull 2 to Australia to break world records over the vast plains there. How serious this project was when it was first mooted, and when it was expected to happen, is hard to establish. Philip Wills had close family and company connections with Adelaide in South Australia. He knew the country. It is just possible that this venture was in mind as early as 1938, and if so it may have been one of the factors in Slingsby's decision to produce this two-seater. Nothing came of it post-war because the Gull 2 was not made available. Despite protests it remained in ATC hands until 1951 when, at last, it was released and allocated a BGA registration. After an overhaul in the Slingsby factory the Gull was painted silver overall.

Serious test flying began in 1952, the pilot being Alan Pratt, with Ron Helm as observer and ballast in the second seat. During a soaring flight over Sutton Bank extensive spin tests were carried out with satisfactory results, but, even with their differential gearing, application of the ailerons when initiating a turn created strong adverse yaw. In any case, a sailplane of this span would be much slower in the roll than the smaller, lighter aircraft to which pilots were accustomed. The tail unit was modified to increase the fin area and the fuselage may have been lengthened. These alterations were found necessary to improve yawing stability and control. The tail moment arm was relatively short for such a large span.

Very long ailerons, as shown on the published general-arrangement drawings of 1945, were fitted when the Gull 2 was first built. During the development flying in 1952 they were greatly shortened, by six rib bays, at the inner ends. The intended effect was to lighten the feel of the lateral controls without much or any loss of control effect. At the same time, reduction of the twisting loads on the wing imposed by aileron deflections at high airspeeds reduced the likelihood of control reversal. Despite these improvements the Gull 2's ailerons were never good, and what they were like before the changes must be wondered. Roy Procter, who became a member of the owning syndicate after 1957, wrote:

At low speeds there was really excessive (adverse) drag which could not always be countered with the rudder. It was often better to make turns with full rudder and opposite aileron to use aileron drag to get some turn going! This took a bit of getting used to, but was OK once you got the hang of it. At high speeds the aileron stick forces were very high and produced little effect on the flight path. This was due to insufficient torsional stiffness of the wing. The hinge moment caused the outer wing to rotate about a spanwise centre in the opposite sense to the aileron. Result—nil. You could watch the wing and aileron rotating in opposite directions from the cockpit, which was interesting.

A fault that was even less easily overcome was the ground attitude. The wheel was slightly in front of the loaded c.g. so the tailskid was down even when two pilots were in the cockpit. Before take-off the wing was at or very close to its stalling angle. As a result, aileron control during the critical moments of a take-off run was quite inadequate. Normally a wingtip runner will keep a sailplane's wings level for a few yards but is quickly left behind. When the runner let go if the tail had not by then been raised, the Gull 2 would be moving forward with a stalled wing and little or no aileron control. If a wingtip went down, which it often did, it could not easily be brought up again and a dangerous ground loop would result unless the pilot released from the tow at once. The awkward moment could be avoided by holding the control column forward to bring the tail up immediately. After this the trick was to keep the sailplane rolling on the wheel in a flying attitude until it was ready to leave the ground, which it tended to do rather abruptly. Once airborne it behaved better.

Nearly 15 years late the Gull 2 was given its Certificate of Airworthiness. It was by now considered out-of-date, since new low drag 'laminar flow' wing profiles had come into use and had produced large improvements in sailplane performance. Wing loadings had increased. Slingsby's own Type 42 Eagle, a tandem two-seater with the new profiles, came into service in 1952 with a wing loading of over 26kg/m^2 (5.33lb/ft^2). Soaring techniques had changed. In competitions, floating away downwind to an unpredictable destination was no longer good enough. Flights were now navigated along prescribed courses with speed points in competitions for those who completed the set tasks. Yet in the hands of a skilful pilot the Gull 2 showed itself to be capable of very fine achievements under these new circumstances. The aircraft now belonged to a syndicate including Roy and Ann Procter and Brennig James. The group improved the ground attitude by fitting a longer, leaf-spring tailskid with a castering wheel. This reduced the wing's angle of attack slightly, made ground loops less damaging and helped ground handling. The group painted it yellow overall, the only markings being the BGA number 664 in small characters at the base of the fin.

James entered it in League 1 of the British National Championships, held at Lasham in July and August 1957. It was up against the latest single-seat sailplanes, Skylarks 2 and 3 and an Olympia 403, as well as some older types. A couple of Slingsby two-seat Eagles also entered this league. During the competition James in the Gull 2 established new National two-seater records, for speed round a 100km (62 mile) triangle and speed to a declared goal of 100km. The latter stood for 25 years, though this was perhaps because no-one actually bothered to attack it. On 31 July 1957 the Gull 2 missed the 200km (124 mile) triangular task speed record by 5 min, the award actually going to Derek Piggott, in the Eagle, at 35.8kmh (22.2mph). But James's crossing of the aerial start line was missed by the official timers, which cost him well over 5 min. The Gull 2 actually completed the course faster than the T-42. After seven contest days James placed 14th in a field of 28. Piggott was only two places (31 points) ahead, and the other Eagle was 22nd. All of the race times were very slow by modern standards, but the style of contest indicated the substantial change in emphasis since the Gull 2 was conceived. That the Type 14 was capable of holding its own against modern aircraft nearly 20 years after it had been first planned at Kirbymoorside says a great deal about the vision that inspired it.

On another occasion, Brennig James climbed the Gull 2 in cloud to more than 4,200m (14,000ft). It was, he said, 'a super ship, and gave us a lot of fun'. Unfortunately it did not survive much longer, being totally destroyed in an accident at Lasham owing to the lack of aileron control during the take-off. Roy Procter, who himself had had some adventures with the Gull, described the result when a new syndicate member attempted his first flight in it:

A wing touched on aero tow take-off and despite a thorough pre-flight briefing he didn't pull off. Full opposite rudder could not stop the yaw. The ailerons could not be deflected as the ground prevented this. When considerable yaw had developed, the pilot realised he could not continue and pulled off. Relieved of the pull of the tow hook, yaw got to about 90° and the aircraft became airborne, sideways. Rotation continued and the tail came up so that the machine finally hit the ground in a vertical nose-down position travelling bottom side first. The cockpit was smashed, the fuselage was in at least two pieces and one wing was reduced to matchwood. The rest wasn't in very good shape either.

The pilot was unhurt but very much chastened. Brennig James bought the wreck from the insurance company and gave it to the ATC, but it was not considered worth repairing.

Had Slingsby been able to develop the Gull 2 in 1945, he could have corrected its faults and might have marketed a two-seater with a performance in advance of anything available elsewhere. He evidently did consider the possibility of building a new prototype. A solitary sketch plan for a new version Gull 2 was found in the factory archives. It showed a redesigned fuselage, lengthened, with greatly enlarged vertical tail areas and a simpler, stepped type of transparent cockpit canopy instead of the contoured, built-up Plexiglas panelled type. There would have been large airbrakes, opening above and below the wing, similar to those

that were subsequently used for the Slingsby T-34 Sky. The flaps were retained, and also the very long ailerons of the original prototype before modification. Slingsby must have decided that it would not have succeeded in repaying the necessary investment and abandoned the project.

Gull 2 data

Dimensions

Wingspan	19.91m (65.33ft)
Wing area	21.74m^2 (234ft^2)
Aspect ratio	18.23
Wing sections:	
Root	NACA 4421
Mid-span	NACA 4418
Tip	NACA RAF. 34
Length o.a.	7.70m (21.98ft)

Weights

Tare	293.5kg (651lb)
Flying	458.6kg (1,011lb)
Wing loading	21.0kg/m^2 (4.3lb/ft^2)

Performance

Best glide ratio (estimate) 27:1

The Gull 2 nearing completion. Fred Slingsby (right) and an unknown assistant check the controls. Note the 'butterfly' type canopy. In the background are the A frame and wings of a Slingsby primary glider bearing the old golden eagle trade mark. (*Slingsby collection*)

The Gull 2 on aero-tow in 1957, before competing in the National Championships. The enlarged fin is well shown here, and a trim tab has been added to the elevator. This was probably not adjustable in flight. The tow release is on the belly of the aircraft. A small castering tail-wheel has been added. This also reduced the ground angle, assisting lateral control in the early stages of a take-off run. (*Charles E. Brown, RAF Museum, Hendon, neg No. 6712-8*)

Although this photograph is rather dark, the short ailerons and the flaps may be seen. (*Charles E. Brown, RAF Museum, Hendon, neg No. 6712-12*)

The Gull 2 fuselage outside the workshop, showing a wing root template clipped temporarily in place. (*Slingsby collection*)

A photograph of unknown origin, but probably showing preparations for a test flight about 1952. The long tube may have been used to suspend a static bomb below the fuselage when in flight, to check the position error of the air speed indicator. Note the 'Ottfur' aero-tow release. Later photographs show this taped over, with the towline attached to the belly hook.

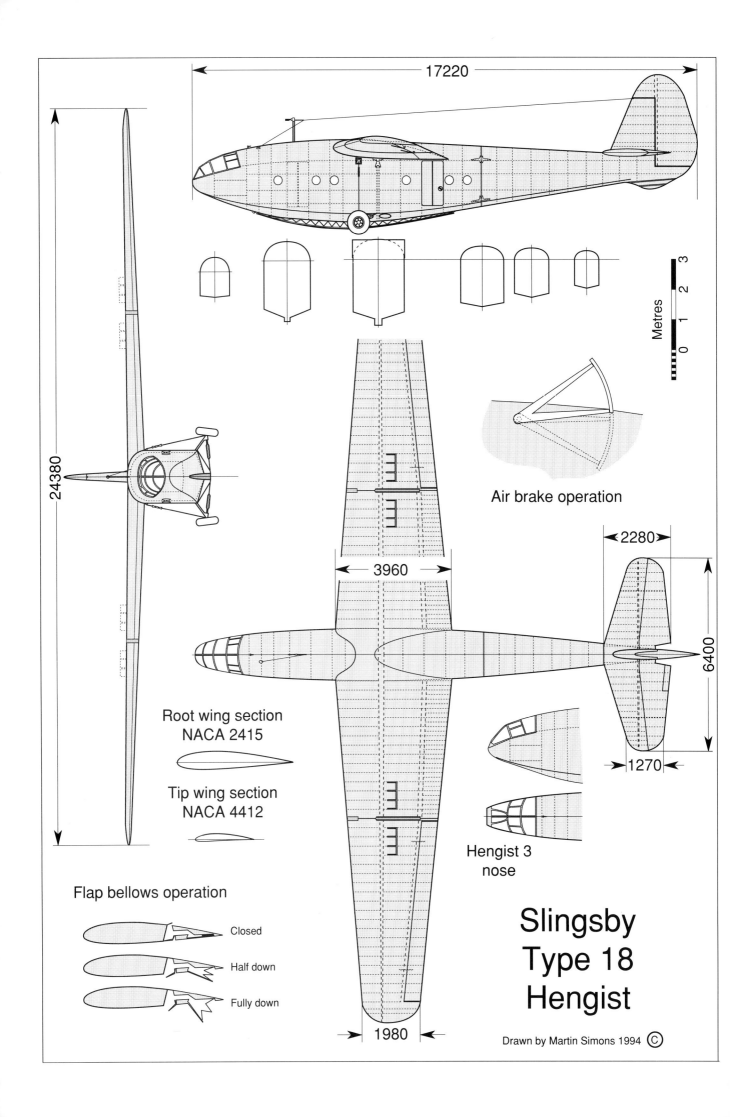

17220

24380

3960

1980

2280

6400

1270

Air brake operation

Root wing section
NACA 2415

Tip wing section
NACA 4412

Hengist 3
nose

Flap bellows operation

Closed

Half down

Fully down

Metres

0 1 2 3

Slingsby
Type 18
Hengist

Drawn by Martin Simons 1994 ©

Type 18, Hengist

At the outbreak of the Second World War, Slingsby was in process of shifting his works from the premises in Kirbymoorside village to a new factory off Ings Lane, a short distance to the south. Major J. E. D. Shaw, who had encouraged and helped the previous relocation to Kirbymoorside from Scarborough, underwrote the move, and the company was reorganised with increased capital. It seemed the wrong time for such a costly expansion. The outbreak of war brought civilian flying to a standstill, and the orderbooks emptied overnight. The Gull 2 was completed but immediately put into storage. Slingsby's Type 16 was never built. It was an interesting project for a small sailplane using the outer wings of the two-seat Gull 2 adapted to fit the fuselage of the Kite 1 and the tailplane of the Gull 1. Nothing beyond a speculative general-arrangement drawing was ever done. A subcontract for rudders for Avro Ansons kept the factory going, and a little work was done preparing gliders for radar trials on the south coast of England.

Exactly when the idea of using gliders to carry troops into battle originated, and who thought of it, is not really known. There is a tradition that, when passing through Munich airport in 1934, Adolf Hitler saw the huge Obs meteorological research sailplane and inspected it. Hitler was in Munich for a political meeting, the Obs for a meteorological conference. The glider spanned 26m (85ft) and could carry three people and a large quantity of meteorological instruments. Very possibly the almighty Führer made some remark or asked a question about the possibilities of using such aircraft in war. Early warnings of aircraft approaching at that time relied on sound detectors and eyesight. Neither was dependable and a glider, or a whole fleet of them, might arrive silently at a chosen objective in the early hours of dawn and deploy troops before the enemy even knew an attack was imminent. If Hitler said anything of the kind, his minions might have felt obliged to take it seriously. Ernst Udet, too, is credited with the original suggestion that the Obs could be adapted for carrying soldiers on secret surprise attacks. Certainly Kurt Student, who eventually

became commander of German airborne forces, saw military transport gliders in the USSR in 1936 and remembered them when he needed vehicles capable of delivering heavy equipment and troops into action. The soldiers would arrive in the gliders with their commanders in organised groups and have heavy equipment immediately available, rather than being scattered individually by parachute over large areas and having to find a rendezvous, then locate and unpack containers which might be equally scattered or even lost.

Whatever the origins of the idea, by 1937 the German military command had a prototype glider, the DFS 230, capable of carrying nine fully-equipped soldiers. After extensive tests by Student and his men it was secretly put into large-scale production in 1939. On 10 May 1940 a highly successful early dawn attack by gliders on Fort Eben Emael and bridges nearby in Belgium shocked military minds all over the world. In Britain, as in the USA and other countries, glider forces were planned and specifications for suitable aircraft were drafted.

Slingsby became involved immediately, and tendered an outline design, the Type 17, in response to the first Air Ministry specification for an eight-seat troop carrying glider. It had a cantilever gull wing of 21.34m (70ft) span. The official requirement at this time was for a glider that would be towed to a great height to make a long, silent approach to an objective, relying on surprise for success. The Slingsby design was not accepted, the General Aircraft Hotspur being approved instead. The Kirbymoorside factory built 13 Hotspurs under contract.

A new specification, X. 25/40, was issued very soon afterwards. This called for a larger glider capable of carrying 15 fully armed paratroops, the intention now being that the gliders would be towed in pairs for the soldiers to jump from them over their target, the gliders then being towed home again. Slingsby responded promptly. A mock-up of the design was ready for inspection by 22 January 1941. Construction of the prototype began, and it was completed 12 months later to fly at Dishforth, towed by an Armstrong Whitworth Whitley bomber.

The Hengist, as it was called, was by far the largest aircraft built at Kirbymoorside, with a span of 24.3m (80ft) and an empty weight of 2,104kg (4,629lb). The wing was a simple tapered form with the NACA 2415 profile at the root and 4412 at the tip. For approach control, split trailing-edge flaps and airbrakes on the upper side of the wing were fitted. Both were of unusual design. Rather than simple hinged spoilers or the parallel ruler action of the Schempp-Hirth brakes used in Germany, the brake paddles of the Hengist were plates curved on a transverse axis and housed vertically inside the wing at the mid-chord station, with their concave side facing forward. In action they pivoted around a centre some distance in front, emerging from their letterbox-like slots to present their concave side to the airflow, braced by radial arms. The landing flaps had a highly ingenious system of bellows to assist the pilot in operation. To lower them, air scoops opened into the high-pressure zone under the wing and filled the bellows, which expanded to force the flaps down. To raise them the scoops were closed and the bellows then vented to the upper, low-pressure side of the wing and the flaps came up. This scheme, developed and patented by Slingsby with advice from the RAE at Farnborough, worked very well.

The wing was built in three pieces. A centre section was mounted directly on the fuselage, carrying the flaps and one set of brakes. The outer sections, port and starboard, carried the ailerons and the second set of brakes. The wing structure was similar to that of sporting sailplanes, comprising a single mainspar, built-up ribs and a light auxiliary spar to carry the control surfaces. The whole wing was skinned with plywood.

The fuselage was basically rectangular in cross-section, but with a round back and a V shaped underside, cross-frames and longerons, all skinned with plywood. In side view it was gracefully streamlined. The pilot and copilot had a fully enclosed cabin with the transparent canopy built on a wooden frame of hoops with curved sheets of transparent plastic. The roof of the crew compartment could be jettisoned to allow rapid exit in an emergency. The two-seat cockpit had dual controls. The ailerons were operated by cables from large pulleys attached to the back of wheel-type controls and thence to the wing via bellcranks and pushrods. The auxiliary controls, flaps, tow release, trimmers and brakes were between the seats. A rudimentary instrument panel was fitted, and a standard Service compass was mounted under the pilot's left knee. The seats for the troops were comfortably shaped plywood mouldings with steel supporting frames, facing inwards in two cabins under the wing, one ahead of the main frame and one behind. Folding doors, one on the starboard side forward of the wing and one to port under the trailing edge, allowed parachutists to exit simultaneously from the front and rear cabins. Cylindrical chutes for dropping equipment

were built in, and various other items required by the authorities, including radio, were fitted.

Aft of the rear cabin the fuselage could be hinged sideways to reduce the length of the component for transport on the ground. A long landing skid sprung with an inflated rubber tube extended along most of its length, and there was a tailskid, also with pneumatic springing. A wheeled undercarriage was provided for ground handling, to be jettisoned after take-off. The tail unit was a straightforward wooden structure with ribs and plywood skin. The elevator had inset hinges to provide aerodynamic balance, and a trim tab. The rudder was horn balanced.

Early test flying proved the basic design to be satisfactory and the controls light in operation, although the second prototype was wrecked in an accident at Dishforth in 1943. Position could be maintained on tow without strain, although some lateral instability was apparent. A diving descent after release to reduce the time exposed to attack could be made at 80kt. A suitable approach speed for landing was 56kt and with flaps deployed touchdown was at 35kt.

Modifications were made to the undercarriage and to the shape of the front cockpit canopy, replacing the curved panels at the extreme front with flat sheets to provide an undistorted view directly ahead. The final outcome was the Hengist Mark 3, and a further 14 were built. The only serious problem was the tailskid, which became overheated by friction during tows along the ground. If no tail dolly was available the tailskid had to be constantly cooled by buckets of water to prevent it setting the aircraft on fire. Tailwheels would have been necessary if the Hengist had been produced in large numbers.

By the time the Hengist was ready for production, official policies had changed again. Paratroops would be dropped from powered aircraft. Gliders would be towed at low altitude until very near their designated landing zone, and after release would get down as quickly as possible with heavy equipment. The Hengist fuselage was not wide enough to carry vehicles or field guns and could not easily be adapted to do so. The Airspeed Horsa and the American Waco CG-4 Hadrian were preferred, and Hengist production ceased. Most of the 18 were stored, but one or two were used experimentally, all being scrapped by 1946.

The Hengist was a good-looking aircraft, but perhaps too much like a sailplane for its intended purpose. It met the specification for which it had been designed and incorporated some ingenious ideas in the flaps and airbrakes. Slingsby did not build any military gliders after this, but was involved with servicing and modifications of the Waco CG-4 Hadrian when it began arriving in quantities from the USA.

Half-a-dozen experimental target gliders of 4.88m (16ft) span, designated Type 19, were made by Slingsby under contract to the International Model Aircraft Company of Merton, south west London. Some quantities of these were produced by Lines Brothers Ltd, the toy company associated with IMAC.

The Bat, a tailless glider of 10.15m (33.33ft) span was built at Kirbymoorside in 1943. This was to establish the feasibility of a tank with wings which could be towed to a battle area, glide down to land and discard the wings to go immediately into battle. The originator of this idea was Leslie E. Baynes, designer of the Scud sailplanes. The Bat flew successfully in 1943, but the winged tank scheme was not taken further in Britain. Instead, the General Aircraft Hamilcar glider, which could carry a 7-ton tank, was designed and produced in quantity. In the USSR the Krylia Tank, a T-60 6-ton tank with a set of biplane wings and a tail on twin booms, was flown briefly in 1941 but proved to be impractical.

During and after 1943 the Slingsby works became much occupied with production, repair and maintenance of Cadet gliders for the ATC.

Hengist data

Dimensions

Wingspan	24.38m (80ft)
Wing area	72.46m² (780ft²)
Aspect ratio	8.2
Wing sections:	
Root	NACA 2415
Tip	NACA 4412
Length o.a.	17.22m (56.5ft)

Weights

Tare	2,100kg (4,629lb)
Flying	3,788kg (8,350lb)
Wing loading	52.3kg/m² (10.7lb/ft²)

Performance
Best glide ratio (estimate) 14 :1

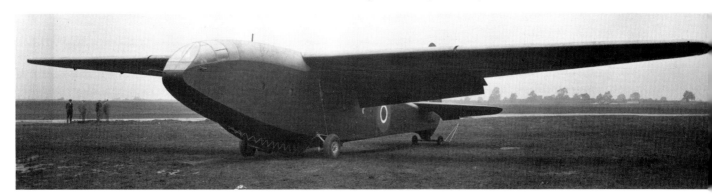

HENGIST I (GLIDER)
OCT. 1942

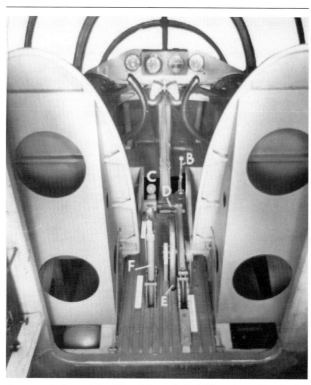

A general view of the Hengist cockpit. (*Slingsby collection*)

Folding doors for the paratroops to jump from. Note the seats folded away on either side. (*Slingsby collection*)

The forward cabin, with seats for paratroops. When not in use the seats could be folded up against the wall. The cockpit is visible in front. (*Slingsby collection*)

The rear cabin, with seats and a view down to the tail inside the fuselage. Chutes for supply dropping are visible in the floor. (*Slingsby collection*)

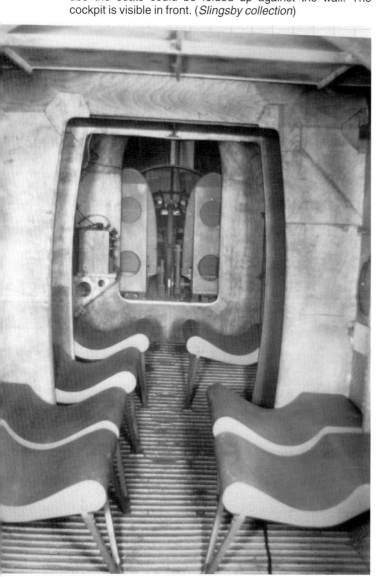

The Hengist prototype with rounded nose. The tail dolly was necessary to prevent the tail-skid overheating when dragged over the bitumen runway. (*Slingsby collection*)

The cockpit, with wheel-type controls. The compass is mounted on the floor. (*Slingsby collection*)

The undercarriage, a long, sprung skid with wheels. (*Slingsby collection*)

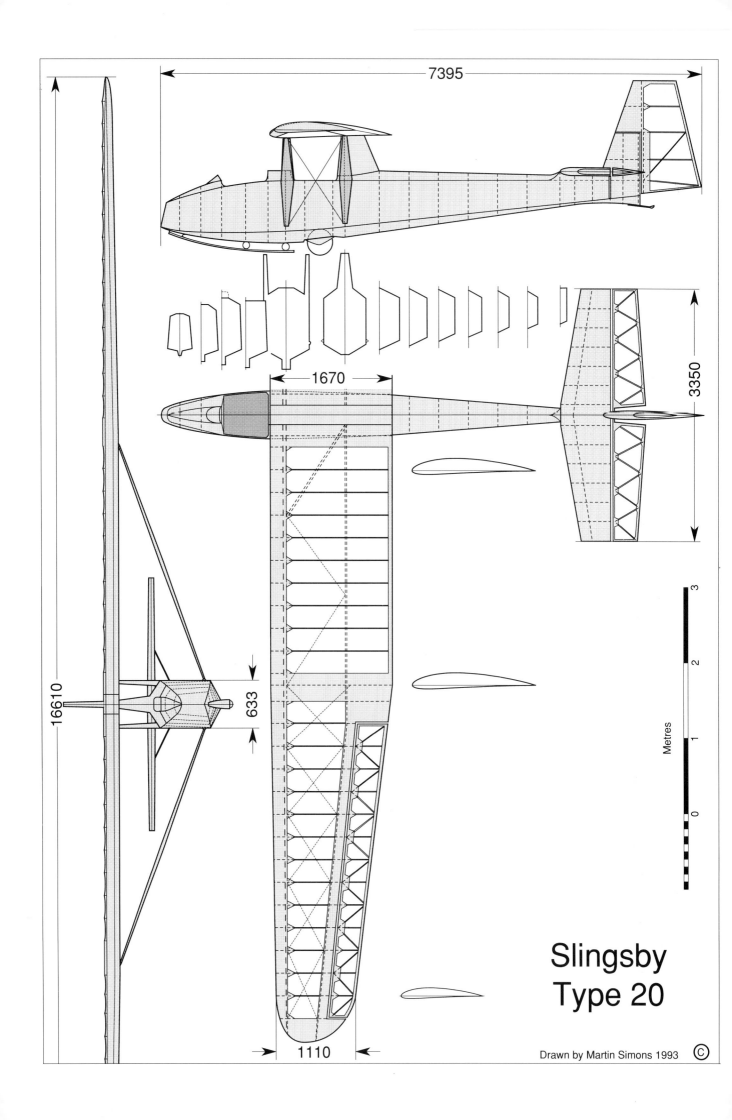

7395

1670

3350

16610

633

1110

Metres

3   2   1   0

Slingsby
Type 20

Drawn by Martin Simons 1993   ©

Type 20

The ATC was still using solo training methods. As he contemplated the numerous broken gliders that came in for rebuilding, Slingsby recognised the need for some inexpensive and robust two-seat training gliders, and as a private venture set about the design of two, his Types 20 and 21. Both first flew in 1944.

By ordinary standards the T-20 failed. Only the prototype was built, and it was not ordered by the ATC. No attempt seems to have been made to sell it to the civilian clubs in post-war years. It never achieved BGA or Air Ministry registration, and, except for a few people who were directly concerned with it, it is now almost totally forgotten. Yet this aircraft had a remarkable career and met a unique fate.

There is a good deal of doubt concerning the details of the design. The general-arrangement drawing published by Slingsby in March 1945 differs considerably from the few known photographs, and the accompanying drawing is the best that can be made from the available evidence. (If any further information is available, the author would be glad to hear of it.) Probably there never were any very detailed drawings, much of the layout work being done by direct lofting in the workshops. Such jigs and tools as were needed were probably stored for a while and destroyed when it became clear that the type would not go into production.

The wing was based on that of the very successful Type 8 Tutor but considerably enlarged. It was fabric covered, and had two spars with internal torsion resisting diagonal members, parallel struts and wire bracing. A light plywood skinning of the leading edge gave a smooth entry for the airflow, but contributed little to the strength. The wing section was NACA 4412. Apparently spoilers were fitted, although these were not shown on the published drawing. The drawing also showed V struts and a rounded rudder, which do not appear on photographs of the aircraft. As explained below, flaps were added later.

The central cabane was similar to that of the earlier Falcon 1, with two vertical struts forward and a single pylon aft so that the wing sat high above the rear cockpit. Aileron cables were partly external, running from bellcranks on either side of the rear cockpit into the wing. The fuselage was very simple, being hexagonal in cross-section with the two cockpits in tandem. There was a landing wheel mounted slightly aft of the loaded c.g., with a main skid sprung with the usual hard rubber doughnuts. The tail unit was equally straightforward, the rudder resembling that of an enlarged Tutor with a tailskid to protect it. The tail unit design may have been used again for the prototype T-21 and for a later two-seater, the T-24, but this is not certain. The outlines were similar. It is not known definitely whether the fuselage of the T-20 was plywood skinned or whether, like a succession of later Slingsby types, it was a fabric covered, open framed structure.

The T-20 in wartime paint and bearing RAF roundels was tested and, according to Slingsby, approved by the ATC but disliked by RAF Training Command, who had the final say. It was not ordered.

Soaring was still forbidden, but most qualified glider pilots by now were either serving members of the fighting forces or ATC instructors, so on many occasions the letter of the law was not followed. On at least one day several sailplanes were launched to soar illegally in the slope lift at Sutton Bank, including the Type 20 and Prince Bira's Cantilever Gull 3. Philip Wills and his son Christopher, then in his early teens, flew the T-20 and found it to their liking. The T-21 remained in the hangar. It was stated in December 1944 that both of the new two-seaters had achieved many flying hours, but neither was accepted by official test pilots. The two prototypes languished in store.

In 1945 John Sproule, designer of the original Kirby Kadet and Tutor, and now a naval officer, arrived at the Slingsby works and took the T-20 away. It was wanted by the Admiralty. Sproule wrote later:

At 10.30 on the morning of May 29th, 1945, I was airborne in a Slingsby T-20 two-seat glider about 300ft over the waters of the Irish Sea, in a position about ten miles off the north-east coast of the Isle of Man. It struck me at the time that this was a very funny place to be flying a glider.

Many accidents on or behind aircraft carriers had been attributed to air turbulence aft of the ship. Wind tunnel tests on models at the National Physical Laboratory revealed no very obvious cause but the number of occasions on which a pilot lost control just before arriving over the flight deck convinced the Royal Navy that systematic tests needed to be done at sea. According to Sproule:

> After discarding all sorts of ideas, from streaming smoke to towing balloons, someone hit on the idea of towing a glider from a carrier and getting the pilot to explore the whole of the airspace behind the ship in a methodical manner. The glider was to be equipped with recording instruments to indicate roll and pitch with great accuracy, so that, provided the glider could be maintained at fixed levels, the up trends and down trends in the ship's air wake could be deduced. Accordingly the call went out for *someone who knew about gliders* to find a suitable machine and, if possible, perform as the pilot thereof.

In view of his pre-war experience, the lot fell upon Sproule. He, as it happened, was glad to avoid an imminent posting to India. Instead he was despatched inland to look for a suitable glider and found the Type 20 unloved and asleep at Kirbymoorside.

After testing it by soaring it at Sutton Bank (with ample excuses), Sproule took the aircraft to Wombleton Aerodrome for modifications. Since it was to be towed over the sea at a relatively slow rate of knots it was necessary to get the stalling speed down. Drag was not important, since there should be no lack of power. Large fixed flaps were designed and fitted, locked down at 30°. With a 10ft towing rope attached to a car, the T-20 could be towed across the aerodrome a few feet off the ground at a brisk trotting pace. Meanwhile, the Admiralty research scientists devised an instrument package which was installed in the rear cockpit, with various probes and flow indicators attached to the wings and struts.

The aircraft carrier *Pretoria Castle* was based in the Clyde, and there Sproule and the scientists went with the glider. On 29 May the sailplane on the flight deck was attached to the winch cable as the ship turned into wind. Sproule was in the front cockpit, wearing a life jacket:

> The T-20, positioned about 60ft forward of the round-down, had been equipped with walkie-talkie-type radio and rope pennants on each wingtip. And a loop of rope on the centre section to hold on to if the worst came to the worst! Sailors were stationed on each of the tip ropes and at the nose to keep the machine steady until I gave the word to go. When the ship was on course into the wind and with 35mph on my ASI, I got the green flag from the batsman and no sooner had I given the word than I was airborne. My Elisha-like vertical ascent was surprisingly easy as I pulled back against the tow cable and I let the glider ride at about 50ft above the deck. The glider controlled in normal fashion so I used the lift spoilers to

> jockey my way down to the deck of the ship again, where the aircraft handlers were waiting to grab me.

The exercise was repeated successfully a few times before Sproule called on the winch driver to pay out more line. Now he climbed smoothly to about 250ft, watching the deck recede until he was hovering a ship's length behind. The air was perfectly smooth here and he was able to move up, down and far out to each side without trouble.

Suddenly he noticed a drastic loss of airspeed. The ship was at full speed but had sailed into a lull in the surface wind, and the T-20 began to lose height. Sproule called anxiously for more power. At the crucial moment the winch motor stalled and the glider continued to wallow downwards. With the huge flaps fixed down there was no chance for the sailplane to penetrate upwind to reach the deck. The deck officer hastily tried to organise a rope heaving party but Sproule prepared for a ducking. At the last moment the winch was restarted. With a mighty jerk the cable tightened and the T-20 quickly rose again to 200ft. Rather shaken, Sproule flew himself back to the deck. He had little to report about the air motions in the ship's wake except that he had found no turbulence or unexpected difficulties until the wind dropped.

The scientists were not pleased with their records, and found it necessary to redesign the instruments. The party returned to shore for further work on the apparatus, and Sproule was posted temporarily away to learn to fly helicopters. Eventually the new package was ready for testing and the group reassembled at Wombleton. There was further towing of the glider round and round a few feet up until the 'boffins' were satisfied.

After another interval of several months, during which the fleet was rather busy with other matters, the sea-going tests were resumed, this time from the deck of HMS *Illustrious* in the English Channel. Sproule now had a deputy who was to take turns with him in the glider. He made several flights himself first to prove the system, and all went well. His deputy, who was an experienced pilot with some gliding time, now climbed into the cockpit and received a careful briefing:

> On the word 'Go' the glider was released in the normal manner, but this time, instead of pulling back on the stick and getting well clear of the deck, as had been carefully explained, my friend continued to fly about three or four feet above the deck in a zero incidence condition. In this unsatisfactory situation he allowed the T-20 to begin to weave left and right until, for some reason which I still do not understand, he weaved right across over the starboard side of the flight deck still only about ten feet above the take-off level.

The tow cable became tangled with one of the radio masts, which were lowered to the horizontal position during flying operations. The T-20 disappeared over the side, the wing scraping the hull as it flopped into the sea. Those on deck saw it reappear in the wake, bobbing like a duck on the waves, the pilot having promptly got out of the cockpit on to the wing to clutch the rope which Sproule had installed there for this very purpose. The guard destroyer rescued him, but the glider remained afloat.

After a quick conference it was decided that the sailplane was not worth saving. By this time the Navy was well into the helicopter era, and if any further wake tests behind aircraft carriers were needed they could be done more efficiently with these aircraft. Sproule himself saw no future in gliding from the flight deck. To prevent it becoming a hazard to shipping in the Channel, the glider was rammed and broken into small pieces by the destroyer.

So ended the Slingsby T-20. It was the only glider ever to be flown from an aircraft carrier at sea, both taking off and landing on, and the only sailplane ever to be sunk by the Royal Navy.

Slingsby Type 20 data

Dimensions

Wingspan	16.61 m (54ft 6in)
Wing area	26.94m² (290ft²)
Aspect ratio	10.0
Wing sections:	NACA 4412
Length o.a.	7.39m (24ft 3in)

Weights

Tare	231kg (509lb)
Flying	453.6kg (1,000lb)
Wing loading	17.6kg/m² (3.63lb/ft²)

Performance
Max L/D 18:1 (Claimed)

Under test on dry land. Fitted with flaps, the T-20 was towed by car across Wombleton aerodrome. With flaps locked down at 30°, the stalling speed was reduced well below 22mph (35 kmh). The prominent end-plates on the inner end of the flaps were intended to improve the airflow but were evidently found unnecessary and were removed before the sea trials. (*J. S. Sproule*)

The cockpits. The front cockpit at this time had two instruments only, an altimeter and airspeed indicator, housed in a small console which also acted as a windscreen. There seems also to have been a spirit or bubble level mounted below them. Note the external aileron cable, with turnbuckle. The tow release knob is on the left of the cockpit. (*Slingsby collection*)

Soon after completion at Kirbymoorside. The T-20 in a carefully posed head-on view. (*F. N. Slingsby*)

Preparations for a hand launch. The T-20, with pilot and instruments aboard, is airborne but is still held by some of the deck crew. (*Admiralty photo from J. S. Sproule*)

Fully airborne, with wing-tip ropes still held by the crew. (*Admiralty photo from J. S. Sproule*)

Now fully flying, only the wing-tip ropes to let go. (*Admiralty photo from J. S. Sproule*)

A view from the bridge. The T-20 is just airborne, restrained by the crew. The winch, and a small tractor, are seen in the right foreground. (*Admiralty photo from J. S Sproule*)

Landing on. The crew wait to grab the glider as it comes down. The winch, having pulled the cable in, stands idle. (*Admiralty photo from J. S. Sproule*)

Rising on the cable with the wing-tip ropes trailing. (*Admiralty photo from J. S. Sproule*)

Over the side of the ship! Note the guard destroyer which rescued the pilot, and, subsequently, destroyed and sank the glider by ramming. (*Admiralty*)

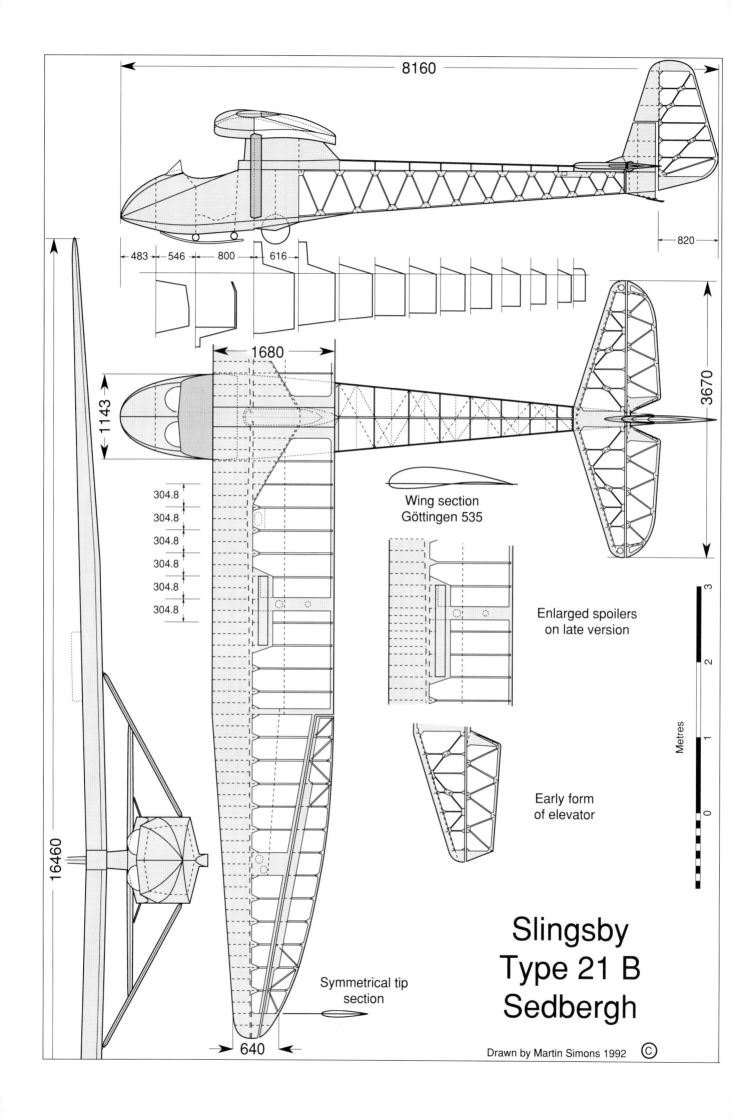

8160

820

483 · 546 · 800 · 616

1680

1143

3670

304.8
304.8
304.8
304.8
304.8
304.8

Wing section
Göttingen 535

Enlarged spoilers
on late version

Early form
of elevator

16460

640

Symmetrical tip
section

Metres

3
2
1
0

Slingsby
Type 21 B
Sedbergh

Drawn by Martin Simons 1992 ©

Type 21, Sedbergh

Although it became one of Slingsby's most successful sailplanes, the T-21 showed few signs of its eventual popularity when the prototype flew in 1944. Looking ahead to the revival of civilian soaring clubs after the war, Slingsby recognised that, as well as being safer, a reliable two-seater sailplane would save its initial capital outlay in a short time. The real costs of primary glider training were never properly accounted. Delays and frustrations cost the clubs new members, and repair bills mounted up rapidly, soon totalling more than the initial cost of the glider. An experienced ATC instructor writing in the magazine *Sailplane and Gliding* in April 1947 remarked that solo training using the Kirby Cadet was 'far from economical in practice, the glider damage rate being sufficiently high to put the average civilian club on the financial rocks in a very short space of time'. He went on to say 'I think there is little or no doubt that by far the best method of elementary training is on high-performance two-seater gliders such as the Kranich, but so far there is no suitable two-seater yet built in this country'. Slingsby was convinced that training two-seaters would be in demand for the clubs once they started operating again. There was also a large potential market in the ATC, although the future of this organisation was not very certain. The gliding schools might be severely cut or even closed down entirely once the war ended. (In the event they survived on a much reduced scale.)

A student pilot would suffer few problems if the two-seat trainer had similar handling characteristics to early solo aircraft. In this case the corresponding solo aircraft was the Grunau Baby. Slingsby enlarged this basic design to carry two pilots sitting side-by-side with dual controls. He had done much the same kind of thing years before with the Falcon and Falcon 3. The T-21 wing was aerodynamically the same as that of the Baby but with a span of 15.24m (50ft) and proportionately greater area. The same Göttingen 535 aerofoil section was used, with the same amount of wing washout to the thin symmetrical profile at the tip. There was no dihedral, but the outer wing panels, approximately elliptical in plan, were tapered on the underside.

The wing structure also followed Grunau Baby practice, comprising a single mainspar with a plywood skinned torsion resisting leading edge and simple supporting struts. The light auxiliary spar was intended only to stiffen the ribs against sideways distortion. Spoilers, rather than the more expensive dive brakes, were fitted. The aileron hinges were very simple, with fabric strips stuck on above and below to seal the inch-wide gap. Some photographs show a bracing wire from the extreme nose of the fuselage to the strut fitting on the wings, but this was evidently superfluous and was removed before long. The spoiler control cables ran externally in guides along the rear edges of the struts.

The side-by-side seating necessitated a wide fuselage. A tall, narrow pylon with an unfaired square-cut front was used to provide the central wing mounting. For reasons of balance the cockpit was placed under the leading edge of the mainplane. This was the weakest feature of the layout, since it was impossible for the pilots to look horizontally into the turn when banking. The danger of colliding with another glider was barely considered. Except in competitions, there were very few sailplanes in the air at any one time over a typical club site, and the T-21 was not seriously considered as a competition aircraft. It was not realised that at the bigger clubs many sailplanes would soon be sharing thermals and hill lift.

The older generation of instructors still maintained that the student glider pilot ought to feel the airflow as directly as possible and should learn to fly entirely without instruments. In a fully open primary glider a badly flown turn with slip or skid was instantly apparent. Airspeed variations could be sensed directly. In performing a circuit, the angle of the glider relative to the intended touchdown point was, and indeed still is, a better guide for making the approach than the altimeter. A well developed sense of what the air is doing is necessary for soaring flight, and the sooner the student learns this, the better for future performance. So it was said and there was some validity in such arguments. To satisfy such opinions the entire upper decking ahead of the seats on the T-21 was made removable so that the pupil and instructor could sit entirely in the open, as if on the seat of a Dagling. The forward deck could be put in place in cold weather, or when the pupil had developed the necessary sense of feel to manage without the rush of air all over.

The front part of the fuselage was an orthodox structure of cross-frames and longerons skinned with birch plywood. Behind the wing pylon, Slingsby used a girder system built up on four substantial spruce longerons with light diagonal struts, making a completely triangulated space frame reinforced with ply 'biscuits' at every joint. This was covered with fabric, except for plywood skinning on the underside. The fuselage was light and relatively cheap, yet strong and easily inspected and repaired. There was a large landing wheel just behind the loaded c.g. and a rubber-sprung laminated ash skid ahead of it. An aero tow release hook was mounted in the extreme nose, but the winch launching hook was under the belly just ahead of the front skid fitting. The tailplane was strut-braced, and the rudder had a large aerodynamic balance ahead of the hinge line.

Like the Type 20, the T-21 was not admired by the Air Ministry, who did not approve of Slingsby's going ahead privately with this prototype, using valuable materials and labour during wartime. What other work the factory could have been doing if it were not something of this sort is unclear, but Slingsby seems to have doubted his own judgement in producing the aircraft. Like the T-20, the T-21P (P for prototype) went into store and was almost abandoned.

It was resurrected almost accidentally. Writing about it many years afterwards, Dudley Hiscox, a founder member of the London Gliding Club, explained:

At the time the Allied armies were landing in Normandy [6 June 1944] the gliding instructors of ATC Central Command were on a course of soaring instruction and experience at Sutton Bank. There, within the more or less deserted hangar of the Yorkshire Gliding Club, was to be seen a dismantled side-by-side two-seater glider obviously of recent construction. Whatever was it and where had it come from?

Hiscox described the aircraft accurately as 'to all intents and purposes a blown-up Grunau Baby'. Slingsby ruefully told him the story. Hiscox continued:

[When] the London Gliding Club [was] about to start flying again at Dunstable, I remembered that dismantled two-seater up in Yorkshire and asked 'Sling' to let us have the use of it to help us get started. He agreed to let us fetch it so long as we promised not to write afterwards telling him what a monstrosity he had produced. There was a good soaring wind on Dunstable Downs the day we rigged and checked out the 'ugly duckling'. Sling got a letter from us all right, but not in the tone he expected. We informed him in glowing terms that his big Baby was a honey; a splendid soarer with reasonably well-balanced controls and that we wanted to buy it, not borrow it. Everyone was delighted with the acquisition.

In this way, about April 1946 the Type 21P (BGA No. 675) came to Dunstable. It was flown sometimes with the fully exposed seats, but before long the advantages of having at least some fairing over the nose and some protection for the pilots in cold weather were recognised and the decking was left on more or less permanently. The club did not immediately go over completely to dual training. Two primary gliders were ordered in 1947, as well as another two-seater. It was not until October 1947 that the club reported using the T-21P regularly for student pilot training. A fatal accident to a Dagling at the Southdown Gliding Club in August that year, and a similar though less serious crash in the same weekend at Camphill (the author being the injured pilot in this case), apparently convinced most clubs that traditional training methods should be modified. The two-seater was regarded at first only as a supplement to the usual routine of ground slides, low hops and high hops in the Dagling. At Dunstable Daglings remained in use throughout 1950, with damage reported fairly often.

In July 1948 a Tutor flown by an experienced pilot of powered aircraft who was on a gliding course and attempting a 5hr soaring flight for the 'Silver C' badge, collided with the T-21P. The Tutor lost a large part of its tailplane and crashed, killing the pilot. The two-seater's nose and wingtip were damaged, but it landed safely. In September 1949 the T-21P at Dunstable was involved in a second mid-air collision which was attributed in part to the poor view from the cockpit in turns. The other sailplane was the famous cross-Channel Kirby Gull, which crashed into bushes near the foot of the hill, the pilot luckily surviving unharmed. The T-21P again landed safely. (The Gull was rebuilt.) These accidents led to a tightening up of the hill soaring rules at Dunstable where the skies were becoming crowded, and it was emphasised that the field of view from the two-seater was restricted. At this time the club had 139 members and was easily the largest gliding club in Britain. By the end of 1952 the T-21P had flown more than 1,000hr with the club.

In 1947 Slingsby produced and exhibited an improved design, the T-21A (BGA No. 683), which appeared, without competing, at the first post-war British National Contests held in June at the Royal Naval Air Station at Bramcote, near Nuneaton. It was made available for inspection and some trial flights. Although the fuselage seemed enormously wide when compared with those of the German Kranich and the graceful Swiss Spalinger 25 which were in the contest, the new Slingsby design looked quite modern alongside the old Falcon 3, which was also present. Those who had a chance to fly it were very impressed. The large, open cockpit undoubtedly created a lot of drag, but most of the gliding instructors liked the side-by-side arrangement. They could converse easily with their pupils, observe facial expressions and see exactly what the student's hands and feet were doing. The T-21 did behave very like a large, sedate, Grunau Baby, and its performance at low speeds was quite adequate for training.

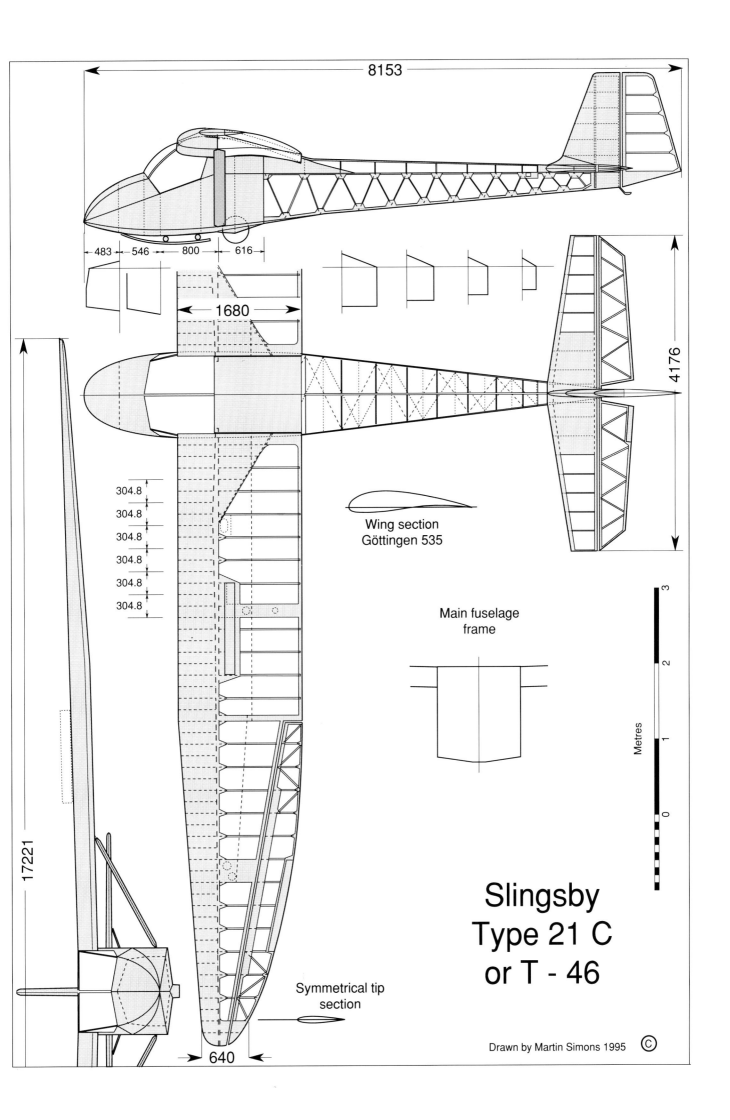

8153

483 546 800 616

1680

4176

304.8
304.8
304.8
304.8
304.8
304.8

Wing section
Göttingen 535

Main fuselage
frame

17221

Symmetrical tip
section

640

Metres

3
2
1
0

Slingsby
Type 21 C
or T - 46

Drawn by Martin Simons 1995 ©

The most important aerodynamic improvement in the T-21A was an increase in wingspan from 15.24m to nearly 16.5m (54ft). This alone gave the aircraft a better performance. A little dihedral was added, but otherwise the wing was much the same. The spoiler drive cables were rerouted internally via the fuselage pylon. There were considerable alterations to the fuselage. The depth was increased all the way from nose to tail. Where previously the pilots had been exposed from the chest upwards, even with the detachable decking in place, now only their heads protruded and two small yet quite effective windscreens were fitted. At normal flying speeds very little breeze was felt, although the student pilot's hair would be ruffled. Skids and slips in flight were instantly apparent as before.

There was now an instrument panel which had room for an altimeter, an air speed indicator, a variometer and, if required, a turn and slip indicator and compass. There were large glove compartments on either side. The spoiler handle was mounted centrally between the seats for use by either the pupil or the instructor, and the tow release knob was also central, just below the instrument panel. The cockpit sides were cut low enough to make entry and egress easy and there was room for parachutes. The pylon for the wing mounting was improved, widened slightly and given a rounded front. The fabric covered frame structure aft of the wing was similar to that of the T-21P, but stiffer because of the increased external dimensions. The rudder was redesigned with a rounded tip, mainly to improve appearance. All British gliders by now were fitted with the Ottfur safety release. The front release was eliminated, as the belly hook was quite suitable for aero towing as well as winch launching. At the correct speed and with the c.g. within limits, the T-21 would climb very well on the winch without a hand on the controls.

The T-21B first flew in December 1947. At first it was designated Type 28, but it differed only in minor details from the 21A and the old type number was retained after all. It was ordered for the ATC (after the fiasco of the Slingsby Type 24, which is described in the next chapter). The T-21B became the standard production version of the type. For the ATC it was christened the Sedbergh TX. Mk 1, after the well-known Yorkshire public school. Civil clubs usually used the original designation, T-21B but often added names which became quite famous. *Daisy* belonged to the combined Imperial College and Surrey clubs at Redhill, and was the first to be used for regular *ab initio* training. It was soon joined by *Buttercup. Dragonfly, Butterfly* and later *Firefly* flew at Dunstable, the Cambridge club had *Bluebell*, and there was even a *Lady Godiva* at Coventry.

One relatively minor design defect was corrected after a few weeks' experience. After landing on the sloping ground of the Dunstable field, the London Club's T-21B rolled backwards a few feet before the pilots could leave the cockpit to restrain it. The elevator had a sharp corner at the outer end which, in the down position, dug into the ground and shattered. All subsequent T-21s had the elevator reshaped with a rounded corner to avoid this problem.

By January 1948 Slingsby reported that three leading gliding clubs, the London, the Derbyshire and Lancashire and the Midland, had taken delivery of the T-21B. The Midland Club, based at the Long Mynd, had been doing no *ab initio* training at all during 1947, but reported that dual instruction with the T-21B began as soon as it was delivered.

Production of the 21B continued with no major changes to the design. The first to be exported was delivered to the Swedish Royal Aero Club in March 1948. Others went to Egypt, India, Jordan, Kenya, Malaya, Pakistan and South Africa . The RAF and RN Gliding and Soaring Associations ordered the type. For the British gliding clubs and overseas customers 126 were produced. In addition kits were sold, one to Leighton Park School for completion under skilled supervision by the boys. (*Min*, named after Minnie Bannister in the Goon Show, first flew in 1958.)

In 1949 tests were carried out by the Airborne Forces Experimental Establishment to prove that the Auster V was a suitable tug for the Sedbergh. It took ten minutes to reach a height of 2,000ft at an airspeed of 53kt. The ATC took a total of 73 Sedberghs from Kirbymoorside, introducing them into service in 1950, and a further 19 for the ATC were built under licence by Martin Hearn Ltd at Hooton Park. The total production was 218. The only British sailplane before or since to surpass this figure was the Slingsby T-7 Cadet. Long after production ceased, the factory at Kirbymoorside was kept busy with T-21 repairs and spares.

The changeover from solo training was not immediate throughout the land. As late as the winter of 1952 Ann Douglas (later Welch) commented in the magazine *Gliding* that a few clubs persisted with the solo method. She quoted official figures which showed that during the first six months of that year, when both systems were in use side by side in the ATC gliding schools, the accident rate was three times as great with solo training. It was also shown to be much less effective in producing pilots qualified up to the B certificate, or circuit flying, stage. Among the few civilian clubs still using solo training, two pupils had been killed. There were no fatal accidents with the two-seaters.

Intended from the beginning as a trainer, the T-21B was hardly regarded as a competitive cross-country sailplane. Despite this, three entered the 1950 National Competitions held at Camphill, Derbyshire, in July. John Furlong's *Dragonfly* had been there in 1949 but was used only for joy rides and air experience flights. In 1950 two Sedberghs entered the lists from the ATC Gliding Schools, and another came from the RAF Flying Training Command. The intention of the ATC entries was not to win the championships, but to give the instructors and cadets some worthwhile experience. It was also felt desirable for the ATC to 'show the flag' among the civilian gliding enthusiasts. Points in this competition were awarded chiefly for cross-country flying, with a large bonus for reaching a pre-declared goal, but altitude gains were also worth something, so there was a chance for the ATC aircraft to score even without leaving the site. Some of the launches were by the old method of rubber bungee from the hill top, directly into the slope lift, so any soaring flight was necessarily also a scoring flight. It was not long before the ATC crews showed they had not come merely to perform circuits. One of the most interesting flights of the meeting was that by the Sedbergh flown by Flt Lt Anderson and Wg Cdr Peter Mallett, who reached their goal at North Coates, Lincolnshire, a distance of 120km (75 miles). It was far from the longest flight of the day but it was a remarkably good effort for a training two-seater.

In the 1951 Nationals, again at Camphill, the ATC brought three of its Sedberghs and the Imperial College Gliding Club entered with *Daisy*. This was a most exciting competition with many long-distance and goal flights, Lorne Welch reaching Kent in a Weihe. On another occasion standing waves assisted many pilots on their way to the east coast, and there was a goal race to Dunstable. On the final Sunday, for the first time in a British national competition, a successful closed-circuit speed task was completed; out and return to Derby. Conditions were difficult. Philip Wills, in his Weihe, scraped home by the narrowest of margins after flying *under* telephone wires on the west facing slope of Camphill, finding a weak thermal over the valley and finally crossing the boundary of the field at a height of four or five feet to land. There was a moral victory for an ATC Sedbergh. George Charman Thomas, with a cadet in the right-hand seat, completed the task in 4hr, while several more famous pilots in far superior cross-country sailplanes did not get home.

More remarkable achievements were still to come. In May 1952 a Sedbergh from Detling, flown by Meddings and Reilly, flew 146km (91 miles) westwards to Chilbolton, winning the Seager Cup for two-seater distance flights. It became normal for the T-21B to fly across-country.

In the 1953 Nationals, a special trophy was offered by Slingsby for the most meritorious flight in a Sedbergh and John Furlong offered another for the Sedbergh with the highest total score. This 27 July Camphill meeting began with heavy rain, but with a partial clearance in the afternoon large cumulus clouds developed. Derek Piggott with cadet Brian Whateley declared for Grimsby and scratched away from the site in their Sedbergh. Over Sheffield they found strong lift under, and very soon inside, a dark cloud. Enduring bitter cold, heavy icing and turbulence which made the cadet sick and almost reduced him to unconsciousness, they climbed to more than 5,100m (17,000ft) a.s.l., a gain of 4,572m (15,240ft) from the lowest previous point of the flight. They had no oxygen supply, but Piggott reported afterwards that he did not notice any problem other than the cold, which froze his hand to the stick. The only blind flying instruments were the turn-and-slip indicator and the airspeed indicator.

On emerging from the cloud near its top the glide to Grimsby was easy, and Piggott could have gone much further but for the coast. The flight not only broke the National altitude record for two-seaters, but also set the 100km speed record for flight to a goal. The climb stood as a UK record until 1964, although it was broken before this by British pilots flying overseas. This Sedbergh was equipped with one of the first electrical-audio variometers, invented by Peter Temple. Instead of the traditional red and green indicators in vertical tubes, the instrument made clicking sounds and flashed lights, the rate of the clicks indicating the rapidity of ascent. A total-energy venturi devised by Frank Irving was also used. It did not ice up, which was surprising. One of the two barographs carried was equipped to record the airspeed on the chart as well as altitude.

Nevertheless, the main function of the type remained that of a basic trainer. The T-21B became and remained the standard, indispensable workhorse in British gliding clubs throughout the 1950s and well into the late 1960s. Its position was only gradually eroded by the introduction of newer types.

Belief in the importance of the open cockpit for training weakened as more and more early solo sailplanes were fully enclosed. In 1954 the Army Gliding Club fitted their T-21B with a neat transparent canopy which proved very popular. Influenced by this, Slingsby looked again at the design and decided it would be worth developing an improved model, the T-21C, or as it was eventually called, the T-46. The wing, hardly changed otherwise, was brought down to shoulder level, as the roots now joined directly to the wide fuselage frames instead of the narrow pylon, the span when rigged was increased to 17.22m (56.48ft). The struts were retained. The view over the banked wing in turns was somewhat improved but the pilots' heads were now inside the leading edge, so the outlook laterally was still not perfect. A capacious transparent canopy enclosed the cockpit. The tail unit was completely redesigned, necessitating some restressing before a Certificate of Airworthiness could be granted. The T-46 flew in October 1957. Although it proved satisfactory it had very few advantages as a trainer over the original T-21. It cost more, and its performance in advanced flying was limited severely by its old-fashioned wing. Aerodynamically it was still a Grunau Baby. After the sale of the prototype no further examples were produced. Slingsby went on to consider the design of a superior trainer which, a few years later, appeared as the Type 49 Capstan.

In 1983 the ATC announced that it would re-equip throughout with aircraft of glassfibre reinforced plastic structure. The remaining ATC wooden gliders, including all the surviving Sedberghs, were put up for sale, many in need of repair and restoration. Most were bought by private syndicates, examples being sold in Holland, the USA, Australia and other countries as well as in the UK.

It became a point of pride with some of the owners to show what the T-21 could do. A seven-person syndicate at Husbands Bosworth achieved more than 2,000km (1,240 miles) total distance in their T-21, many of the flights being over 200km (125 miles). In 1984, the longest cross-country by a T-21 was flown by Lou Frank and Norman James from Husbands Bosworth to a landing in Central Park, Plymouth, a distance of 317km (196 miles). Flown by a solo pilot, it would qualify for a 'Gold C' and Diamond. On 23 August 1986 the same pilots flew the T-21 from Husbands Bosworth to the Isle of Wight. A thermal over the Solent helped them across the water with sufficient altitude to continue soaring for some time before landing at Sandown. Apart from these, other T-21s have done wave flights over 3,000m (10,000ft) at the Long Mynd and Sutton Bank. Such adventures are likely to continue. There is no apparent limit to the age of a wooden sailplane. With proper care and maintenance the T-21B will continue in service indefinitely. *Bluebell* still flies with the Cambridge Gliding club, who have owned it since it was new.

Type 21 data

	Type 21P	Type 21B
Dimensions		
Wingspan	15.24m (50ft)	16.46m (54ft)
Wing area	22.4m^2* (241ft^2)	24.2m^2 (260.4ft^2)
Aspect ratio	10.37*	11.2
Length o. a.	8.16m (26ft 8in)	8.16m
Wing sections		
Root	Göttingen 535 modified	
Tip	Symmetrical	
Weights		
Tare	272kg (598lb)	
Flying	476kg (1,047lb)	
Wing loading	19.6kg/ m^2 (4lb/ft^2)	

Performance
Best L/D (claimed) 1:21
* Figures for the T-21P are approximate

The original T-21P with its truly open cockpit. Other details of interest are the 'Sutton' harness made of canvas webbing, the instructor's hand on the tow release knob, and the aero-tow release visible in the extreme nose. The bracing wire sometimes fitted from the nose to the strut fitting is not present. (*Slingsby collection*)

A close-up of the nose of Sedbergh WB924, showing the cylindrical ballast housing fitted to many ATC Sedberghs to allow solo flying without fuss. The pitot guard is removed before flight. (*M. Simons*)

Preparing for take off in the T-21P. The external spoiler cable running up the back of the strut may be seen. The nose bracing wire is absent. The passenger carries a microphone,

and the antenna sticking out of the nose indicates that this was a special flight for a radio feature programme broadcast by the BBC. (*M. Eacock*)

The instrument panel of an ex-ATC Sedbergh. The panel is quite typical, with, left to right, an airspeed indicator, turn-and-slip indicator, Cobb-Slater pellet-type variometer, and an altimeter. A compass was often mounted on the decking behind the windscreen. The central knob is the tow release, and the spoiler control handle is on the central console between the pilots. Rudder pedals and control columns are clearly visible. (*M. Simons*)

Dragonfly attended the National Gliding Competitions at Camphill in 1949, although not competing. Here it is launched by bungee from the crest of the west-facing slope. The smoke comes from the large cement works with its 400ft chimney. Above the port wing the local club's T-21 is visible, much higher. (*G. Thompson*)

John Furlong's *Dragonfly* was loaned to the London Gliding Club and flew regularly there for many years until bought by the club. Compare the cockpit arrangement with that of the T-21P. (*M. Eacock*)

Only one T-46, often called the T-21C, was built. The wing remained similar to that of the T-21 but was mounted on the fuselage at shoulder level, with a tidy enclosed canopy. The tail unit was also redesigned, but the improvements were not considered sufficient to justify series production of the type. (*I. Tunstall*)

The T-21P preparing for launch. The pilot in the left seat seems to have mixed feelings. (*M. Eacock*)

A rare shot of the T-21P in flight, on a winch launch at Dunstable. (*M. Eacock*)

One of the first clubs to take delivery of a T-21B was the Derbyshire and Lancashire Gliding Club. Their two-seater had blue stripes on the rudder and clear-doped fabric covered wings and tail, but was otherwise painted cream. It is soaring here over the west-facing slope at Camphill. The photo was taken by George Thompson from the club's Grunau Baby.

Imperial College Gliding Club's T-21 (*Daisy*) on aero-tow at Lasham, with contest number 40. The pitot tube carries an 'Irving' total energy venturi. The fabric-covered frame of the rear fuselage is well shown here. (*C. E. Brown*)

Sedbergh WB920 of the Empire Test Pilot's School Gliding Club was painted silver overall, with yellow bands around wings and fuselage and RAF type roundels. The pilots are fully equipped with oxygen breathing apparatus. (*C. E. Brown*)

Another picture of the EPTS Sedbergh on aero-tow. The large triangular inspection panel in the fuselage was not fitted to the early models of the T-21B.

Rigging a Sedbergh at Dunstable in recent times. This aircraft is one of those sold by the ATC during the last few years. It is painted in the standard Air Cadets colour scheme, with serial number and roundels. (*M. Simons*)

Another Air Cadets Sedbergh, showing the colours applied to the wings. This T-21B belongs now to a Dutch group and has been fitted with the steel guards ahead of the cockpit, as required by the Netherlands authorities. These are intended to protect the pilots from decapitation in the event of hitting telephone or power lines when outlanding. (*M. Simons*)

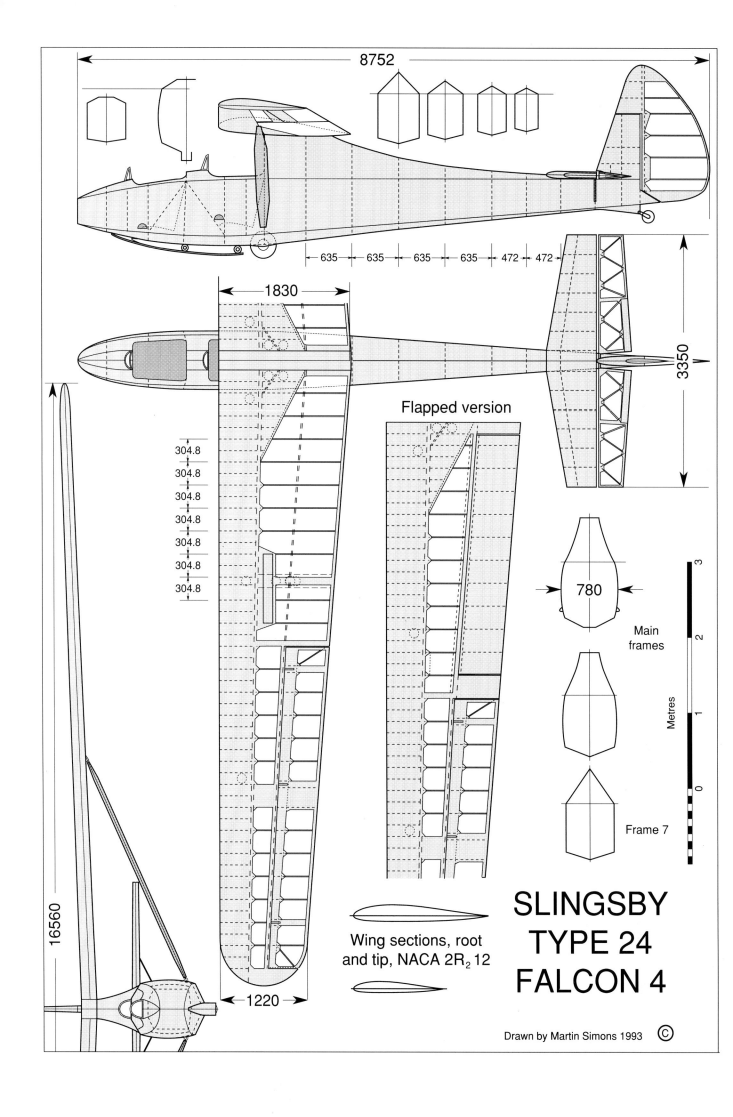

8752

635 — 635 — 635 — 635 — 472 — 472

1830

3350

Flapped version

304.8
304.8
304.8
304.8
304.8
304.8
304.8

780

Main frames

Metres

Frame 7

16560

1220

Wing sections, root and tip, NACA 2R$_2$12

3

2

1

0

SLINGSBY TYPE 24 FALCON 4

Drawn by Martin Simons 1993 ©

Type 24, TX.8/45 Falcon 4

The first post-war British National Gliding Contests at RNAS Bramcote base opened in a certain amount of confusion on 21 June 1947. The weather on the practice day was not very good. The pilots and crews, mostly with Olympia sailplanes built by Elliotts of Newbury, assembled and waited for the organisation to sort things out. They did a little flying, but mostly wandered round to admire each other's sailplanes, special attention being devoted to the four very superior Weihes imported by devious means from the ruins of Germany and a beautifully-made Swiss Moswey 3. A couple of German Kranich two-seaters belonging to the Royal Naval Gliding Club were also competing. One of them, flown by Christopher Nicholson and Peter Blake, had broken the British two-seater goal and distance record with a flight to Bramcote from Yeovilton during the previous days.

Then, without prior announcement, a large yellow glider carrying RAF roundels arrived overhead, towed by an Auster. The glider's span was much larger than that of the tug. It released, circled the aerodrome and landed, looking at once very much out of place among the competing sailplanes. This unexpected visitor was the Slingsby Type 24, designed to Ministry of Aircraft Production Specification TX.8/45 and christened Falcon 4. Flown by Slingsby's chief engineer, John Leach, it had been towed from Kirbymoorside in two hours. It did not attract much admiration. No-one seems even to have taken a photograph. It was dragged away and parked in a hangar which had been reserved for the ATC, and it stood there for a few days alongside a number of Cadets TX Mk.1. Later it was towed away again, and as far as the civilian gliding fraternity were concerned that was the last ever seen of it.

After the T-21 Slingsby had intended to produce a new version of the pre-war Petrel, with a revised cockpit canopy and a few other small changes. This would have been the Type 22, but with the Olympia now available the Petrel 2, based on the old Rhönadler designed originally in 1932, was too slow for modern cross-country flying. No one ordered it and the T-22 was never built. One T-23, an improved version of the Kirby Kite, was produced, but also lacked sales appeal (see the relevant chapter). So it was that the Slingsby type numbers reached 24.

An advocate of two-seater training at the time said that what was needed was a two-seater with: 'sufficiently high-performance to allow a useful time to be spent airborne after release on a winch circuit even on a stable windless day, that can be operated within the financial limits of British Clubs, and is sufficiently simple from the instructor's point of view to allow instruction to be given by [the] comparatively inexperienced'. He added: 'The TX.8/45 was produced for the ATC with that end in view'.

The ATC in 1944 had not approved of either the T-20 or the T-21, so the Ministry of Aircraft Production drew up an official specification. This document, dated 4 April 1945 and emanating from the Directorate of Technical Development (DTD), seemed very reasonable at a first reading. It asked for a two-seater which would perform and handle in the air as much like the Kirby Cadet as possible. It had to be light and structurally simple though robust. The seats were to be in tandem, with a good view from both cockpits. Flaps were to be fitted to aid take-off and landing and to keep speed under control in rapid descents. The only instruments mentioned were an airspeed indicator and an altimeter. Just why the T-21 or even the T-20, which had tandem seats, did not meet the specification was not apparent, but Slingsby embarked on a new design which owed nothing to these existing types.

A contract was signed for three prototypes, but there was more in the bureaucratic mind than Slingsby could have reckoned with or than showed up in the outline specification. It was said later: 'The type was loaded up with the requirements of almost every department of the Royal Aircraft Establishment'. When detailed work began, Slingsby's team was compelled to delve into 'general requirements given in the following paragraphs of DTD 1028 (Issue No. IV) and amendment No. 1: 1.01-3.01, 3.07; 4.01-4.02, 5.01-5.02, 5.04-11.01 (all inclusive)'. The designers had to discover and comply with Chapters 203, 206, 208, 800, 801, 803, 804,

805 and 806 of Air Publication 970. They had to study Section 1 of ATN 127 (Issue II), and were to consult the RAE and RD (Airb) about the cables used for towing and to 'agree with this Department about strength requirements for launching and landing'. Airworthiness Technical Note 127 (Issue II) had to be complied with. Buried in the various paragraphs was a demand for copper binding on wingtips and rudder trailing edges, and an intercom system for the pilots to communicate with each other. Probably those who were consulted about the design envisaged the TX.8/45 as nothing else than a military training aeroplane which lacked only one thing, an engine, to distinguish it from standard RAF equipment.

During discussions with the various official bodies some relaxations were allowed. A demand for picketing safely in a 90kt wind was eased, and the required maximum aero-towing speed was reduced from the 195kph (120mph) originally demanded to 128kph (80mph). There may have been other concessions.

The actual construction work was undertaken under sub-contract by Martin Hearn Ltd. Martin Hearn had been in the Avro 504 joyriding business and had gradually established a small company at Hooton Park in Cheshire, near Ellesmere Port, repairing and building wooden aircraft. During the war the firm expanded to undertake repair work on Avro Ansons and sub-contracts for Mosquito parts. Some Slingsby Cadets and Tutors had been built for the ATC. It was hoped to continue with this kind of work, and a close relationship with Slingsby Sailplanes was established in the post-war period.

When the Falcon 4 with all the required equipment finally emerged it was a glider with a high, strut-braced single-spar wing of 16.56m (54ft 4in) span, about 80kg (175lb) heavier than either the T-20 or or the T-21 and costing more. The wing, of tapered planform and slightly swept forward to give a straight leading edge, was well proportioned, but the aerofoil section, NACA 2R-12, of reflexed form, was very far from the type of profile normally seen on sailplanes. It was probably thought that the flaps would be used to improve the low-speed glide, but this choice of section is puzzling. It is unlikely to have been Slingsby's personal preference. The plywood-skinned flaps were large, and the fabric-covered ailerons also were of wide chord. The third prototype was fitted with simple spoilers and no flaps, coming out about 10kg (20lb) lighter than the others.

The fuselage, with a tall pylon to carry the wing 1.7m (5.5ft) above the ground, had high cockpit sides, so footholds were necessary to allow the pilots to climb in. The front seat had an excellent field of view, but the rear pilot was well back under the leading edge of the wing. As usual with tandem-seated sailplanes, space for the rear set of rudder pedals had to be made on either side of the front seat, so the fuselage was 780mm (30in) wide at this point. Rather than having a plain slab-sided cross-section, the sides were slightly bulged, making the cockpits unusually roomy. A landing wheel with skid and a tailwheel were fitted in accordance with the requirements. The tail unit was straightforward and the elevator had trim tabs.

The prototype, with flaps and the military serial VM109, flew in April 1946, almost exactly a year after the issuing of the specification. It was delivered in July to Beaulieu in Hampshire for trials by the Airborne Forces Experimental Establishment (AFEE). The second of the three aircraft, VM113, was written off in an accident at Wombleton in December 1946. The last, with spoilers, VM118, arrived at Beaulieu in September 1947.

It became obvious quite soon that the T-24 was not what the ATC had been hoping for, and advertisements placed by Martin Hearn in the civilian magazines drew no orders from the clubs. The T-24 was judged too costly and too heavy. It offered no advantages whatever over the T-21B, and at this stage the Air Staff decided in future to buy their gliders 'off the shelf'.

The two remaining aircraft were not immediately abandoned. Tests were carried out late in 1947 by the AFEE to determine whether the TX.8/45 would be suitable for the aircraft carrier wake surveys which (as described in an earlier chapter) were actually done with the Slingsby T-20. Incidental to this investigation, the Auster VI aeroplane was evaluated as a tug. The rate of climb achieved to 600m (2,000ft) with a single pilot in the glider was 69m/min (230ft/min). Practicable towing airspeeds were between 45 and 64kt.

The T-24 project delayed the decision to use the Sedbergh for ATC service until 1950, so there was an immediate shortage of two-seat gliders. It was therefore decided to carry out further performance and handling trials so that an official clearance might be issued for the TX.8/45 to be flown by the gliding schools. The AFEE at Beaulieu did the required work between May and December 1948, fitting in the test flights between other more urgent operations. Most of the flying was done with the spoiler-equipped VM118. The take-off speed was found to be 35kt. On aero-tow slight lateral and longitudinal instability was discovered, but this, it was reported, was no worse than on any other glider. The ailerons were unduly heavy, the forces required to move them being out of proportion to the other controls. The elevator trim was not effective enough to cover all conditions of flight on tow, especially in the low tow position below the tug slipstream.

In free flight the TX.8/45 was judged pleasant to fly, although the ailerons were still too heavy and the trimmer inadequate for the extreme c.g. positions. Stalling tests revealed no abnormalities. The aircraft could not be made to spin more than half a turn, falling out into a spiral dive. Winch launching tests showed nothing untoward, though a very low maximum airspeed on the winch cable of 39kt was imposed and the recommended landing approach speed was 38kt, only one knot slower. In performance trials a minimum rate of descent of approximately 78m/min (260ft/min or 4.3ft/sec) was measured at an airspeed of 35kt This placed the TX.8/45 firmly in the circuit training category.

An important defect of the aircraft was aileron flutter, which showed up at airspeeds above 65kt. This was almost certainly because the ailerons were of unusually broad chord and large area, with their centre of mass behind the hinge line. Mass balancing, which might have cured or at least alleviated the problem, would have added more to the total weight of the aircraft which was already heavy enough.

During the winch launching trials in August 1948 an accident led to the writing-off of VM118. Only one TX.8/45 remained. In January 1949 VM109 passed from Beaulieu to the No. 168 Gliding School of the ATC at Detling, where it remained until March 1950. It then moved on to other ATC units, spending most of one year in storage before being sold to the Western Area Gliding Club at Cosford in March 1953. What became of it then is not known.

Type 24 Falcon 4 data

Dimensions

Wingspan	16.56m (54ft 4in)
Wing area	24.7m^2 (266ft^2)
Aspect ratio	11.1
Wing section	NACA 2R-12

Weights

Tare	360kg (792lb) (VM109)
	351kg (775lb) (VM118)
All-up	544kg (1,197lb) (VM109)
	528kg (1,162lb) (VM118)
Wing loading (max)	22.0kg/m^2 (4.5lb/ft^2)
	21.3kg/m^2 (4.4lb/ft^2)

The nose section of the fuselage, showing the cockpit area under construction. The substantial wheel bearers are visible, with the steel strut fittings protruding from the sides of the main frame. The footholds for climbing into the cockpits can be seen. (*Slingsby collection*)

The T-24 under construction at Hooton Park. The fuselage, inverted during assembly, is shown on its jig. The framework was based on four main longerons and a substantial keel member, with light cross-frames. Plywood skinning was added later. (*Slingsby collection*)

The starboard wing of the flapped T-24, seen from the underside and showing how the hinge points for both flaps and ailerons were positioned flush with the underside of the wing. To carry the flaps, the secondary spar had to be quite substantial. (*Slingsby collection*)

The starboard wing of the spoiler-equipped T-24 almost ready for the covering. The very light secondary spar functioned only to prevent the wing ribs from distorting sideways under the tension of the doped fabric aft of the main spar. (*Slingsby collection*)

Very few photographs of the completed T-24 in flying trim exist. For official purposes, the sailplane was photographed on the ground from four aspects. A head-on, profile, three-quarter front and three-quarter rear views accompanied the official AFEE report. These show VM109, the prototype with flaps, which was the last survivor of the three built. It was painted standard RAF training yellow all over, with roundels on fuselage sides with the 'P' prototype marking and the red, white and blue fin flash. Large roundels were painted above and below both wings. The lettering on the rudder cannot be deciphered. (*Public Record Office, Avia 21/300*)

The only other known photograph of the T-24 is this head-on view which survives in the RAF Museum collection at Hendon.

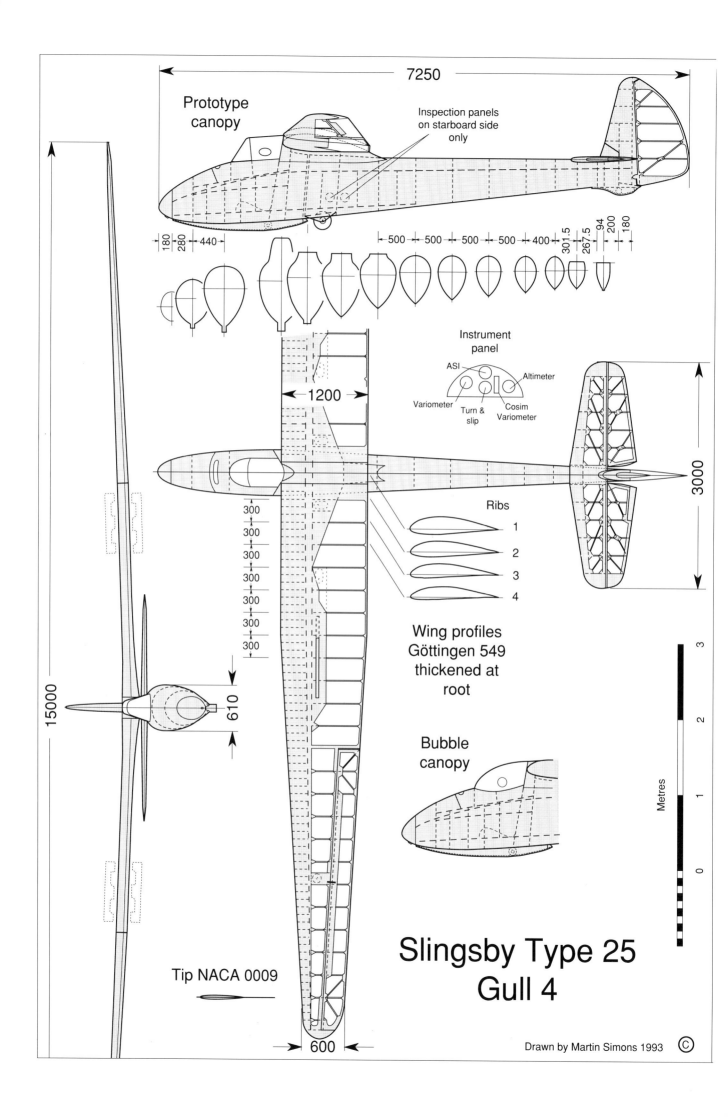

7250

Prototype
canopy

Inspection panels
on starboard side
only

180
280
440

500 — 500 — 500 — 500 — 400 — 301.5 — 267.5 — 94 — 200 — 180

1200

Instrument
panel

ASI
Altimeter

Variometer
Turn &
slip
Cosim
Variometer

3000

300
300
300
300
300
300
300

610

Ribs

1
2
3
4

Wing profiles
Göttingen 549
thickened at
root

15000

Bubble
canopy

600

Tip NACA 0009

Metres

3

2

1

0

Slingsby Type 25
Gull 4

Drawn by Martin Simons 1993 ©

Type 25, Gull 4

A small mystery surrounds the birth of the Slingsby Type 25 Gull 4. Despite its type number, the prototype appeared about nine months later than the Type 26 Kite 2. Partly as a result, the Gull 4 missed the market which it deserved. It was an excellent sailplane but not a commercial success. It is not clear why Slingsby did not give it the priority it should have had. He may have misjudged the temper of the British gliding movement and underestimated the demand that would appear for a good, up-to-date 15m high-performance sailplane. He seems also to have over-estimated the potential of the Kite 2.

The advertising brochure which Slingsby issued in 1947, by which time the Kite 2 was already available, indicated that the Kirby Gull 4 would have the same root wing profile as the Gull 3, NACA 4415, and a similar wingspan, 15.32m (50.25ft). The tail unit also was similar to that of the old Gull. There was to be a new fuselage with a longer tail moment arm and better cockpit. The wing would have straight dihedral instead of the old-fashioned and more expensive gull form. What Slingsby had in mind was an improved version of the most successful single-seat sailplane he had produced in the years of peace.

He would probably have done much better by sticking to this plan, if it would have resulted in the new aircraft becoming available in 1946 instead of a year later. But these preliminary ideas were almost completely abandoned, and Slingsby began speaking of the Gull 4 as a replacement for the Olympia. It should rather have been a direct competitor, and would have been so had it been on the market sooner. As early as December 1944 it was claimed that the new Gull would have a better performance than the Olympia. What the Yorkshire company needed to do was to get one into the air as soon as possible and demonstrate this.

It had been agreed before the outbreak of the Second World War that the Olympic Games scheduled for 1940 would include a soaring contest. To place the emphasis on skill rather than equipment, it was determined that all competitors should fly the same type of aircraft. A specification was drawn up for a suitable 15m span sailplane capable of being built from easily obtained materials without costly machine tools. A design competition was held and six prototypes, from Germany, Poland, Switzerland and Italy, were flown for assessment at a special meeting at Sezze in Italy in 1939. The Meise, designed by Hans Jacobs and built by DFS, won this competition.

The Meise was a smaller version of the 18m Weihe which was already in production and had achieved a great reputation. It was constructed of wood along orthodox lines, was fully up to specification in strength and handling, and it had no complications or costly metal fittings. Straight dihedral was used as the expensive traditional gull wing form was, at last, recognised to be unnecessary. It had powerful airbrakes of Schempp-Hirth 'parallel ruler' type rather than units of the DFS's own design, which were more complicated and less effective. The elevator had a trim tab, and the cockpit was roomy and comfortable — at least for pilots of average height. Tall pilots found their heads well back inside the leading edge of the wing, which restricted their view to some extent.

After the decision at Sezze, the Meise became known outside Germany as the Olympic sailplane, or Olympia. Complete sets of working drawings were made available to all the nations likely to compete. However the war began and the 1940 Games were cancelled. Gliding has never since featured in the Olympics, but the Meise was produced in large numbers in Germany and became well known and well liked there.

At the end of hostilities Philip Wills visited Germany and test flew a number of sailplanes. In his report on the Meise he said it was 'one of the finest pieces of balanced aerodynamic poetry which has been created by man'. Compared with almost any other 15m sailplane the Meise/Olympia was incomparably better; the controls were light, well balanced and harmonised, and stability was good without making the type pedestrian. It required some deliberate persuasion to make it spin, but it would do so when required and it was capable of all the usual sailplane aerobatics. The performance was not as good as that of the bigger, heavier Weihe, but was in advance of anything else available in the immediate post-war period. Although at the time there was no recognised system for classifying sailplanes, the Olympia established a concept which had profound influence on sailplane development throughout the world and led eventually to the International Standard Class specification.

Early in 1945 Slingsby mentioned plans to manufacture the Olympia, but the Chilton Aircraft Company was already promoting its own version, and soon claimed that more orders for the Chilton Olympia had been received than for any other high-performance sailplane ever built or sold in Britain. This was true, though it did not mean very much because the only moderately high-performance sailplane built in Britain, the Kirby Gull, had not achieved double figures in production. Very few others had ever been imported. According to Slingsby's own account, the Kirbymoorside factory was still fully occupied with wartime contracts, and he evidently decided not to compete directly. He said it was mainly to keep his small design team occupied that he decided to proceed with a new high-performance design which became the Type 25 Gull 4. The Type 26 Kite 2 was already in production but was proving a disappointment.

The field was thus open to his competitors. Elliotts of Newbury, after the rights were taken over from Chilton, manufactured the Olympia in quantity. A hundred were built and were followed later by another batch of 50. The first reached British customers early in 1947, and Slingsby had nothing comparable to offer. The prototype of the Gull 4 did not fly until late in 1947, the first photographs and BGA test group flying assessments being published in January 1948. By now the limited British market was virtually flooded with the Newbury products. Only four Gull 4s were built.

The aerodynamic design of the T-25 was obviously influenced by German experience. The cantilever wing, of 15m span with a rectangular centre section and tapered outer panels, had a slightly higher aspect ratio than that of the Olympia. The original intention to use the NACA wing profiles like those on the Gull 1 and Gull 3 was abandoned. After extensive comparative testing in Germany the Göttingen 549 wing profile had been chosen by the DFS for the Reiher, a very advanced sailplane, in 1936-37, and for many later designs including the Weihe and Olympia. The Gull 4 used the same root section, tapered to the symmetrical NACA 0009 at the tip, with 5° washout. This arrangement was thoroughly orthodox. To comply with revised British strength requirements while reducing the weight and cost of central fittings, the wing was thickened generously over the last few rib bays near the roots. Schempp-Hirth speed limiting brakes were fitted, and were enlarged after first tests of the prototype. The structure was of the usual wooden monospar type, with stressed plywood skin over the leading edge. The sub-ribs ahead of the spar were spaced at 100mm intervals, rather than the more usual 150mm. This

added to the torsional stiffness. Fabric covering was used behind the spar and for the ailerons.

The fuselage was also straightforward, being a semi-monocoque construction with light wooden frames and longerons skinned throughout with plywood. Most of the frames were shared with the T-26 Kite 2. The wing was mounted on a slight neck or pylon which faired neatly into the cockpit canopy. It avoided the rather awkward air trap under the wing which was a significant aerodynamic defect on the Olympia. A landing wheel was fitted, with a sprung ash skid, and there was a tailskid.

The tail unit was orthodox, with ample torsional stiffeners. The prototype had no trim tab, but instead the tailplane was made adjustable. This was soon changed to the more practical trim tab arrangement.

The cockpit canopy was built up from several sheets of transparent plastic. Plastic bubble blowing at this time was often rather imprecise, the resulting canopies sometimes not fitting very well, although they gave the pilot an excellent, unobstructed field of vision. The Gull 4 canopy was a good fit but not so aerodynamically pleasing. The cockpit itself was comfortable for large pilots and, since the headrest was wholly in front of the wing, the view was better.

It was generally accepted that the Gull 4 was slightly superior to the Olympia in handling, although perhaps not such a finely balanced piece of poetry. The controls generally had a crisper feel and a quicker response. Stability was good. The wing loading was a little greater and the stalling speed higher.

A well-known Swedish pilot estimated that the new Slingsby type was 10 per cent better all round than the Olympia. Performance tests in flight were carried out on the second Gull 4 to be built (though not until 1950), and the results compared with similar tests of the Weihe and Olympia. The best glide ratio was measured at 1:24.2, the Olympia at 1:22.5; and 1:29 for the 18m Weihe. The minimum rates of sink of the two 15m sailplanes were very similar, but the Olympia, capable of flying more slowly, would probably have had a very small advantage when circling tightly in narrow thermals. At high speeds the Gull 4 was better than the Olympia up to 60kt but not as good as the Weihe.

The first post-war International Soaring Championship was held at Samedan in Switzerland during July 1948. In a field of 37 the British team of six aircraft included two Gull 4s, two Elliott Olympias and two Weihes, the last pair coming from the RAF clubs in occupied Germany. The Gulls were on loan from Slingsby and the Olympias from Elliotts. Philip Wills and Christopher Nicholson flew the Gulls. This competition was the first in which points were gained on some days for speed around closed circuits or to fixed goals, but points were also awarded for height climbs, and most of the tasks were simply flights to goals of the pilot's choice, scored primarily for distance with bonuses for actually reaching the goal.

It was a tragic competition for the British. On 28 July Donald Greig in an Olympia and Chris Nicholson in a

Gull 4 were killed in separate accidents. Greig, flying close to a valley side, struck one of the steel cables common in this region for carrying bales of hay or logs down from the summer pastures. The Olympia lost a large piece of its port wing and spun 65m (200ft) down into the rocks, killing Greig instantly. Nicholson in the Gull 4, on the other side of the same mountain, was evidently circling in lift funnelled up in a narrow gully near Chiavenna, just across the Italian frontier. He had mountain walls on three sides and was close to an *arête* or saw-toothed ridge. Probably, as he climbed, cloud formed in the gully below and swept up around him. Blinded, he was confronted suddenly with the jagged spine of rock immediately ahead, pulled up to try to clear it, stalled and crashed just over the other side at the summit 3,000m (10,000ft) above sea level. He was found quickly by a shepherd and lived for some hours, but died before he could be brought to a hospital.

Wills, flying the other Gull, would have placed fourth in the final standing, but on the first day of the contest his barograph failed and he lost the 4,000 points which he should have earned for a climb to 6,000m (20,000ft) above sea level. The Gull 4 was, he said, the best 15m sailplane he had ever flown. He used airspeeds up to 75kt to escape severe downdraughts and pushed the speed up to 85kt when starting in one of the races. The Gull 4 was rock steady at these speeds and quieter than the average machine flying slowly. He established the British National speed record for the 100km triangle at 47kmh (29.2mph). Unfortunately, these results were too late to assist Slingsby with sales.

After the Internationals, the Gull 4 that Wills had flown at Samedan was exported to the Sydney Soaring Club in Australia, where it arrived in May 1949 and immediately became popular with the members of this small group. It was fitted with two-way radio, being one of the first sailplanes in the world so equipped. The club used the radio for their annual Christmas gliding safari, launching the sailplane by aero-tow each morning with a different pilot for a cross-country flight. The rest of the party followed by road and air to launch another member the next day from a different site, to complete a soaring tour of the vast inner plains of New South Wales and Victoria. Fred Hoinville used the Gull 4 to earn the first Australian 'Gold C' badge in January 1950.

On a stormy day, 30 December 1950, Martin Warner took off from Narromine in New South Wales and circled up in the Gull 4 to cloud base at 1,800m (6,000ft). Using the turn-and-slip indicator, which was the only gyro instrument fitted, he continued climbing at a very great rate, measured subsequently on the barograph chart as 660m/min (2,200ft/min). He had no oxygen supply, but made no attempt to get down until 6,600m (22,000ft), at which height he opened the air-brakes and tried to straighten out on a northerly heading. He lost some height at first, but then encountered heavy turbulence and even stronger lift which carried him, brakes open, to 7,050m (23,500ft) above sea level. Lack of oxygen rendered him almost help-

less, and he did not regain control fully until he was down to about 450m (1,500ft) in an extremely violent downdraught, still in the cloud with hail and heavy rain. When he emerged suddenly into clear air he was 30m (100ft) above the bush in hilly, rock-strewn country. He had no option but to make a crash landing into the trees, which wrecked the aircraft without serious injury to himself. The flight broke the Australian records for gain of height and absolute altitude. The Australian Gull 4 was rebuilt and flew again in Victoria, but was again seriously damaged in a winch-launching accident. Its remains still exist at Tocumwal in New South Wales, but no serious attempt has been made to rebuild it.

In Britain, the prototype Gull 4 was bought in 1948 by the London Gliding Club and served as a popular club sailplane for several years. It was entered in the National Competitions in 1949, coming fifth in the team placings (an Olympia was third). In 1950 it was ninth. It was severely damaged in an accident on the Dunstable hillside, but the wings were repaired and fitted to the fuselage of a Kite 2. In this form it still survives.

The other Gull 4 was bought by the RAF Gliding and Soaring Association and flew with the Moonrakers club. This aircraft went with the British team to the Internationals in Sweden in 1950. On the second contest day the canopy came off in the air, and Peter Mallett, the pilot, struggled on for another 46km (28.5 miles) before landing, but inevitably made a relatively poor distance. A new canopy was immediately flown out from England, but the Gull 4 did not distinguish itself in the later days of the contest. After years of good service including many cross-country flights and competitions, this aircraft was finally written off in an accident in 1967.

The Gull 4 never achieved the popularity and success it deserved. It demonstrated that Slingsby Sailplanes in 1947 could design and build a sailplane that was slightly better all round than the German Meise of 1939. The next move seemed almost automatic. A 15m sailplane wing will never perform as well as one with a few extra metres of span. Plans were soon made for the Gull 4 to be stretched to 18m.

Type 25 Gull 4 data

Dimensions

Wingspan	15 m (49ft 2½in)
Wing area	14.49m² (156ft²)
Aspect ratio	15.52
Length o.a.	7.25m (23ft 9½in)
Wing sections	
Root	Göttingen 549 thickened
Mid-span	Göttingen 549
Tip	NACA 0009

Weights

Tare	211.8kg (476lb)
Flying	317.5kg (700lb)
Wing loading	21.97kg/m² (4.5lb/ft²)

The crashed Gull 4 in the Australian bush near Narromine after Martin Warner's 23,500ft record-breaking climb in a cumulonimbus. The Gull was rebuilt and flew again for several more years. (*M. Waghorn*)

The rebuilt Australian Gull 4, here seen with a Grunau Baby in Victoria. The rather angular cockpit canopy was replaced by a blown bubble which improved the appearance and reduced drag slightly. The skid and wheel fairings were also improved. (*G. Hearn*)

The London Gliding Club's Gull 4 at Camphill in 1949. Note the Schempp-Hirth-type airbrakes, opening above and below the wing. The club name was in block letters, shadow shaded. In the background is the famous cross-Channel Gull 1. (*M. Simons*)

The prototype Gull 4 at Redhill during test flying by the BGA Test Group 1. (*C. E. Brown, RAF Museum, Hendon, neg No. 6208-90*)

Anne Welch flying the prototype Gull 4 over Redhill. The cockpit canopy, built up from separate sections of Perspex, gave very adequate visibility but was unfavourably compared with the bubble canopies of the Elliott Olympia. (*C. Brown*)

Christopher Nicholson preparing for a flight in the Gull 4. Not long afterwards he was killed while competing in the first post-war International Championships, at Samedan in Switzerland. (*Wills collection*)

The Moonraker club Gull 4 preparing to take off. The wings in this case were clear-varnished all over, showing the natural plywood and fabric tones, but the fuselage was painted.

Philip Wills in the cockpit before going to the competitions in Switzerland. Note the thickening of the wing roots to allow a deeper spar, and the aero tow release just in front of the skid fitting. (*Wills collection*)

The Gull 4 at Camden Aerodrome, south of Sydney, in May 1949 immediately after delivery. The markings put on for the international competition are still on the aircraft. Members of the Sydney Soaring Club, from left to right, are Keith Collyer, Selwyn Owen, Martin Warner and Mervyn Waghorn. (*M. Waghorn*)

Wills, in the cockpit, and Slingsby, confer. The skids of the Gull 4s taken to Samedan were lengthened to fair in better with the wheel. The prototype, which was sold to the London Gliding Club, had a shorter skid. Also visible is the winch launching release. (*Wills collection*)

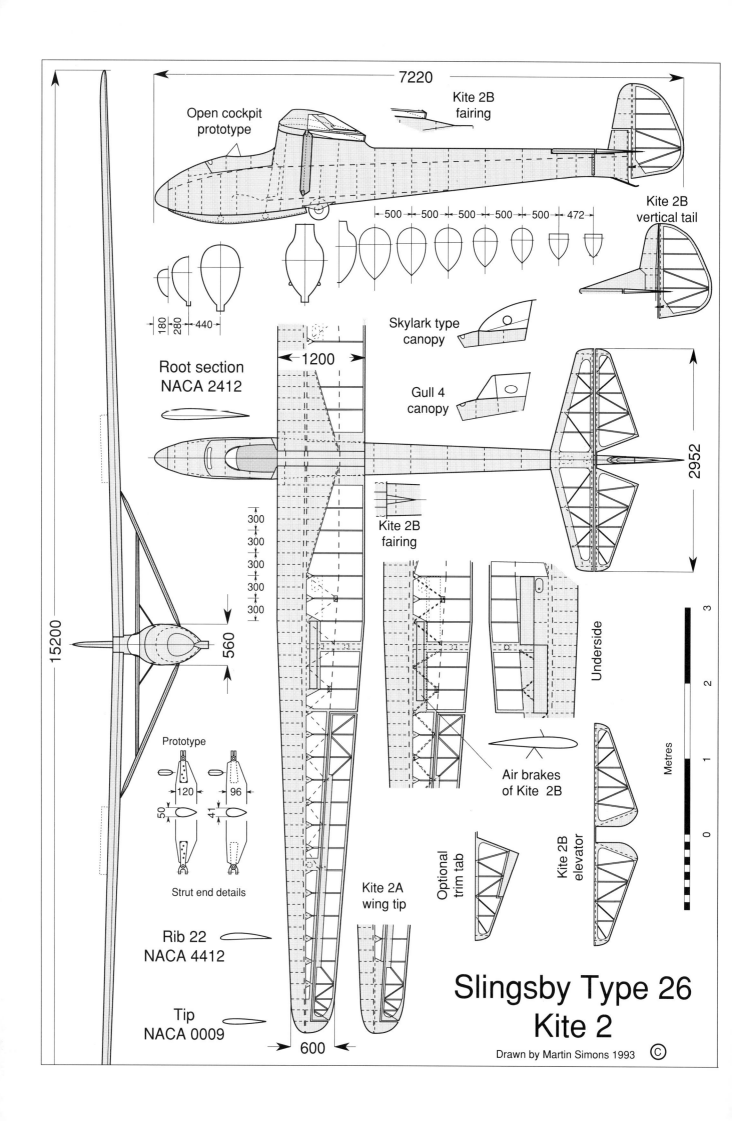

7220

Kite 2B
fairing

Open cockpit
prototype

Kite 2B
vertical tail

500 500 500 500 500 472

Skylark type
canopy

180 280 440

Root section
NACA 2412

Gull 4
canopy

1200

2952

300
300
300
300
300

Kite 2B
fairing

Underside

560

15200

Air brakes
of Kite 2B

Prototype

120 96

50 41

Optional
trim tab

Kite 2B
elevator

Strut end details

Kite 2A
wing tip

Rib 22
NACA 4412

Metres

0 1 2 3

Tip
NACA 0009

600

Slingsby Type 26
Kite 2

Drawn by Martin Simons 1993 ©

Type 26, Kite 2

Slingsby's Type 23 Kite 1A, of which only one was built, mated the wing and tail unit of the old Kite 1 with an improved fuselage. There was no measurable improvement in performance or handling, so Slingsby decided to adopt a more radical approach. Although the aircraft that emerged as the Kite 2 was described as a development of the old Kite, it owed little to the pre-war aircraft except its tail unit.

It is not clear who, under Slingsby himself, was chiefly responsible for the design of the Kite 2.

The Type 26 had a strut-braced wing and tailplane, which was by now considered old-fashioned for a high-performance sailplane, but the Kite 2 was never intended as a very advanced aircraft. Seen as replacing the Kite 1, a step up from the ubiquitous Grunau Baby, it was to be inexpensive, easily maintained and safe to fly, with a moderately good cross-country performance. Struts allowed a good deal of weight to be saved, especially in the main wing spars, and there was no need for expensive or elaborate metal fittings.

Publicity brochures for the Kite 2 advanced another argument in favour of strut bracing. By using a strut the wing could be made considerably thinner, and the resulting saving in wing profile drag at high airspeeds ought to compensate for the parasitic drag of the struts. The Kite 2 wing was only 12 per cent of the chord in thickness at the root end, compared with 16 per cent or more for contemporary cantilever sailplanes of similar span. It was held that the high speed glide, or 'penetration', would not suffer. For cross-country soaring the ability to fly at high airspeeds without losing too much height is more important than minimal weight. On any reasonably good day, gaining altitude is not very difficult. Even a relatively crude training glider will go up in a strong upcurrent, but to make distance a pilot needs to find and use a whole series of thermals. After a climb, reaching the next thermal often requires a long glide through lifeless or even sinking air. A light, slow glider will gain height easily in any rising air, but loses most of it on the way to the next lift and might have to land before getting there. It spends too long in the bad air.

A heavier, faster sailplane may not climb quite so rapidly, but penetrates downcurrents quickly. A good glide at high airspeeds demands minimal parasitic and wing profile drag, together with a high wing loading.

All of this was now understood in Britain. (It had been known longer in Germany.) Saving weight was no longer considered very important; reducing parasitic and wing profile drag were most necessary. Heavily-cambered thick aerofoil sections such as the Göttingen 535 used on the famous Kranich and Rhönsperber and on the Kite 1, were replaced by less-cambered forms, the sections often being increased in thickness at the root ends to give adequate depth for spars. Even so, the wooden mainspar of a typical cantilever sailplane might contribute half the total structure weight of the aircraft.

It is probably significant that the most advanced sailplane built at Kirbymoorside up to this time, Mungo Buxton's King Kite of 1937, had increased profile camber at the wingtips and only a moderate negative twist or 'washout'. This arrangement is common on the most modern sailplanes now. (As mentioned previously the King Kite failed not because the wing design was in error, but because it was incorrectly jigged when being built in the factory.) Increasing the camber towards the tip of a wing and combining this with a only few degrees of washout was in direct contrast to the older design technique. Hitherto, almost all sailplane designers had tapered the wing to a symmetrical section at the tip, but this necessitated very large amounts of washout, sometimes as much as 8° or even 10° to prevent wing tip stalling. This excessive washout had the serious disadvantage of causing the outer part of the wing to reach negative angles of attack at quite moderate airspeeds. The tips on such aircraft as the Rhönsperber and Rhönadler would bend down increasingly under the reversed loads, and this tended to ruin the performance at the high speeds needed for inter-thermal cruising.

At the root, the Kite 2 wing section was NACA 2412 with, as the first digit shows, only 2 per cent camber.

This section extended unchanged over the inner wing panel, which had constant chord. The tapered section of the wing outboard of the strut had a progressive change of section to the NACA 4412 with 4 per cent camber at rib station 22. Contemporary wind tunnel test results from the USA indicated that the 4412 section would stall at a geometric angle of attack about 2° less than the 2412, but the stronger camber enabled the 4412 to reach a higher maximum lift coefficient. To prevent the outer wing from stalling first, which would be dangerous, there was 4° of washout between ribs 8 and 22. This gave a safety margin of about 2° at the stall. At low angle of attacks in high-speed flight the 4412 would reach its aerodynamic zero lift angle of attack at about –4°, the 2412 at –2°. Hence, even with the 4° of washout the outer wing would still be yielding useful lift at high airspeeds. The reversed loads would not appear until the sailplane was diving quite steeply.

So far, so good. It is not easy to understand the rest. From rib 22 to the tip of the wing the Kite 2 wing section changed very quickly to the fully symmetrical NACA 0009, with 2° of geometric wash-in, (*i.e.* wing twist in the other direction). The 0009 section stalls at a much lower lift coefficient than the 4412 and at a smaller aerodynamic angle of attack. Inevitably, the outermost wing panels of the Kite 2 would stall early.

The wing of the prototype drew puzzled comments from those who examined it. The oddity was quite apparent as a distinct kink in the leading edge of the outermost wing panels and a rapid change of both section and angle of incidence. (It was not for junior club members to ask too many awkward questions.) There was, this time, no question of a factory jigging error. Frank Irving subsequently remarked that the geometry of the wing between ribs 22 and 27 looked very weird on the original drawings.

Another unusual feature of the new sailplane was the very high angle of incidence of the wing relative to the fuselage. This, too, was apparent at a glance. The angle of the root chord to the datum line was 8° and when the tail was on the ground it appeared even more extreme. Once again, the pre-war King Kite might have had some influence. The argument here concerned landing speeds. For a perfect landing the wing should stall just as the wheel touches down. On many sailplanes the tailskid would hit the ground before the wing could reach the stalling angle, so they had to be 'flown on' at a higher airspeed than was strictly desirable. For relatively inexperienced pilots the minimum possible landing speed was required, so the Kite 2 wing was rigged at a suitably high angle. In normal flight this necessarily gave the aircraft a marked nose-down attitude which, to anyone who did not know the cause, made the Kite 2 appear always to be flying very fast. (Although hardly in a comparable field of aviation, the Armstrong Whitworth Whitley twin-engined bomber had a similar arrangement of rigging angles and likewise appeared distinctly nose-down when flying straight and level.)

Other features of the Kite 2 were less unorthodox. The tail unit was virtually identical to that of the old Kite 1 and similarly lacking in refinement. The fuselage was longer, increasing the tail volume coefficients and hence improving stability. A landing wheel was fitted aft of the loaded c.g., with a nose skid. The cockpit of the prototype was open and had a windscreen, but a fully enclosed, rather angular canopy built up from Perspex was offered as an option. The wooden structure throughout was of standard type. The wing, despite the normal D-nose plywood skinning, had extensive internal diagonal bracing. This was probably incorporated because the profile was thinner than usual and additional torsional stiffness was thought desirable. The ailerons were simple, with the open type of hinge line sealed merely with strips of fabric, doped on above and below. Such control surfaces were easily constructed, readily inspected and uncomplicated to repair, though lacking aerodynamic elegance. The simplest type of upper-surface spoilers were incorporated. The rudder pedals were easily adjusted but on the prototype there was no elevator trimmer.

Despite its type number 26 the Kirby Kite 2 was designed, completed and flown at Kirbymoorside about a year before the Type 25 Gull 4. It was advertised that production would be under subcontract by Martin Hearn Ltd at Hooton Park in Cheshire.

Early in 1947 the prototype was sent on a tour of the British gliding clubs, to be flown and assessed. Martin Hearn's representatives visited the clubs with the aircraft, which was soon accompanied by the first off the production line. After a rally at the North Somerset Gliding Club late in March it was reported in *Sailplane and Glider* that: 'The Kite 2 is definitely in a class of its own and constitutes the ideal club soaring machine, salient features being the cleverly designed wing, robust construction and very easy ground handling allowed by the built-in wheel'. The two aircraft quickly moved on to take part in a successful rally at Ratcliffe, near Leicester, over Easter and early in April the prototype went to the Derbyshire and Lancashire Gliding Club site at Camphill. Here the Kite 2 was flown by the club instructors, who commented quite favourably although their praise was a little faint. The first of the Olympia type had already arrived at this club from Elliotts of Newbury, and with perfect handling, powerful airbrakes, an enclosed cockpit, an elevator trimmer and excellent performance it had made a very great impression. By comparison, the Kite 2 seemed rather pedestrian. It was emphasised by the salesmen that the Kite 2 was for club pilots and not intended to compete directly in the high-performance field. Nevertheless, unfavourable comparisons were made.

At Camphill this week was a visiting group from the Cambridge University Gliding club on vacation. After several satisfactory flights, on 10 April the prototype Kite 2 spun down into the trees halfway down the hill at the southern end of the west facing slope. It was a total wreck. Reporting the accident, the Cambridge Club scribe wrote in *Sailplane and Glider*:

The stall and spin of this aircraft were found to be vicious and Hookings on his second flight had the misfortune to spin it in from 300ft above the ridge. By a miracle he escaped unhurt. Three of the new Elliott Olympias, owned by syndicates, were flying at Camphill during our visit. The Cambridge one is expected very shortly and reports already received show the Elliott Olympia is an outstanding aircraft.

The juxtaposition of paragraphs could hardly have been accidental. (Gordon Hookings survived to become a Professor of Mathematics in New Zealand, and did much to promote the gliding movement in that country.)

News of the crash spread almost instantly through the British gliding movement, and the prospects for large sales of the Kite 2 disappeared almost overnight. Nobody wanted an intermediate sailplane for pilots with small experience which could behave like that.

At the first post-war British national gliding competitions at Bramcote in June, a fine display of aerobatics including full spins and quick recoveries was put on by Martin Hearn's demonstrator pilot in a very smart black and white Kite 2. This aircraft was made available for flying by possible buyers, but the harm had been done. The two Kites entered in the contest placed nowhere, and no orders were placed. When the subcontracting agreement between Hearn and Slingsby ended, eight unsold and unfinished Kite 2s were in storage. These went to Kirbymoorside, where Slingsby had three others. The total built was 11 including the crashed prototype. Slingsby was determined to sort out the spinning problem, finish and sell these aircraft if possible.

After reconsideration of the wing design and some experimental studies a modification was undertaken. Taking one of the sailplanes, the plywood was stripped off the tips from rib 22 outwards, and this part of the wing was twisted 5° in the washout direction before being reskinned with ply back to the aileron spar. The extreme wingtip was now rigged at 1° relative to the fuselage datum, a total washout of 7°. Initial test flights indicated that the misbehaviour at the stall had been cured. The aircraft went to BGA Test Group 1 in 1951 for evaluation before the type was submitted for formal certification by the Air Registration Board, as required at that period. The BGA test programme, carried out mainly by Frank Irving and Lorne Welch, was very thorough and demonstrated that the modifications had been quite successful. The sailplane, though not without small faults, now handled in a satisfactory manner, and certification followed. All of the aircraft were modified to become Kites Mark 2A. They were offered with optional elevator trim tabs and enclosed cockpit canopies, and all were eventually sold and proved satisfactory in service with private owners. Handling was still not entirely satisfactory, but the type was not dangerous. The performance was quite good, and some owners believed their Kites to be about equal to the Olympia.

Most of the Kite 2s, however, ended in spinning accidents, and only three or four now survive. These have all, at some time, been fitted with blown bubble canopies. One of them, BGA 689, after a long history of repairs and even rebuilding, has been immaculately restored by Peter Warren and is in regular use. Another survivor, BGA 663, which was the Kite 2 tested by Irving and Welch after the modifications in 1951, was extensively modified further by Irving and his partners, who owned it afterwards. In Irving's words, the objective was 'to stop the tendency to oscillate in yaw, to give it some decent airbrakes and to clean it up'. The most important changes are indicated in the accompanying drawing and photographs. This became the unique Kite 2B. Another Kite 2 was at some time fitted with a Skylark 2B vertical tail, presumably in another attempt to improve yawing stability. This was sold in recent times to the USA, where it remains.

If the outer wing panels had been better designed in the first place there would have been a market in the late 1940s for a robust club sailplane of this type. The Kite 2 was strong, uncomplicated and easily maintained and repaired. It had a flying performance quite good enough for early cross-country flights, but after the Camphill accident the Olympia had the field virtually to itself.

Type 26 Kite 2 data

Dimensions

Wingspan	15.2m (49ft 10½in)
Wing area	14.49m² (156ft²)
Aspect ratio	15.52
Length o.a.	7.22m (23ft 8½in)

Wing sections

Root	NACA 2412
Station 8	NACA 2412
Station 22	NACA 4412
Tip	NACA 0009

Incidence angles relative to fuselage datum and section chord lines

	Kite 2	Kite 2A
Root:	8°	8°
Station rib 8	8°	8°
Station rib 22	4°	4°
Station rib 27	6°	1°

Weights

Tare	190.5kg (420lb)
Flying	281.2kg (620lb)
Wing loading	19.53kg/m² (4lb/ft²)

Photographs of the unmodified Kite 2 prototype with open cockpit are rare. This is one of the few, taken from Slingsby's own archives. It shows the Kite 2 at the start of a winch launch. The skid at this stage was not faired and the cockpit was open. It is just possible to detect the change of wing section and wash-in at the wing-tips, causing a marked upward bend in the leading edge. (Slingsby collection)

Apparently in an attempt to improve the airflow, a Kite 2 was fitted with tip bodies for experiments at Kirbymoorside. Details are not known and the results were not reported. (Slingsby collection)

BGA 663 being given a winch launch at Lasham in 1951. The pilot is Ralph Hooper. The only hook provided was in the nose, the advantages of a rear hook mounting not having been recognised at this time. The canopy is the original type, similar to that used on the Gull 4. (F. Irving)

Two photographs of the Kite 2A at Dunstable where it was owned and flown frequently by an enthusiastic private syndicate.

The only example of the Kite 2B, BGA 663, at Dunstable during a vintage glider meeting. Note the modified rudder and increased fin area, the shortened skid and improved wheel fairing, and the wing root fairing. (M. Simons)

The instrument panel of Kite 2A BGA 689, *Percy*. From left to right the instruments are, airspeed indicator, turn-and-slip indicator, accelerometer (above), altimeter, Cobb-Slater pellet-type variometer and Cook electric variometer. The spoiler handle is just visible on the left, the tow release knob hangs below the instrument panel. The rudder pedals and control column are also visible. (*P. Warren*)

The Kite 2A named *Percy*, belonging to Peter Warren, fully restored to its original condition and paint scheme. Note the large wing angle of incidence relative to the ground. In flight, the Kite 2 always appeared nose-down. (*P. Warren*)

Peter Warren in the cockpit of *Percy*. (*P. Warren*)

Detail of Kite 2A *Percy*. (*P. Warren*)

Percy, a head-on view. (*P. Warren*)

A Kite 2A on aero-tow at Lasham. (*C. Brown*)

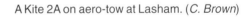

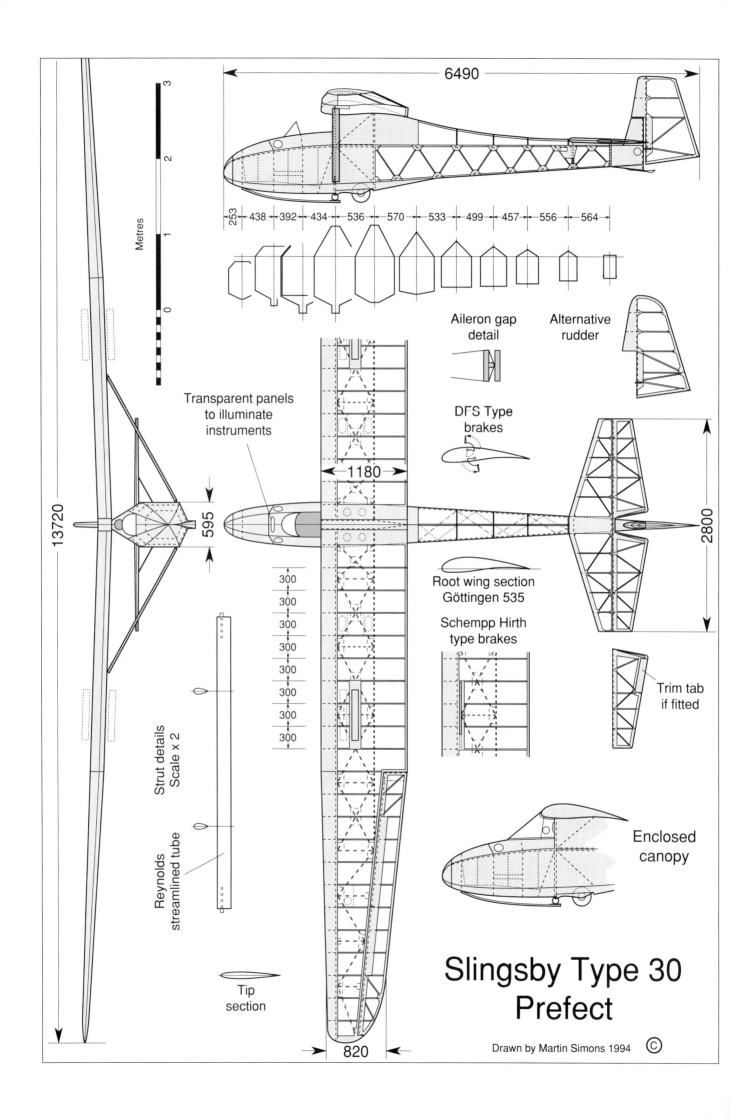

6490

253 438 392 434 536 570 533 499 457 556 564

Metres

13720

Transparent panels to illuminate instruments

Aileron gap detail

Alternative rudder

DFS Type brakes

1180

595

Root wing section Göttingen 535

Schempp Hirth type brakes

2800

300
300
300
300
300
300
300
300

Trim tab if fitted

Strut details Scale x 2

Reynolds streamlined tube

Tip section

820

Enclosed canopy

Slingsby Type 30
Prefect

Drawn by Martin Simons 1994 ©

Type 30, Prefect

Slingsby's Type 27 project, abandoned before completion, was for an unusual two-seater comprising twin Cadet fuselages joined by a central section of wing, with Tutor wing panels outboard. It was nicknamed the 'Widow' because of its supposed resemblance to the Northrop P-61 Black Widow nightfighter. The idea, which never caught on, was to give dual training in this aircraft so that on transferring to a single-seater the student pilot would find the cockpit and outlook almost identical.

The type number T-28 was applied originally to the redesigned T-21 which became the T-21B Sedbergh, and Type 29 was the Motor Tutor. Slingsby thus arrived at his sailplane type number 30, the Prefect.

The Prefect first flew in June 1948, and was advertised at a price of £425. It was an unpretentious design intended as a replacement for the Grunau Baby, which it resembled externally. The Grunau Baby was regarded as an intermediate type to come between the Tutor and a high-performance sailplane such as the Olympia or Gull 4, and this was the niche the Prefect was also expected to occupy. Like the Grunau Baby it would be suitable for the 5hr duration, 1,000m height gain and 50km cross-country tasks for the 'Silver C' badge. It was well understood that anyone who wished to progress to longer-distance flights and competitions would require something much better.

The T-30 was not without rivals. Elliotts of Newbury, whose Olympia had captured the British market for high-performance sailplanes, was now also producing a version of the Grunau Baby, the EON Baby, which threatened to dominate the 'intermediate' field. Nearly 50 Elliott Babies were built, including some assembled by amateur constructors from kits. This seemed to leave little room for the new type from Kirbymoorside.

The Prefect was not merely a copy of the Grunau Baby. The general layout was similar, with only slightly increased span and the same basic wing profiles, Göttingen 535 changing to a symmetrical section at the tips, with washout to prevent tip stalling. The only obvious external difference was the simplified wing plan, with straight taper over the outer panels instead of the elliptical tips of the Baby. The flying weight was somewhat greater and the wing loading higher. However, a great deal of thought went into structural simplification and cost cutting without sacrificing performance and strength or increasing the weight. Wherever possible metal fittings, bearings and other small components were adapted from those used in the Cadet and Tutor. It was argued very reasonably that having standardised and interchangeable spare parts available from stock would be an important consideration for clubs operating and servicing these earlier types of Slingsby aircraft.

Instead of the usual stressed plywood skin torsion box ahead of a single mainspar, the Prefect wing had two spars with extensive internal cross-bracing, like the Tutor, but the leading-edge plywood skinning was counted as part of the primary structure, recognising its contribution to torsional stiffness. This allowed the twin struts of the Tutor to be replaced by a single strut on the Prefect. The strut itself was a length of streamlined steel tubing of suitable size, sawn to length and given end fittings. The ailerons were simple, with a longitudinal plywood box spar to resist torsional loads. The gap along the hinge line was closed with a 'half round' strip of wood and a fabric shroud.

On the early production models the airbrakes were of the old German DFS type. The blades lay flush with the wing surfaces in normal flight. To open, they pivoted around transverse axes, requiring quite a complicated drive mechanism with bellcranks and separate bearings for each blade. The air pressure on the lower paddles moving down and back, tending to force them open, balanced the load on the upper blades as they moved up and forward against the airflow. After a few Prefects had been built the brakes were changed to the Schempp-Hirth type, which were simpler to install and opened like parallel rulers vertically above and below the wing. Although the designations are not entirely clear, it seems that the Prefect with Schempp-Hirth brakes was registered as the Type 30B.

The fuselage of the T-30 was also structurally quite different from that of the Baby and followed the pattern established by the T-21. Some notable weak-nesses of the Grunau Baby design, especially the front skid attachment, were improved. Instead of having a stressed plywood skin, the fuselage behind the wing was a wooden space frame covered with fabric. The method of assembly was similar to that used for many model aircraft. The two identical fuselage sides were assembled with longerons and diagonal cross-braces, each joint being reinforced with plywood gussets or 'biscuits' on both sides. The completed sides were then placed in a jig with the main cross-frames for the wing and tail supports and the cockpit. Cross-struts and the corresponding diagonal members to make a com-pletely triangulated frame were glued in top and bottom, forming a square-section box extending from the rear of the cockpit back to the sternpost. It was light, strong, easily built, and easily maintained and repaired. The upper part of the fuselage between wing and tail was merely a fairing with light vertical formers and a single longeron along the top. Plywood skinning was used on the front of the fuselage around the cockpit, on the main frames of the wing pylon, and underneath to reduce damage from small stones and rough ground.

The cockpit was normally fitted with a semi-enclosed canopy and windscreen, though like the Grunau Baby it was possible to fly the Prefect without any canopy at all. A fully enclosed cockpit cover was offered as an option. There was provision for a back-type parachute, though not many Prefect pilots ever bothered to carry one. The undercarriage consisted of a single wheel with a simple rubber sprung ash skid and a steel spring tailskid. The tailplane, with struts, was closely modelled on that of the Grunau Baby, but the rudder was taken directly from the Kirby Cadet, using the same drawings.

Despite the competition from Newbury there was some demand for the Prefect, although sales were very slow at first. Slingsby adopted a policy which had proved successful before. In January 1949 he lent a Prefect to the London Gliding Club, still the largest in Britain, for a season. The loan gave anyone who wanted to assess the aircraft a chance to fly it, and to discuss it with people who had been operating and ser-vicing it regularly. Club members used the Prefect for their 'Silver C' badge. It made many 5hr duration flights over the hill at Dunstable, plenty of 1,000m ascents in thermals, and several cross-country excursions of 50km or more. Before the end of the year it had become an indispensable member of the fleet, and in 1950 the club, having bought this aircraft, discovered it had accumulated more flying than any other club machine, 329hr, surpassing even the two-seaters.

Meanwhile, the Cambridge University Gliding Club had bought one, and a few others were sold elsewhere. One for the Royal Navy was fitted with instruments and a camera for more tests of aircraft-carrier wake air-flows following the loss at sea of the T-20, though these further experiments were never carried out. Gradually the Prefect established itself as a very safe, useful and popular sailplane. A total of 30 were bought by civilian clubs over the next few years, with exports to New Zealand, Israel, Egypt and Holland. Sixteen were bought for the ATC, where the type was known as the Prefect TX Mk.1. The eventual total of 46 built in the factory almost equalled the production of the EON Baby and, as with the Baby, a few were built from kits by amateurs.

As the Prefect became established, British gliding clubs were gradually being persuaded to abandon solo training with Daglings or Cadets. Dual instruction was becoming general. However, the old tradition was a long time a-dying.

In a school for powered flying the transition from dual to solo flying was, and is, simple. After a previous successful circuit, the instructor leaves the aircraft and waves the pupil off immediately to do the same thing again with the least possible fuss. Not so in gliding during the 1940s, '50s and even '60s. The glider pilot, who had been brought up to the required standard usually in a T-21B, was not then launched for the first solo in the familiar aircraft. The first-soloist was taken out of the two-seater and put into a single-seater. To the inevitable tensions associated with such an occa-sion were added all those strains associated with an unfamiliar cockpit, a different seating position, and different outlook, different control feel and response.

One reason for this was that flying the T-21B solo with its side-by-side seats required ballast to be carried to make up for the weight of the instructor. With only one seat occupied the c.g. would be much too far back for safety. The T-21B had provision for ballast, but fitting the necessary weights required the cockpit to be vacated and the aircraft to be taken off the launching line while someone delved into the nose with the appropriate lumps of lead, to clamp them down in the proper place and in the right quantity, allowing for the weight of the solitary pilot. The ATC Sedberghs were eventually adapted to carry trimming ballast in cylin-drical housings accessible from outside the cockpit, but this was almost unheard of in the civilian clubs. While all this business with ballast was going on, other pupils were impatiently waiting their turn to fly in the two-seater and the student preparing to go off alone had time to contemplate everything that might go wrong. Often enough the weather would change in the middle of the operation requiring at least a special briefing, more fuss and possibly even a postponement until another day. Another factor was economic. A typical gliding club possessed only one two-seater. If it was put out of action the entire training programme came to a standstill until it was flying again. If its T-21 were badly damaged or written off, a small club might collapse. Club committees therefore were very reluc-tant to let the two-seater be used for first solos. It was accepted that the chances of damage to the precious aircraft were greater. The argument that no instructor should send a pupil off solo in any type of aircraft at all if there was a serious risk of accident found little support.

It seemed much easier, then, to have a suitable single-seat aircraft standing by, and the first-solo pilot would be given a thorough briefing before being sent off alone in it. In some clubs the first solo flights would be gentle 'low hops' in a Tutor, so that at least the pupil would have something of a feel for the aircraft before taking a launch to full height and doing a circuit. Sometimes the policy was even to go back to the old Dagling or one of the later types of primary glider and begin the process of solo training again almost from scratch. Progress to full circuit flying was then quick, but there was great frustration at being put on to such an aircraft after at least a taste of soaring in the T-21. Usually, when the trainee was judged ready to leave the T-21, the next flight was a full circuit from a winch launch in a totally different aircraft. There were not many serious accidents.

Although the Prefect was aerodynamically similar to the T-21B, the first-solo pilot had to adjust to considerable changes. Some found the cockpit quite cramped and even claustrophobic after the very wide open arrangement of the two-seater, and a few exceptionally tall pilots could not get into it at all. The view in all directions was much better because the wing no longer obstructed vision overhead, and on the left there was no person to cut off the view on that side. The nervous pilot could find all this quite frightening. Paradoxically, to sit in a Prefect after training in a T-21, could make the pupil feel both tightly enclosed and unduly exposed. The instruments were invariably different and were often positioned differently on the panel. The familiar spoiler handle was replaced by an airbrake lever. All the controls felt strange even before taking off.

In flight, the mere fact that the Prefect was a smaller aircraft made it more responsive and lighter on all the controls than the T-21. A particularly noticeable difference was the tendency of the Prefect to take up a very steep climbing attitude on winch launches, so that during the early stages of the climb it needed to be held down with a little forward elevator until sufficient height had been gained to enable safe recovery if the winch cable should break. All in all, the first-solo pilot needed a very careful briefing, but the Prefect was docile and well behaved even when handled roughly. Once the first few solos had been successfully accomplished the Prefect was both pleasant and easy to fly. It soared well. Confidence built rapidly. Before long, the 'C' soaring badge would be gained, and progression to more advanced flying could be quite rapid.

Training aircraft are not often allowed to make very long excursions from the home site, and club Prefects were used mostly for circuit and local soaring flights. Nevertheless, some notable achievements were made in the type. J. C. Riddell made a height gain of 3,090m (10,300ft) when cloud flying a Prefect over the Long Mynd in 1953. S. H. Georgeson first flew the Prefect at Dunstable in 1949 and did his 5hr in it there. He took one to New Zealand with him and described this Prefect, registered ZK-GAB, as ideal for making exploratory flights over hitherto unknown soaring territory because it could be landed 'on a pocket handkerchief'. With it, he twice broke the New Zealand national height record with flights in wave near Christchurch, the first to 3,180m (10,600ft) asl in December 1952, and the second, some months later, to 3,900m (13,000ft) asl, both without oxygen. He could have gone much higher if he had had the requisite apparatus on board. These were among the first substantial wave soaring flights in New Zealand, and had a considerable influence on the subsequent development of soaring in that country.

Meanwhile, in England, as the old Tutor was phased out the Prefect became a standard first-solo aircraft and there were exports. The type became well-known in the Netherlands, where nine were in service. The prototype itself, which was originally registered G-ALLF in Britain, became PH-1 in Holland and later still returned again to Britain. Five went to Egypt, and Belgium, Israel and New Zealand took others.

At the time of writing a few Prefects remain in service. Most were written-off eventually after being seriously damaged in training accidents, and one was destroyed by fire at the Bristol Gliding Club's site in 1973. Those that remain are cherished vintage sailplanes in the hands of private owners. Some of these have been modified in various small ways; G-ALLF for instance, flying with an enlarged rudder. At the Vintage Glider Club Rally at Terlet in Holland in 1992, the strength and reliability of the Prefect was amply demonstrated when PH-192, built in the early 1950s, gave a demonstration of aerobatics which amazed those who had, themselves, used the type for a few tentative circuits 40 years previously.

Type 30 Prefect data

Dimensions

Wingspan	13.72m (45ft)
Wing area	14.25m^2 (154ft^2)
Aspect ratio	13.2
Wing sections:	
Root	Göttingen 535
Tip	Symmetrical
Length o.a.	6.49m (21ft 3½in)

Weights

Tare	176.9kg (390lb)
Flying	279kg (614lb)
Wing loading	19.5kg/m^2 (4lb/ft^2)

G-ALPC, the second Prefect built, is shown here at Dunstable in 1950. Note that the airbrakes were of the old DFS pattern. On later Prefects these were replaced by the vertical 'parallel-ruler' brakes of Schempp-Hirth type. In the left background is the wing of the two-seat Hawkridge Venture G-ALMF. (*Slingsby collection*)

Prefect G-ALLF in its modern guise and in perfect condition. Full registration letters were required for a short period during 1949-50, when Certificates of Airworthiness were issued by the Air Registration Board. The law was changed before long and registration letters disappeared from gliders. In this case the restorers decided to restore them as well. (*Neville Churcher*)

A Prefect at a vintage glider rally at Sutton Bank. A T-31 is being rigged in the background and beyond are the Scud 2 and the Kirby Kite. (*Ray Ash*)

It was possible to fly the Prefect without the cockpit canopy and windscreen. For tall pilots this was sometimes the only way. (*P. Selinger*)

Prefect G-ALLF was built in 1948. It has had a long and varied history, having operated at Staverton, the Long Mynd and Dunstable, and has done well over 14,000hrs of flying. Numerous repairs were necessary over the years, and a major restoration was done in the 1970s. The elevator is of a non-standard pattern, possibly taken from an old Grunau Baby, and the rudder was enlarged with a rounded top at some time. (*Neville Churcher*)

Prefects (including, in the background, G-ALLF in earlier guise) at Brienne le Château during the vintage glider rally of 1978. (*P. Selinger*)

PH193, one of the Dutch Prefects, in flight. (*P. Selinger*)

The Prefect has always been popular in the Netherlands. PH193 and 192 are shown here at the 1978 Brienne rally. (*M. Simons*)

ZK-GAB was an early production Prefect exported to New Zealand, where, flown from Simons Hill by Dick Georgeson, it pioneered wave soaring in that country. (*Slingsby collection*)

A Prefect at Terlet in 1992. (*M. Simons*)

PH-192 in flight, with enclosed canopy. (*M. Simons*)

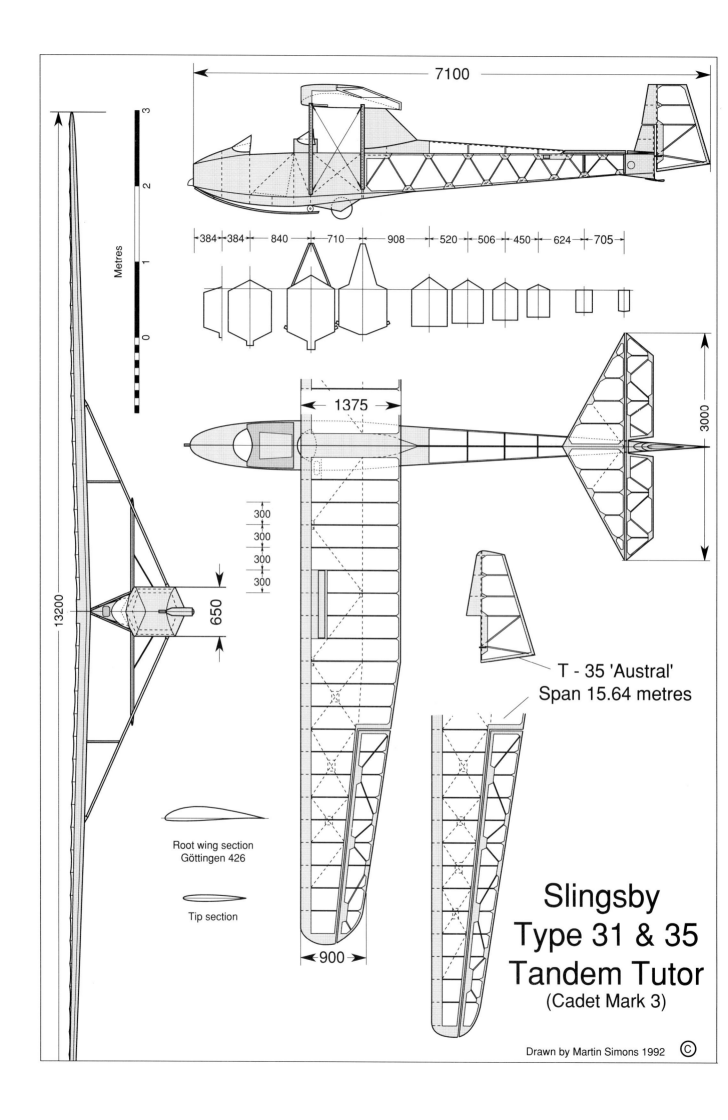

7100

384 384 840 710 908 520 506 450 624 705

Metres

1375

300
300
300
300

650

13200

3000

900

Root wing section
Göttingen 426

Tip section

T - 35 'Austral'
Span 15.64 metres

Slingsby
Type 31 & 35
Tandem Tutor
(Cadet Mark 3)

Drawn by Martin Simons 1992 ©

Type 31 Tandem Tutor (TX Mk 3 Cadet) and T-35 Austral

By 1950 it was at last recognised throughout the British gliding movement that the old solo method of primary training should be abandoned, and that two-seaters should be used. The main impediment for the small clubs was the greater capital cost of such otherwise excellent training aircraft as the T-21B Sedbergh which had been available since 1947. It was also felt in some quarters that a good two-seater should have the seats in tandem, so that the pupil would have the least possible adjustment to make on going solo. The advantage claimed for side-by-side seating was that the instructor could see and talk easily to the student, and *vice versa*. Some people maintained that too much conversation in the cockpit was undesirable because instructors talked too much anyway! The tandem arrangement allowed the instructor to speak when necessary but otherwise, after the first few flights, the pupil could learn to be self-reliant and get the feel of flying alone.

In 1948 Slingsby already had the main components of a new tandem-seated, inexpensive training glider. The original Type 8 Tutor single-seater had flown first in 1937, and subsequent minor redesign and strengthening had established the Tutor or Cadet Mark 2 as a standard training sailplane suitable for first-solo flying. The Type 29 Motor Tutor, of which two had been built in 1948-49, used Tutor wings and tail unit with a new fuselage. In the Motor Tutor the pilot sat immediately underneath the wing, which was supported on a simple cabane. The motor was mounted in front. The rear fuselage was a fabric covered wooden space frame of the style already well proved in the T-21.

It was a very simple exercise to redesign the fuselage of the Motor Tutor to take a pupil pilot instead of the engine. It would almost have been feasible to cut the cockpit off an existing Tutor and scarf it on to the Motor Tutor fuselage. However, to accommodate the instructor's feet on either side of the pupil's seat in front, the fuselage had to be widened slightly. The landing wheel and skid were taken directly from the Tutor. Many of the same jigs as for the Motor Tutor were used, and the prototype T-31 flew in 1949. It was finished in silver dope and carried the 'B conditions' marking G-26-2 on either side of the rear fuselage. Apart from the new fuselage, the only other important change was the addition of half a degree of dihedral to the wing. The cockpits remained open, with small windscreens. At this stage no airbrakes or spoilers were fitted. The expected price was about 60 per cent of the cost of a T-21.

One group which had supported the idea of a tandem trainer was the Derbyshire and Lancashire Gliding Club, whose site at Camphill had been created from about a dozen small fields. The roots of dry stone walls were still extant under the turf all over the landing area, and caused many good landings to finish in a series of fairly heavy thumps. (Digging up wall roots was a favourite occupation in bad flying weather at this site until well into the 1960s.) The need for a very robust and easily repaired trainer was particularly obvious under these conditions, and it was therefore natural that the prototype T-31 should be tested and flown in service by this club. The first flight at Camphill was on 23 July 1949, when it flew about a dozen circuits. Three days later the pupil (who had begun training on primary gliders) was flying solo.

The test flights required for certification were done mostly by the Derby Club's chief instructor, Gerard O. Smith, at Camphill and other sites, with winch and aero-towed launches, and control and c.g. position checks. It was found that the T-31 handled well although it lacked any trim tab or spring trim for the elevator. If the student pilot was heavy enough to bring the c.g. to the forward limit, a constant pull of four pounds was required on the stick to hold the airspeed down to 40kt. The stalling speed at maximum all-up weight was measured at 33kt. A fully developed spin, even with the c.g. fully aft, was almost impossible, the maximum number of turns achieved being only one-and-a-half. The only minor abnormality was in side-slipping. The T-31 could hold a sideslip with the fuselage yawed 40° but with wings level and ailerons neutral.

As expected, the performance of the sailplane was between those of the Slingsby Cadet and Tutor. The additional weight and drag of the instructor and the higher wing loading ensured that the T-31 would be less capable of soaring in weak upcurrents than the Tutor, but its greater wing span and aspect ratio gave it an advantage over the Cadet.

Certification having been completed, the T-31 entered production. The prototype acquired the BGA number 667 in 1951 and became known as the T-31A. Subsequent models, either in the factory or by retrospective modification, had small spoilers well forward on the upper surface of the wing and became the T-31 B or Cadet TX Mk.3 in the ATC. For aero-towing a small additional strut was added to prevent rather alarming vibrations of the front lift strut under certain conditions of airspeed and loading. These struts had first appeared on the Motor Tutor.

The T-31 had the same type of mainspar design as the original Tutor. The ribs were threaded on to the spars to be glued in their places, after which strips of spruce were added above and below the spar flanges between the ribs to provide gluing area for the plywood nose skin. After long service these were found to cause compression shakes in the spars, so retrospective modifications were required.

The T-31B was greeted with enthusiasm by the ATC, and 131 Cadets TX Mk.3 were built under Air Ministry contract. Painted in the official para-military colour scheme with roundels and the bold lettering AIR CADETS on either side of the front fuselage, the Cadet Mk.3 became a great favourite with the many youngsters who had their first flying experience in one of these gliders. The main purpose of the cadet training scheme was to bring students up to solo standard, and there was little emphasis on gaining certificates for soaring. Many of the cadets finished when they had reached the B certificate stage, which required only a few gliding flights from a winch launch. It is recorded that one of the Cadet Mk.3 gliders made over 120,000 flights of about 3min each, a total of 6,000hr. This may not have been typical, but it does indicate the very hard use to which the ATC gliders and instructors became accustomed. In fairly recent times the surviving Cadets Mk.3 no longer required by the ATC have been sold, and some are again in service in civilian hands in Britain and overseas, following restoration.

Civilian clubs in Britain, with a few exceptions, were not greatly enthusiastic about the T-31 despite its relatively low cost. With the emphasis increasingly on cross-country flying, most clubs felt it was essential for the beginner to be introduced as soon as possible to thermal soaring and although the T-31 and the Tutor, its single-seat equivalent, were capable of exploiting thermals when skilfully handled, the T-21 was much better for this. Sales of the T-31 on the civilian home market were relatively few. Many of those which appeared briefly on the BGA register were exported, and it appears that only about a dozen of those built at

Kirbymoorside were ever in regular use in British gliding clubs, although several more were taken up by the RAF Gliding and Soaring Association, and one or two at least by the Royal Naval Gliding and Soaring Association. Of the 69 civilian aircraft produced in the factory, the great majority were exported to such countries as Pakistan, Burma, Jordan, Lebanon, Nyasaland, Israel, Ceylon and Australia. A batch of six kits was sent for assembly in New Zealand, and two went to Australia. Others were built from kits in Britain and elsewhere, and some were assembled from government surplus and spares.

Designed from the outset as a trainer, the T-31 was never expected to make long cross-country flights or achieve great heights, but there were some fine achievements. At the Australian National Championships in 1956 the Royal Australian Navy's T-31, which had been fitted with an enclosure for the cockpits, made a cross-country flight of 93km (58 miles). In New Zealand the Canterbury Gliding Club's T-31 broke the national altitude record with a wave flight over 5,700m (19,000ft) and made many other ascents above 3,000m (10,000ft).

The total of all T-31s ever flown is certainly in excess of 200, and probably about equal to the number of T-21s.

An interesting variant of the T-31 was the T-35, known as the Austral. This was built at Kirbymoorside to a special order for an Australian gliding club. The wingspan was increased to 15.64m (51.3ft) by the addition of extra rib bays on each side, extending the tips, and the rudder was enlarged to assist control of the longer wing in yaw. The result was a worthwhile improvement in soaring performance, and after arrival in Australia the T-35 made a useful contribution to the development of soaring training in that country, flying with various clubs including those at Waikerie and Renmark in South Australia, and with the RAAF Club at Laverton. It appeared as No. 24 on the Gliding Federation of Australia register. Home-built enclosed canopies for both cockpits were fitted at an early stage in its career. The airframe still exists complete in storage at Tocumwal in New South Wales.

Type 31 data

Dimensions
Wingspan	13.2m (43.3ft)
Wing area	15.8m^2 (170ft^2)
Aspect ratio	11
Wing sections:	
Root	Göttingen 426
Tip	Symmetrical
Length o.a.	7.1m (23.3ft)

Weights
Tare	176kg (388lb)
Flying	376kg (829lb)
Wing loading	23.8kg/m^2 (4.88lb/ft^2)

The original T-31 with the B conditions marking G-26-2. Note the absence of auxiliary struts. (*Slingsby collection.*)

The prototype T-31B with the auxiliary bracing strut and spoilers. (*Slingsby collection.*)

A Royal Navy Gliding and Soaring Association T-31 preparing for launch. Another T-31 is in the background. (*Charles E. Brown, RAF Museum, Hendon, neg. No. 6689-12.*)

A T-31B in service with the RAAF support group in Singapore, about 1967. (*J. Wilson*)

The instrument panel of a T-31B in Malaysia, including artificial horizon and other instruments not normally fitted.

A Royal Navy T-31 just after take-off on winch launch in 1951. (*Fox Photos*)

The cockpits and instrument panels of an Air Cadets T-31B. The instruments are an airspeed indicator, altimeter and variometer—all that are required for simple training flights. (*M. Simons*)

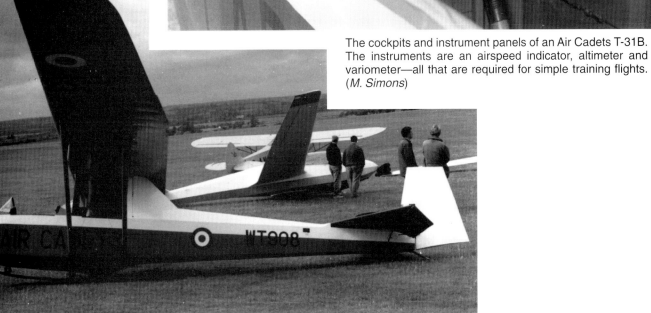

An Air Cadets T-31B at Dunstable in 1990, following restoration after sale on the government surplus market. (*M. Simons*)

A rare photograph of the T-35 Austral in service with the Renmark Gliding Club in South Australia, 1959. (*Alan DeLaine.*)

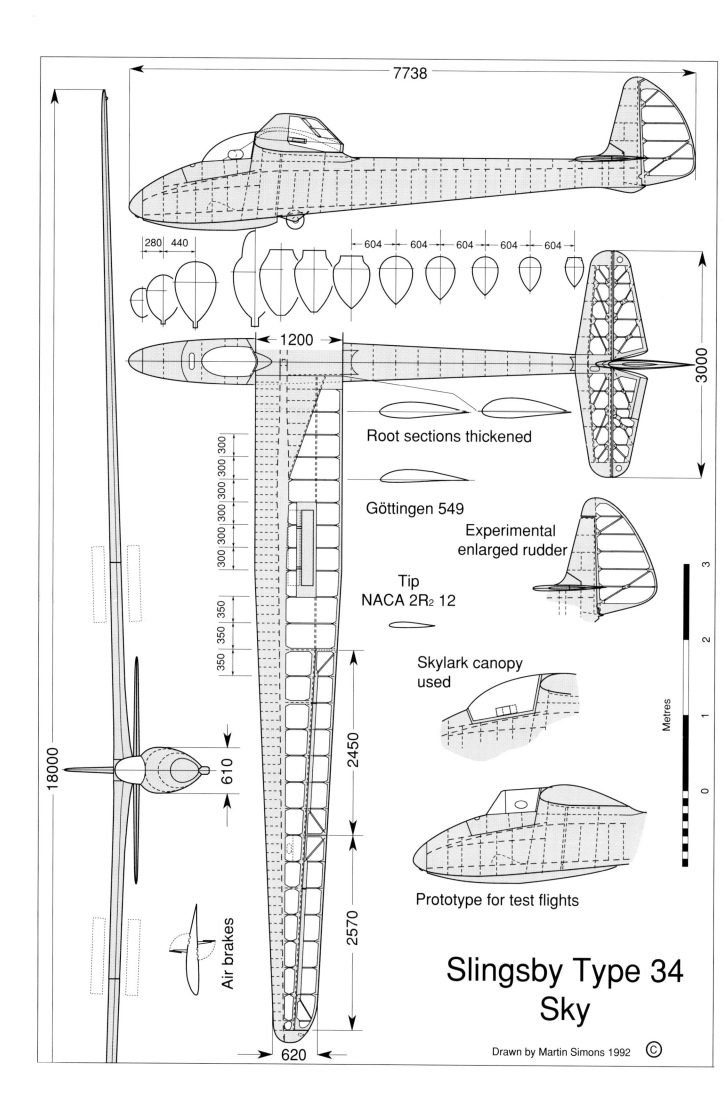

7738

280 | 440

604 — 604 — 604 — 604 — 604

1200

3000

Root sections thickened

Göttingen 549

Experimental
enlarged rudder

Tip
NACA 2R$_2$ 12

Skylark canopy
used

300 | 300 | 300 | 300 | 300 | 300

350 | 350 | 350 | 350

2450

2570

620

610

18000

Air brakes

Prototype for test flights

3

2

1

0

Metres

Slingsby Type 34
Sky

Drawn by Martin Simons 1992 ©

Type 34, Sky

'There is no substitute for span,' Fred Slingsby was once heard to say. In sailplane performance this remains true, and probably always will. The current generation of open-class sailplanes have spans of anything from 23 to 26m (75 to 85ft). In 1950, however, sailplane wing spans of more than 18m (59ft) were considered somewhat too great, and although many earlier German aircraft and Slingsby's own two-seat Gull 2 had reached about 20m (65.6ft), 18m represented an accepted limit. Since sailplanes often have to be transported by road, the wing was normally divisible on the centreline into two equal pieces. A two-wheeled light trailer less than 10m (32.8ft) long could be towed safely by an ordinary car.

The best contest sailplane available at this time was the 18m German Weihe (pronounced approximately 'Vyer', to rhyme with fire), which had been designed in 1938. The Olympia was in effect a 15m version of this famous aircraft. It was almost inevitable that Slingsby should be advised to produce a new sailplane which would meet and beat the Weihe. Types 32 and 33 never advanced beyond the design study stage, so the number allotted to the proposed new high-performance single-seater was T-34. The name Sky was not chosen until after the prototype had flown. It was invented by John Furlong, using the initial letters of Slingsby, Kirbymoorside, Yorkshire. Furlong ordered the first of the new type off the drawing board.

The obvious way of improving the performance of a good small sailplane was to extend the span, and this was what Slingsby proceeded to do. This had the very important advantage that it would allow the re-use of most of the jigging and tooling used to produce the Gull 4, and many of the components would be the same. While such an exercise might seem relatively simple, there are difficulties.

The span increase was achieved by adding two extra bays to the centre section of the wing and increasing the spacing of the outer main ribs to 350mm instead of 300mm. The main spar was a box-type of spruce with plywood shear webs, and the greater span necessitated a complete redesign of this most vital member.

The bending and shear forces at the centre of such a wing are large, and the spar had to be much stronger than that required for the smaller Gull. The spar flanges inboard of bay nine in the centre section were widened in plan view, and the depth of the spar was increased considerably towards the root. The resulting structure was quite complicated, and one aerodynamic consequence was that the aerofoil section at the extreme root end of the wing had to be increased to 22 per cent depth instead of the 13.85 per cent of the standard Göttingen 549 profile. The weight of the main spar so constructed was a quarter of the total structural weight of the sailplane.

The rest of the wing was of standard form with a plywood skinned leading edge, the grain of the birch plywood laid diagonally to resist torsional loads. The plywood over the inner wing panels was 2mm thick, reducing to 1mm near the tips. This stressed skin was supported by numerous light nose ribs to preserve an accurate profile and stiffen the plywood against secondary failure. The outer panels of such a wing tend to flex in bending and torsion during flight, and tip movements up and down of a metre or so had to be allowed for. The need in soaring to change direction frequently in search of the strongest part of thermal upcurrents requires effective ailerons. These on the T-34 were spilt into two segments to prevent them binding at the hinges as the wing distorted, and were driven by tubular steel pushrods rather than cables. Rigging the Sky was facilitated by the simple three-pin system of attaching the wings to one another and to the fuselage, but the weight of the wings was a disadvantage. It was claimed that a trained crew could rig the aircraft from its trailer in 6min, but what was not stated was the number of people required for this exercise. It could not have been fewer than four or five unless trestles and auxiliary wheeled trolleys were available.

The airbrakes used on the Gull 4 had been of the vertical parallel-ruler type developed originally by Schempp-Hirth in Germany. On the Sky these were replaced by the DFS type of brake with paddles above and below the wing which lay flush with the surfaces when retracted. On opening these brakes, the lower paddle moved down and back, the upper paddle up and forward, the aerodynamic loads on the two surfaces tending to balance one another. Some difficulties were found when closing the brakes on the prototype at moderately high airspeeds, which required several modifications before fully satisfactory operating loads were achieved. They were also increased in size.

The fuselage of the Sky from the wing forward was identical to that of the Gull 4. The prototype Sky flew with a rather angular built-up transparent canopy, but in production this was replaced by a blown bubble. Behind the wing, to keep the tail moment arms in proportion to the greater span, the fuselage was stretched, with an increased number of cross-formers and stiffeners while retaining the same cross-section. The tail unit was adapted directly from the Gull's. The rudder proved somewhat too small, and various experiments were tried to improve this before the final arrangement was adopted. A simple landing wheel was fitted, but to reduce drag for major competitions, the Sky was available without the wheel, a drop-off dolly being used for take-off and landings being made on the skid alone.

The prototype T-34 first flew in September 1950, and favourable reports appeared almost at once. It handled well and was safe and strong. Before long, comparison flights against the Weihe were made, and it was claimed that these demonstrated a clear advantage for the new type. In some important respects these claims were justified. The Sky showed measurable improvement over the old German aircraft at high flying speeds. For cross-country flying and racing in anything but the poorest conditions the Sky would certainly do better, gaining speed and distance in the glide, even if not climbing quite so well in weak thermals. It was not made clear in any of the published data that the Sky and Weihe differed in weight and wing loading. The Slingsby type was heavier and stronger, which gave it a greater wing loading and hence a better glide at high speeds. Had the two been compared at identical weight, any performance advantage for the Slingsby type would probably have disappeared.

The BGA later published figures based on flight tests which showed the Sky to have a best glide ratio of about 27.5 at 34kt airspeed, the Weihe reaching 29 at 36kt. The best glide ratio of the Weihe was superior and its minimum rate of sink was fractionally better. In practice the difference between the two types, allowing for experimental error in the test flying, was probably negligible. What was more important was that the Sky was readily available at an attainable cost from a British factory.

Two Skys competed in the British National Contests held at Camphill in July 1951. John Furlong's aircraft was flown by Geoffrey Stephenson, well-known for his cross-Channel soaring flight in the Gull 1 in 1939. The other Sky was piloted by Jock Forbes, who had made a great reputation flying with the British Air Force of Occupation gliding clubs in Germany. Two Weihes, flown by Philip Wills and Lorne Welch, constituted the

main opposition. The contest had several remarkable features. On one day Stephenson's barograph failed to record correctly the height he had gained in a cloud flight, costing him 52 points. On another day Forbes attempted an out-and-return flight to Flamborough Head, relying on a photograph he proposed to take of the lighthouse to prove that he had reached the pre-declared turning point. This was the first occasion ever on which a glider pilot used a camera to prove the rounding of a turning point in a competition. Forbes did reach the lighthouse, but had to land a short distance inland on the return journey. His photo when developed was almost indecipherable. The final result of the competition after seven days' flying depended on whether he could establish that he had in fact rounded the Head, which would give him a small winning margin. After some fairly frantic telephone calls it was established that the lighthouse keeper had seen and logged the appearance to seaward of a red glider at the appropriate time. Forbes won with 877 points over Stephenson, with 873, and Welch and Wills took third and fourth places with 804 and 800.

At the Festival of Britain exhibition, held on the south bank of the Thames in London later in the year, the prototype Sky was suspended in the transport hall among other aircraft as a recognition of its design excellence.

It was not surprising that the British team of Forbes, Stephenson, Wills, Welch and Foster, sent to Madrid for the World Championships in 1952, should be equipped with Slingsby Skys. Two others of the type were flown by the Argentinian team, and one by Ordelman of Holland. To the great delight of the British Wills won the championships from the Frenchman Gerard Pierre, with Forbes in third place. Slingsby's latest product was thus established as one of the great sailplane designs. The Sky had proved itself. Orders came in, with exports as well as sales on the home market, and for a time the T-34 was recognised as the best available contest sailplane. Stephenson won the British Nationals in 1953.

Yet only 16 of the type were built. This was a modest success, but not at all the kind of result Slingsby must have hoped for. For its period the Sky was quite costly, and with much less expensive gliders such as the Olympia on the market there were not many individuals or clubs with the capital to buy one. In other countries during this period new sailplanes with very significant improvements in performance over pre-war German design were beginning to appear.

The 1954 World Championships, held at Camphill (forever remembered because they were almost washed out by rain) were won by the French Breguet 901 flown by Pierre, with Wills in his Sky second. A Weihe 50 from new German production came third, showing that even this old type could still do well, especially in difficult weather. Meanwhile, outstanding work by the aerodynamicist August Raspet and Dick Johnson in the USA had produced the RJ-5 sailplane, which, after very skilful rebuilding, smoothing and sealing, achieved a best glide ratio of 40:1 using NACA low drag '6 Series' wing profiles. The Breguet 901 used these sections and achieved a glide ratio of 36:1. By 1954, it was clear to anyone that design concepts dating back to 1938 were no longer appropriate. The success of the Sky was short-lived. Even so, as late as 1958 in Argentina, Sky sailplanes placed third, fourth and fifth in the National Championships.

Today, several T-34s are flown in Britain and are treasured by their owners. These include BGA 685, the prototype; BGA 686, the third off the production line in May 1951; and BGA 698, first registered in 1953, which has been fitted with a Skylark cockpit canopy. It is not known how many of those that were exported have survived, but some that were sold to Dutch and Swiss owners have more recently been returned to Britain, and one at least has been exported yet again.

Type 34 Sky data

Dimensions

Wingspan	18m (59.06ft)
Wing area	17.37m^2 (187ft^2)
Aspect ratio	18.7
Length o. a.	7.65m (25ft 1in)
Wing sections	
Root	Göttingen 549 thickened
Mid-span	Göttingen 549
Tip	NACA 2R, 12

Weights

Tare	249.5kg (550lb)
Flying	362.9kg (800lb)
Wing loading	20.9kg/m^2 (4.28lb/ft^2.)

An early experiment with a much-enlarged rudder with aerodynamic balance. This was not adopted for production. (*Slingsby collection.*)

The prototype T-34 showing the original built-up cockpit canopy, small rudder and translucent doped fabric covering. (*Slingsby collection.*)

An early production Sky outside the factory at Kirbymoorside. (*Slingsby collection*)

Wills in the Sky taking off on a winch launch. (*Charles E Brown, RAF Museum, Hendon, neg No. 6568*)

Philip Wills flying his Sky with the landing skid instead of the fixed wheel arrangement. Performance tests by the BGA Test Group 1 based at Lasham showed a gain of one point in the best glide ratio for this configuration. (*Charles E. Brown, RAF Museum, Hendon, neg No. 6598-3*)

During the National Championships, a goal race to Dunstable from Camphill was won by Geoffrey Stephenson. Jock Forbes was placed second and Philip Wills, in the Weihe, came third. The two winning Sky aircraft are seen here after landing at Dunstable on 21 July 1951, with the Olympia flown to fourth place on this day by Tony Goodhart behind them, and Wills's Weihe on the left. (*M. Eacock*)

Geoffrey Stephenson in the cockpit, preparing to take off. His wife and crew chief Beryl assists. (*Charles E. Brown, RAF Museum, Hendon, neg No 6613-12*)

Rigging detail of the Sky. Two horizontal pins aligned on the same centre attach one wing to the fuselage. When the other wing is similarly attached the last pin is inserted to join the upper flanges of the main spars. Aileron and brake pushrods are linked with pip pins. (*P. J. Teagle*)

Airbrake detail of the Sky. When retracted, the brake paddle lies flush with the wing. (*M. Simons*)

BGA 685, a restored Sky which has been a frequent participant in vintage rallies in recent times, at Dunstable. (*M. Simons*)

Instrument panel and cockpit details of Sky BGA 686. Instruments, from left to right and top to bottom, are airspeed indicator, electric variometer, altimeter, mechanical variometer (PZL), artificial horizon, turn and slip indicator, Cobb-Slater variometer, oxygen pressure gauge and Cook compass. (*P. J. Teagle*)

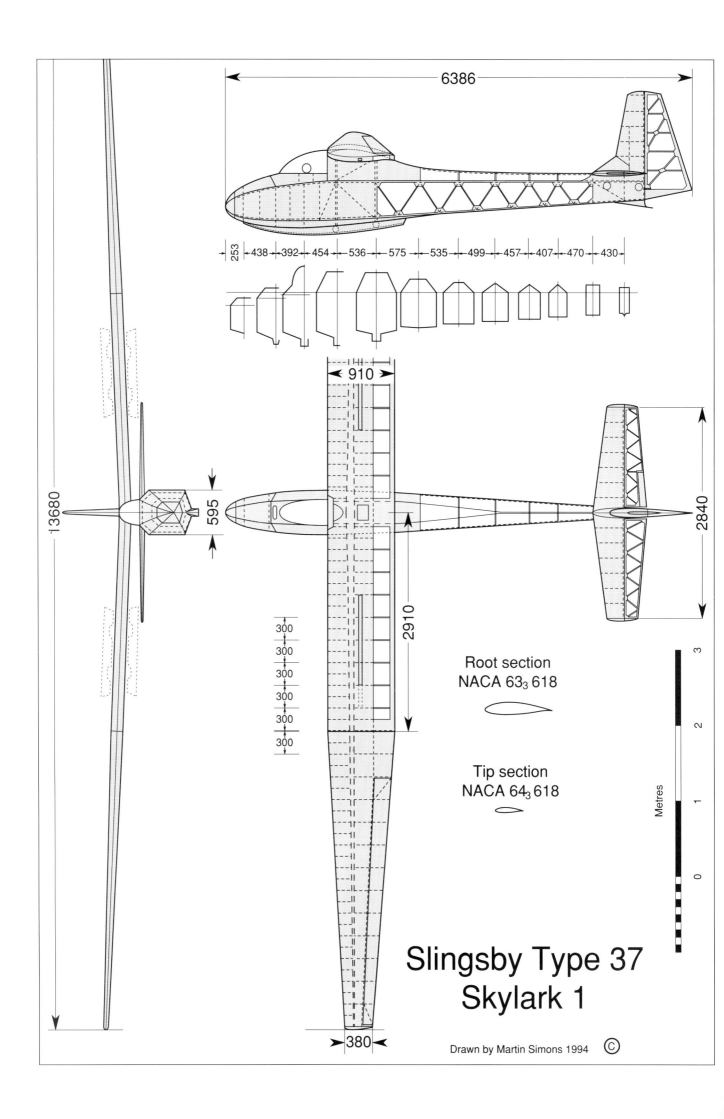

6386

253 438 392 454 536 575 535 499 457 407 470 430

910

13680

595

2840

2910

300
300
300
300
300
300

380

Root section
NACA 63₃ 618

Tip section
NACA 64₃ 618

Metres

0   1   2   3

Slingsby Type 37
Skylark 1

Drawn by Martin Simons 1994 ©

Type 37, Skylark 1

Several lines of thought converged to produce the first Slingsby Skylark, which began test flying in March 1953. According to Slingsby himself, the prototype was built 'for a lark', hence its name. There was a serious purpose behind this 'lark', and with its subsequent development it led to something of a golden age for the Yorkshire company. It was numbered Type 37 in Slingsby's sequence. (The T-35 Austral was the one off extended-span version of the T-31, and the T-36, a projected two-seat development of the T-34 Sky, was never built.)

In a highly competitive market a successful sailplane was judged chiefly by its performance and price. Slingsby argued rightly enough that, despite the advantages of a large wingspan, a small aircraft should always turn out cheaper to produce than a large one using similar materials. If the performance was not much poorer or, with improved aerodynamic design, even superior to contemporary 15m sailplanes such as the Olympia, and if the price was lower, sales of a new type ought to be good. There was also some need for research into the lateral controls of sailplanes which, with their high aspect ratios and relatively large moments of inertia in the rolling plane, tended to be sluggish when changing direction and suffered from severe adverse yaw caused by aileron drag. Moreover, they were occasionally prone to aileron reversal at moderately high speeds. Application of aileron could cause the wing to twist so much that the control became ineffective or reversed (an example being the T-14 Gull 2). Many sailplanes were notoriously heavy on the ailerons. Rudders, in the absence of any slipstream from a propeller, were seldom adequate.

In the autumn of 1952 some preliminary design work was begun. To facilitate the research the wing was designed in three pieces, consisting of a parallel-chord centre section with detachable outer panels which could be changed as required to try out different types of control, including tip spoilers coupled with short-span ailerons, different tip sections and varying amounts of washout. The three-piece design also obviated the need for heavy and expensive metal fittings at the root ends of the wings, where, in orthodox practice, they were joined to one another and to the fuselage at the point of maximum stress. Carrying the mainspar through in one piece, with appropriate dihedral built in, saved both weight and cost, as the fuselage could be suspended below such a wing using the simplest and lightest of fittings. The connection between the outer wing panels and the centre section was made by a single vertical steel pin inserted from above, with very simple automatic alignment and connection of front and rear drag fittings.

At this time Slingsby appointed John Reussner, a qualified engineer from Hull, as draughtsman and designer, and it may have been at Reussner's suggestion that Slingsby decided to use the NACA '6 series' wing sections. The original intention had been to use the older four-digit profiles which had been successful on the Gull 1 before the Second World War. The outstanding performance in the USA of the RJ-5, using the newer so-called laminar flow profiles, caused sailplane designers all over the world to revise their ideas, and a major advance in performance was expected. The sections chosen for the T-37 were the NACA 63_3618 for the centre section, tapering to the 64_3618 at the tip, with $3.5°$ of washout to prevent tip stalling. The 63 section should have a laminar boundary layer to 30 per cent of the chord (as indicated by the second digit), and the 64 section to 40 per cent. As denoted by the last two digits, the wing was 18 per cent of the chord in thickness. The figure 6 relates to the camber, which was large compared with that used for powered aircraft, and the sub-scripted $_3$ referred to the width of the low-drag range, or 'drag bucket', of these profiles. An important advantage of the new sections was that, even though they were thick, their very wide 'drag bucket' allowed a sailplane to perform well at low speeds for soaring and at high speeds for penetrating sinking air between thermals. Preliminary calculations showed that with 13.72m (45ft) span with these low drag profiles, the Skylark would not only be cheaper but would also outperform larger types.

To get the advantage of laminar flow in the boundary

layer, the RJ-5 had proved that it was absolutely necessary to make the wing accurately and to prevent the development of waves and humps, particularly over the forward third of the chord. Quite a small hump or hollow, and even small blobs of paint or fly specks in this region, could cause the boundary layer to become turbulent. A 'low-drag' section with the flow forced into premature turbulence would actually produce more drag than one of the old-fashioned profiles. Dick Johnson had completely rebuilt the wing, and spent many hundreds of hours levelling and smoothing the surfaces of the RJ-5 before the sailplane began to perform up to expectations. To maintain this performance the levelling and smoothing process had to be repeated every season.

Hitherto, production sailplanes had usually been skinned with birch plywood, often with the grain laid diagonally. The ply was as thin as possible consistent with strength and stiffness, to save weight. Hence there were waves in the skin even as a new sailplane emerged from the factory, and after a short time in service these became more prominent as the wood shrank slightly, producing something of a 'starved horse' appearance, with every rib visible from the outside. Where the plywood was glued to the mainspar there was always a marked bump running from tip to tip on both upper and lower surfaces. With the older types of wings the penalties were not very great, but the new profiles demanded much more attention to these details.

Having recognised the problem, Slingsby adopted a radical solution. Instead of thin, high-density birch ply, an African gaboon plywood of low density and greater thickness was used. Gaboon, rather a soft wood, had not been well liked for aircraft construction previously, and the greater stiffness of the material necessitated a different approach to manufacture and surface finish. Thin birch ply can be persuaded without very elaborate moulding techniques to bend right round the leading edge of a wing, so that the skin can be continuous from the bottom round to the top of the mainspar. This was not feasible with gaboon, so the extreme leading edges of the Skylark wing were made from an accurately machined and spindled hollow member of spruce, with rebates top and bottom to accept the edges of the plywood. The skin was then applied in separate panels above and below, with careful attention to the leading-edge joints to prevent irregularities. This was largely successful. The Skylark wings were much more accurate and wave free than those of previous sailplanes, and remained quite good in service. To preserve accuracy over the rest of the wing the plywood skin was carried aft to the auxiliary spar, only a small area of the wing near the trailing edge being fabric-covered. The outer wing panels and ailerons were entirely ply skinned. To protect the rather soft outer veneer, lightweight cotton fabric was doped on to the plywood before painting. Airbrakes of the well tried Schempp-Hirth type were installed and, according to Slingsby,

proved to be very effective, even more powerful than strictly necessary.

The rest of the Skylark 1 was very orthodox, even somewhat crude, since it was regarded as an experimental aircraft. The fuselage was adapted cheaply from that of the T-30 Prefect trainer, being a wooden space frame with a simple cockpit and an upright, rather cramped and uncomfortable seating arrangement. The undercarriage was a simple rubber-sprung skid. The tailplane, like the wing, was skinned with gaboon ply. It was intended to produce a more refined streamlined monocoque fuselage for series production once the wing design had been proved.

After preliminary test flights, the Skylark was flown in the British National Championships by Anthony Deane Drummond, the distinguished soldier and pilot. The BGA handicappers rated it about equal to the much larger and more expensive 18m Sky and Weihe, with a best glide ratio about 27:1. The features that Deane Drummond praised most were the very effective lateral controls and the absence of adverse aileron drag, suggesting that the research had paid off. His chief criticism of the Skylark was that it had a higher wing loading and hence a greater stalling speed and larger circling radius than he had been accustomed to. He thought these were disadvantages for British soaring conditions. In good soaring weather the T-37 was excellent. Deane Drummond was placed fifth in the individual list, a good result considering the limited time he had had to get used to the aircraft.

A second T-37 was built for South African pilot Pat Beatty to fly in the 1954 World Championships at Camphill. In miserable weather which produced a bare minimum four days' flying, in common with several others he scored points on only one day. Afterwards the Skylark was taken to South Africa. What became of it there is not known. The one that remained in Britain was sold by Slingsby and still exists, though it is now very rarely seen or flown.

Technically, the T-37 was a very considerable advance for Slingsby. It is interesting to speculate on what might have happened if he had done as originally intended and produced a new version with exactly the same wing and a superior fuselage and cockpit. The wing loading of 28.8kg/m^2 (5.89lb/ft^2), which was considered so high in 1953, now seems extraordinarily light when sailplane pilots commonly load up their aircraft with large quantities of water ballast to achieve loadings nearly twice as great. Already in 1953 the mighty HKS 1 from Germany was flying successfully with higher wing loadings, and the Breguet 901, which won the wretched 1954 World Championships, had a wing loading comparable to that of Sling's little Skylark. The Breguet, however, had enormous Fowler flaps which enabled it to turn tightly in small, weak thermals. As it was, Slingsby allowed the collective voice of British pilots to convince him that the Skylark should follow a more conservative line of development; more span, more wing area, lower wing loading.

Type 37 Skylark 1 data

Dimensions

Wingspan	13.7m (45ft)
Wing area	10.5m^2 (113ft^2)
Aspect ratio	17.9
Length o. a.	6.39m (20.95ft)
Wing sections	
Root	NACA 63$_3$618
Mid-span	NACA 63$_3$618
Tip	NACA 64$_3$618

Weights

Tare	196.5kg (433lb)
Flying	302kg (665lb)
Wing loading	28.8kg/m^2 (5.89lb/ft^2.)

Tony Deane Drummond taking a winch launch in the prototype Skylark at the 1953 British National Championships at
Camphill. (*Slingsby collection*)

Beatty takes a winch launch at Camphill during the 1954
World Championships. (*M. Eacock*)

The prototype Skylark survives in Britain but is not often
flown. It is shown here, carrying the contest number 234, in
company with the later developments Skylark 2, 3 and 4.
(*Wills collection*)

The Skylark was unusual in having a three-piece wing comprising a central section with two tip sections. The airbrakes were in the centre panel, the ailerons confined to the outer panels.

The prototype Skylark on the ground at Lasham in 1953. The wheeled dolly was used for ground handling. The fuselage was taken with minimal changes from the Prefect training sailplane, the most noticeable alteration being a reduction in height to allow the cantilever wing to be attached on a broader pylon.

Before the 1954 World Championships, the South African pilot Pat Beatty took delivery of the second Skylark and flew it at Dunstable. He is seen here in the cockpit, with the canopy about to be put in place by his countryman, Heli Lasch. (*M. Eacock*)

In this photograph it is Lasch's turn to try the Skylark while Beatty looks on. (*M. Eacock*)

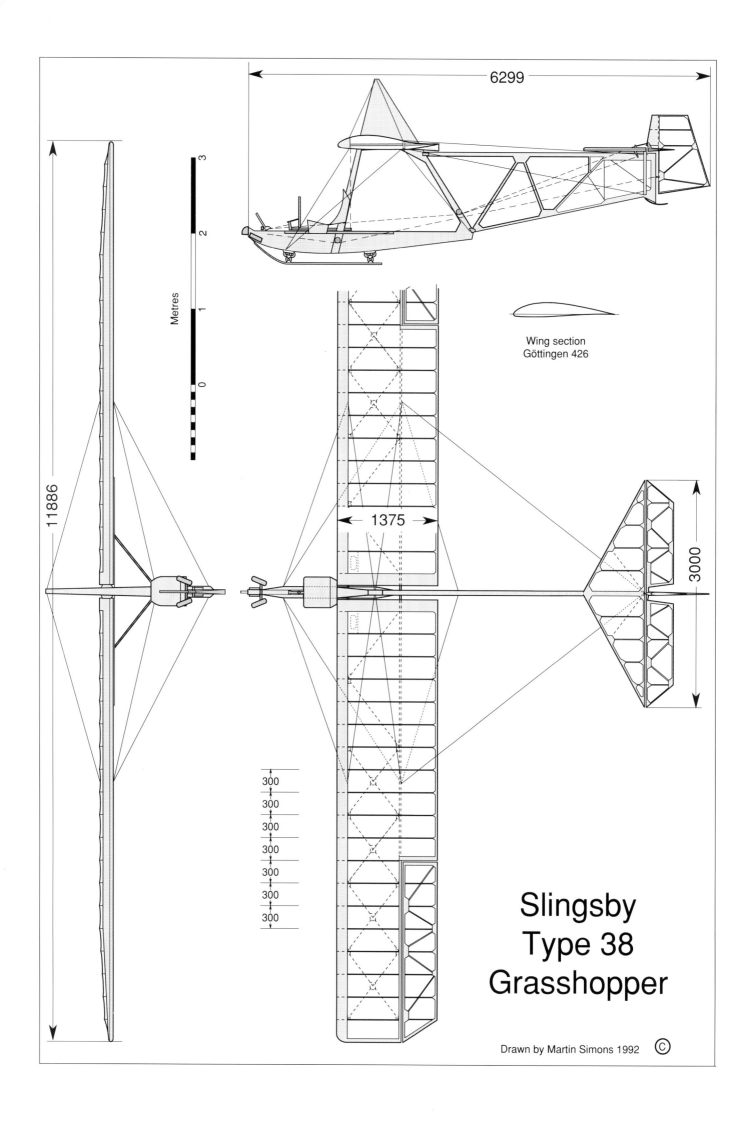

6299

11886

1375

3000

Metres

3

2

1

0

Wing section
Göttingen 426

300
300
300
300
300
300
300

Slingsby
Type 38
Grasshopper

Drawn by Martin Simons 1992 ©

Type 38, Grasshopper

It seems extraordinary at first that while Slingsby was working on the technically advanced and innovative T-37 Skylark 1 in 1952-53, he should revert to the production of a primary glider. The British gliding movement had almost totally abandoned solo training methods by this time, and there was no demand from the civilian clubs for such primitive aircraft. However, there were many schools with Combined Cadet Force units, in which boys could receive some basic military training. The officers were usually schoolmasters who had gained experience in the Services during the Second World War. Boys who were interested in the army had guns to work and drill with, and those who were keen on the Navy could learn to row, sail and navigate boats. There was nothing of similar kind for the air-minded cadets. Members of the Air Council recognised that this was an unsatisfactory state of affairs, and the idea that the cadets could have an elementary glider to play with appealed to the authorities. Such machines could be used for instruction in airmanship, aircraft structures and controls. The cadets could learn how to rig and inspect gliders, and even carry out simple repairs. It would not be necessary for the aircraft to be fully airworthy.

The EON Type 7 primary glider, available new from Elliotts of Newbury, was a straightforward copy of the successful German SG-38, fully certificated for flight including aero-towing. About 90 had been built but many were not sold, being allowed to stand idle in storage. A few, named the Eton TX-1 by the ATC and RAF, were in use. It was, however, remembered that the ATC had a large number of the old Slingsby T-7 Cadet wings, and more spare sets of wings from Cadets were in stock at Kirbymoorside, following conversion of the aircraft into Tutors. A new fuselage frame could be made to take Cadet flying surfaces which would need some servicing and very little modification. It would be possible to produce a large number of suitable, non-airworthy gliders very quickly and more cheaply than buying the Eton.

Slingsby was very happy to undertake the work of overhauling the wings, many of which were quite old and glued with casein. Tail units were also taken from old Cadets. The new fuselage was very similar to that of the SG-38, the only important difference being that the telescopic springing system used on the skid of the German type was replaced by a simpler suspension system of hard rubber rings. Provision was made for ballast weights to be fitted to allow for small and light boy pilots. To prevent the pupil from over-controlling and perhaps even getting the glider off the ground into some dangerous attitude, a locking pin could be inserted to restrict the movement of the elevator.

Flight testing of the T-38 Grasshopper was undertaken by Derek Piggott, launching by aero-tow to 900m (3,000ft). Presumably the aircraft used was carefully checked and was fully airworthy, since it was not feasible to carry a parachute. The ailerons were not differentially geared, and severe adverse yaw was experienced when entering turns. The vertical tail area was found to be too great, it being impossible to yaw the aircraft straight with rudder during the hold-off for a crosswind landing. This was corrected by removing a large area of fabric covering from the rear bays of the gate-like tailboom. The Grasshopper would enter a spin with full up elevator and full rudder and opposite aileron, but would spiral out after about one full turn.

Adopting an idea from the old German gliding schools, the primary glider could be suspended on a *pendelbock* for the boys to get some feel for the controls. The *pendelbock* was a tripod on which the glider could be suspended on a universal joint about its c.g. In a wind the controls would all work correctly, and a boy on the seat could use ailerons, rudder and elevator to change attitude without actually leaving the ground.

Having established that the glider was at least controllable, manufacture, (or remanufacture) began. A total of 115 were delivered. Many spare parts and a great deal of repair work were necessary during the following years, all quite profitable to the company.

A training school for the cadet officers was established at Detling, Kent, where Derek Piggott was working. The procedure was to give each schoolmaster at least one genuine flight in a T-21 Sedbergh to teach the effects of the controls, even allowing the student to do the landing. After this the course was confined to bungee launching the primary glider up and down the airfield. With one person strapped safely on the glider's seat, four on the bungee, a wingtip runner and someone holding back the tail as the bungee was stretched, the work was hard, and at the end of a good day each student would have had four or five ground slides or very low hops. It was exhausting, and Piggott remembers sometimes praying for rain so that they could have a rest. On one occasion a course continued to operate in deep snow, with fog in dead-calm air reducing visibility to 100 yards. The group operating the glider wandered about, launching, hopping and launching again until a fence was encountered, after which the glider was turned and launched again and again until another fence was found. After a short time the group was totally disoriented and did not know in which direction to find the hangar.

The amount learned on these exercises was depressingly small in relation to the physical effort put into them, and eventually winch launching was used to speed things up. Even so, progress was very slow compared with two-seater training. With their new-found skills and a glider, the officers could return to their schools and keep the boys busy for hours. An inexperienced group following the instruction manual could spend most of a day simply rigging the glider, and it would often be wrongly set up at the end.

Each cadet group was supplied with a rubber bungee for ground slides. Strictly, the cadets were not supposed to fly, but many did achieve hops, either intentionally or by accident. The ballast weights provided were often wrongly disposed or not fitted, so a lightweight cadet would sometimes find himself off the ground in a climbing attitude. If the locking pin was in place the restricted stick movement would prevent adequate corrective elevator action, even if the pupil knew what to do. George Locke, who already had achieved his A and B Certificates, contrived to remove the locking pin from

his school's Grasshopper and took off, unfortunately crashing immediately on the hallowed turf of the school cricket pitch. According to him, in their next match the school bowlers made good use of the rut he had gouged. Some school groups broke all the rules by using a double bungee for launching, and hops were achieved in this way. Many of the fields were not large enough to permit even a primary glider to fly without reaching or flying over the boundary. To prevent serious misadventures of this type, Slingsby produced special spoilers which could be fitted to the leading edges of the wings. With these in place it was not possible for the Grasshopper even to hop.

From Slingsby's viewpoint the T-38 was a profitable exercise, and there is no doubt that many boys did learn a good deal—not necessarily about flying—from their exercises with these gliders. They continued in use for many years, and a few have survived until recent times to be resold on the civilian market. They have some nostalgic attraction, but after a very few flights primary gliders tend to lose their novelty and are derigged and stored. One, WZ791, is in the RAF Museum at Hendon, where it was exhibited above the entrance hall in 1992. According to Peter Elliott, the museum staff took six hours to assemble the aircraft. Several others exist in other museums.

Type 38 Grasshopper data

Dimensions

Wingspan	11.8m (39ft)
Wing area	16.16m² (174 ft²)
Aspect ratio	8.73
Length o. a.	6.3m (21ft 1½in)
Wing section	Göttingen 426

Weights

Tare	132.9kg (293lb)
Flying	249kg (550lb)
Wing loading	15.13kg/m² (3.1lb/ft²)

Grasshopper WZ761 after emerging from the factory at Kirbymoorside. The fabric covering of the rear fuselage bay was partly removed following flight tests. (*Slingsby collection*)

Grasshopper WZ754 suspended on its *pendelbock* at Bridlington School in 1976, with cadets. (*P. J. V. Elliott, RAF Museum, Hendon, Ref PO19499*)

WZ754 at Bridlington, apparently just airborne. The bungee crew stand in the background (*P. J. V. Elliott, RAF Museum, Hendon, Ref PO19498*)

Grasshopper WZ791 on display at the RAF Museum, Hendon, in 1992. Although basically a very simple aircraft, rigging a primary glider correctly was not straightforward because the cables had to be correctly tensioned to ensure that the wings and tail unit were accurately aligned. To get this aircraft into position for display occupied the museum staff for 6 hours. (*M. Simons*)

The pilot's seat and controls of the Grasshopper at Hendon. The Ottfur release hook at the extreme nose, the ballast boxes and the rubber ring skid suspension are also shown. (*M. Simons*)

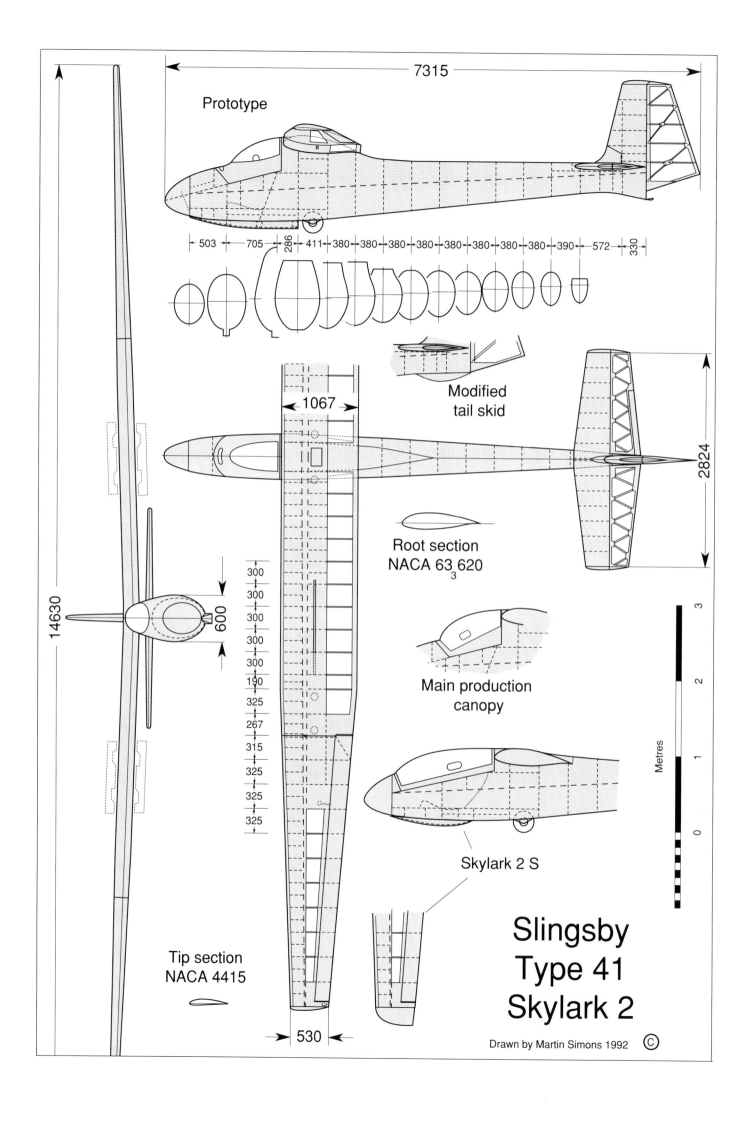

7315

Prototype

503 705 286 411 380 380 380 380 380 380 380 380 390 572 330

Modified
tail skid

1067

2824

Root section
NACA 63$_3$620

14630

600

300
300
300
300
300
190
325
267
315
325
325
325

Main production
canopy

Skylark 2 S

Tip section
NACA 4415

530

Metres

0 1 2 3

Slingsby
Type 41
Skylark 2

Drawn by Martin Simons 1992 ©

Type 41, Skylark 2

The Skylark 2 was envisaged as a straightforward development of the original Skylark, Slingsby's Type 37, and when design work began in 1953 it was described as the T-37B. It was soon apparent that an entirely new design was emerging, and the type number 41 was allocated. (The T-39, an unpiloted target glider, and T-40, a powered racing aeroplane, were never built.) The new Skylark inherited very little from the Skylark 1 except the general concept of a three-piece wing and the low-density gaboon plywood used for the skins. The value of the NACA '6 series' aerofoil sections had been widely recognised by this time, but the T-41 used the 20 per cent thick NACA 63_3 620 profile instead of the 18 per cent thick section of the T-37. The wingtip section was also changed. Slingsby had been advised that the low-drag profiles did not work well at low Reynolds numbers (associated with narrow wing chords at low airspeeds), and reverted to the older NACA 4415 with 3° of aerodynamic washout to prevent tip stalling.

A most important innovation was the use of glass-fibre reinforced plastics (GRP). As long ago as 1944, in articles for the magazine *Sailplane and Glider*, W. R. Scott had suggested that the era of the all-plastic aircraft was approaching. He described various different types and uses of plastics and mentioned impregnated wood, paper and cloth materials, although the possibility of using glass fabric as a structural material had not yet been considered. In the late 1940s, asbestos fibre reinforced plastic materials were used by F. G. Miles's Company in the construction of a prototype wing for the Kendall K 1 two-seat sailplane. Neither the material nor, after six years' work, the K 1 design, proved successful.

When glass-plastic composite materials became readily available, Slingsby was quick to see their potential. Polyester rather than epoxy resins were used at this stage, and there was not yet enough confidence for the new materials to be used for any of the load bearing structure, but it was expected that experience in manufacture and service would lead to their more widespread adoption. The Skylark 2 had a large proportion of its fuselage skin ahead of the wing moulded in one piece, and the wing and tail unit tips and some small fairings were made of the same material. Such three-dimensionally curved parts of sailplanes had previously been built up by scarfing together large numbers of small pieces of plywood. The GRP moulding technique saved a great deal of time in production and gave a much more accurate and stable surface. The Kirbymoorside factory was thus in the forefront of new developments in both aerodynamic design and materials of construction.

The general opinion of the British pilots who had flown the T-37 was that it was somewhat too fast for British conditions, with a higher wing loading and hence higher stalling speed and larger turning circle than required for British thermals. The span of the T-41 was increased to 14.63m (48ft), slightly short of the the 15m which was likely to become the limit for the proposed new Standard Class for contest sailplanes, and the aspect ratio was reduced to 16. Despite the lower aspect ratio the new type would be more satisfactory at low airspeeds. With a better fuselage of semi-monocoque construction, as usual for high-performance sailplanes, the parasitic drag would be reduced, so the T-41 would represent a considerable advance on the original Skylark.

The choice of the 20 per cent thick wing section was guided by study of drag curves from the NACA wind tunnels. These showed that while thick profiles had somewhat higher minimum drag than thin sections at the ideal angle of attack, the thick sections had a very broad range of low drag values. Colloquially, the 'drag bucket' of the thick sections on the wind tunnel charts was wider, although slightly shallower. The best lift-to-drag ratio, or L/D, commonly used as an index of aerodynamic efficiency, is of less importance in soaring than might be expected. A sailplane on a cross-country flight is normally flying slowly, circling to gain height in a thermal, or gliding straight at high airspeed to make distance and reach the next upcurrent with minimum loss of height and time. There is little reason ever to fly at the theoretically ideal minimal drag speed corresponding to the maximum L/D ratio. By using a thick, low-drag section with a wide drag bucket, the Skylark 2 would have a slightly poorer maximum L/D figure than some other sailplanes, but it would climb better and cross the gaps between thermals faster.

All the advantages of the low-drag sections would be lost if the wing surface was not accurate in service, and for this reason the thick, low-density gaboon plywood which proved successful on the T -37 was used again for the Skylark 2, with the same kind of accurately machined spruce leading edge and carefully smoothed joints. The ply skin of the wing centre section was carried right over the mainspar to the rear auxiliary spar, before which the laminar boundary layer would have made its transition to turbulence. Behind this, the wing was fabric covered. Subsequent research, including measurements of the profile drag of the centre section in flight, showed that the Skylark wing profile did achieve the anticipated low-drag figures.

On the outer panels of the wing, which tapered to the 'turbulent flow' tip section, some weight was saved by covering with fabric alone behind the mainspar. The ailerons, plywood skinned to ensure adequate stiffness, were mass balanced. A rather large piece of lead on a steel arm was bolted to the aileron spar but wholly concealed inside the wing. The aileron hinges of the Skylark 2 were very simple and mounted flush with the top skin of the wing, instead of the more usual centre-mounted hinge with elaborate fairing of the gap. The Skylark hinge line was easily sealed with tape, and on the underside the gap that opened when the aileron was raised provided some drag which helped to counteract adverse yaw. This arrangement was one of the outcomes of the research on lateral controls that had been done with the T-37. Airbrakes of the Schempp-Hirth type were fitted.

The centre section of the wing was made almost the same span as the length of the fuselage with rudder, so the two main components of the aircraft could be housed in the trailer side-by-side. This had the disadvantage of making the centre section rather heavy, but the T-41 was not a very large aircraft and the weight was not unreasonable. To rig the Skylark, the fuselage was held upright as the centre section was lowered bodily into position. Two long steel pins, one on each side, were then inserted from the front to join the front and rear fittings to the fuselage main frames. Controls were linked through a central hatch in the wing. The tip panels, joined when rigging with a single vertical steel pin, were much shorter and lighter. Connection to the ailerons was very simple, the drive mechanism being entirely within the centre section, with a short pushrod to the aileron horn at the extreme inner end of the control surface.

The fuselage was a simple streamlined form of oval cross-section, skinned with gaboon plywood aft of the glass-plastic nose. The wing was mounted on a low pylon which faired into the cockpit canopy in front. Behind the trailing edge, the line of the wing profile was continued down to fair neatly into the rear fuselage. The cockpit was large and comfortable, with a fairly upright seating position and a small blown bubble transparent canopy. There was a simple landing wheel with skid. By now, the importance of stability for sailplanes which were to be flown blind in cloud had been well recognised. The Skylark 2 had a long rear fuselage and large tail surfaces of rather angular appearance which ensured safe handling characteristics.

The first flight of the new sailplane was made in November 1953, about eight months after that of the Skylark 1. Test flights by BGA Test Group No 1, based at Lasham, showed everything normal, though Ann Welch had some interesting moments when flying at an extremely far aft c.g. position, the Skylark taking five full turns to come out of a spin after initiation of the recovery procedure. With a normal c.g. there were no problems.

It was at once apparent that the new sailplane was going to be a very successful and safe aircraft with good performance and that, when the International Standard Class rules had been settled, the Skylark 2 would be a contender in the World Championships for this category. The new class rules were framed around the old Olympia 2B with a span limitation of 15m, a wheel and effective airbrakes as leading requirements, and elaborations such as flaps and ballast tanks were not allowed. Slingsby's order books filled rapidly, and the Skylark 2 entered full-scale production. It was ordered by clubs and private groups, a number were exported and a few were built from kits, including two in New Zealand. The total produced was 63, more than any previous Slingsby high-performance sailplane. In production, the original small cockpit bubble was replaced by a much larger canopy which made the cockpit more comfortable and the view better, but did not improve the airflow over the wing.

In July 1955, Derek Piggott in a Skylark 2 made a climb in a thunderstorm over Lasham which broke the British gain of height record. The only gyro instrument fitted was a turn and slip indicator. There was no oxygen breathing equipment. The Skylark was struck several times by lightning and there was damage from hailstones. When he essayed to leave the cloud and descend with airbrakes open, Piggott was carried up and reached almost 7,500m (25,000ft) above sea level before emerging from the cloud. He was very lucky to survive with the aircraft still intact and himself still conscious, though in a strange condition because of repeated shocks and lack of oxygen.

In the 1958 World Championships, held at Leszno in Poland, Philip Wills flew a Skylark 2 in the Standard Class. He was placed 13th out of 24 competitors, which was disappointing, but he insisted that the aircraft could not be blamed. What was probably more important was that, in the inaugural design competition for the Standard Class, the Skylark 2 did not win. The sailplane that took the design award was the Ka 6BR, designed by Rudolf Kaiser of Germany. Although Wills believed that the Skylark had a better performance, the Ka 6 was cheaper and lighter. Within a few years the total number of Ka 6s and variants produced exceeded

700. By 1961 the Skylark 2 was no longer in production, and Slingsby admitted in print that it was, after all, surpassed in performance by the Ka 6.

The Skylark 2 was the basis for some experiments intended to improve its performance. A group at the Bristol Gliding Club set out to clean up the design in detail, reducing the angle of incidence of the wing to cut parasitic drag at high speeds, improving the wing-to-fuselage junction, fairing the wheel and making other changes, all of which combined to make a measurable improvement. The author rebuilt a Skylark 2 during 1965-7. The aircraft was the one used by Piggott for his thunderstorm climb, which, some ten years later, had been almost written off in an accident at Husbands Bosworth. During the reconstruction work, marks from the lightning strikes and hail were discovered in several places. The span was extended to the full 15m with slightly upswept Hörner wingtips to reduce vortex drag, and the wing section was modified at the leading edge in accordance with research and advice from Dr F. X. Wortmann of Stuttgart University. The main fuselage frames were cut down in height by about 150mm, and the wing incidence reduced. The cockpit was redesigned to allow a semi-reclining seat and a Skylark 4 transparent canopy was adapted. These changes did produce a slight improvement in performance, and the aircraft, which still flies regularly, is now known as the Skylark 2S.

Type 41 Skylark 2 data

Dimensions

Wingspan	14.63m (48ft)
Wing area	13.4m^2 (144.3 ft^2)
Aspect ratio	16
Length o.a.	7.315m (24ft)
Wing sections	
Root	NACA 63$_3$ 620
Mid-span	NACA 63$_3$ 620
Tip	NACA 4415

Weights

Tare	209kg (461lb)
Flying	308kg (679lb)
Wing loading	23kg/m^2 (4.715lb/ft^2)

Skylark 2 over Lasham during tests by the BGA Test Group No. 1. (*Charles E. Brown, RAF Museum Hendon, neg No. 6605-4*)

Fred Slingsby with the prototype Skylark 2 under construction. The small cockpit canopy, thick wing section and the aileron pushrod at the outer end of the centre section are visible. Slingsby himself is pressing the remote control button of the camera in this picture. (*F. N. Slingsby*)

The prototype Skylark 2 being flown over Lasham by Ann Welch. (*Charles E. Brown, RAF Museum, Hendon, neg No. PO 35029*)

The Skylark 2 in Western Australia. This aircraft was No 41 on the Gliding Federation of Australia register. (*F. Hamilton*)

Philip Wills in the cockpit of the Skylark 2 at Lasham, with his daughter. (*Charles E. Brown, RAF Museum, Hendon, neg No. PO 35018*)

The production version of the Skylark 2, with much-enlarged cockpit canopy. (*Charles E. Brown, RAF Museum, Hendon, neg No. 6831-8*)

In recent times, the Skylark 2 continues to give good service. This example, with a modified cockpit canopy, participated in a vintage glider rally at Camphill in Derbyshire in 1987. (*M. Simons*)

M. Simons with the rebuilt and modified Skylark 2S at Dunstable in 1987, 20 years after the rebuilding was completed. The emblem, designed by Elizabeth Hargreaves, represents a phoenix rising from the flames. Unkind persons described it as an exploding chicken.

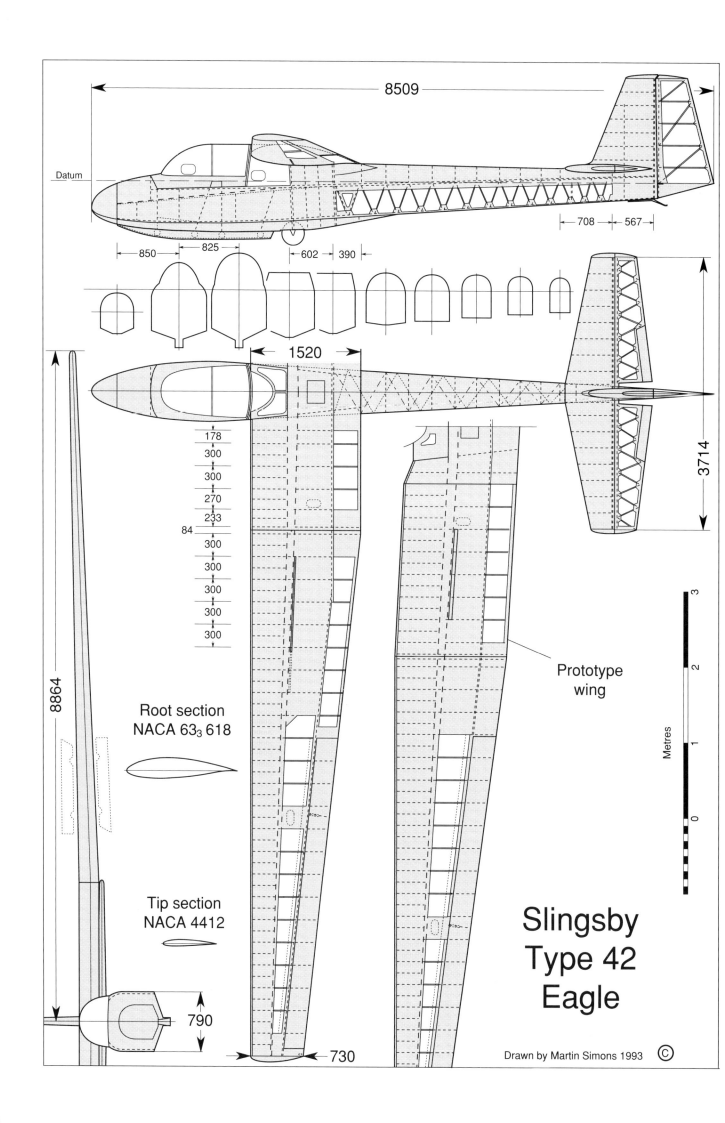

8509

Datum

708 567

850 825 602 390

1520

3714

178
300
300
270
233
84
300
300
300
300
300

8864

Root section
NACA 63₃ 618

Tip section
NACA 4412

Prototype
wing

790

730

Slingsby
Type 42
Eagle

Metres

0 1 2 3

Drawn by Martin Simons 1993 ©

Type 42 Eagle and T-55 Regal

Many useful training two-seat gliders and sailplanes had been built and flown after the Margarete emerged from the Darmstadt Akaflieg in 1923. Its modern counterparts were the Slingsby T-21 and T-31. High-performance two-seaters were rarer, but a few had appeared, notably the German Kranich, which had been built in large numbers and a few of which survived the Second World War. In post-war Britain there was a recognised need for a two-seat sailplane with sufficient performance to give instruction in cross-country flying. The BGA in 1947 organised a two-seat sailplane design competition which produced several very promising projects on paper. The winner was Hugh Kendall's K 1. This was eventually built and flown in 1954, but many late changes were made, including shortening the fuselage and replacing the orthodox tail unit with a V tail. The prototype was found to be extremely dangerous in spins, and the K 1 was abandoned after many attempts to rectify the trouble. The remains were eventually burned at Dunstable in the late 1960s. Slingsby did not enter the BGA competition. He might have submitted an improved version of his Gull 2, which would probably have done very well.

Following the success of the T-34 Sky single-seater there was a project for a two-seat version which would have been the T-36. Some work was done on this in 1952. When the advantages of the NACA low-drag 'laminar flow' wing profiles were realised, a new approach was adopted and the outcome in 1953 was the T-42. Details were announced in the spring of 1954 and the prototype flew in June of that year. The name was chosen by Hulton's, proprietors of the children's comic paper *Eagle*, who sponsored the entry of the aircraft in the World Championships at Camphill.

A major problem with two-seat sailplanes is that, if the seats are side-by-side, the fuselage is unduly broad, which increases drag. Furthermore, such an aircraft cannot be flown solo without the addition of ballast to keep the c.g. forward. With tandem seating the fuselage can be made narrower and the rear pilot can be seated on, or very close to, the point of balance, so that, if the rear seat is empty, the c.g. remains unchanged. With a normal wing layout the rear cockpit has to be located either above, below or within the wing root. The pilot's vision is then severely restricted. Every possible solution to this problem had been tried in the past. Like many earlier types the T-31 trainer had the wing mounted high enough to clear the pilot's head, so the view down was excellent, but in turns the banked wing prevented any outlook to the inside of the turn. This was dangerous for a sailplane in thermals, when other sailplanes were likely to be in the way. The Kranich and the American Schweizer TG-2 had the pilot's head emerging from the centre of the wing, which gave a good view into turns, but there was no view down. The Short Nimbus of 1946 had the second pilot's seat on the main wing spar of a low wing mounting, which gave excellent visibility but produced an unduly deep fuselage and increased the drag almost as much as a side-by-side arrangement would have done.

The USSR's world record breaking KIM 3 Stakhanovetz had shown the best solution, which was to give the wings pronounced forward sweep. This creates some difficulties in design and construction, but if these are overcome the result is very satisfactory. Many modern two-seaters, such as the Janus, the Ka 13 and Twin Astir, use forward sweep together with a shoulder or mid-wing position. The Eagle wing had tandem seating and the high mounted wing was swept forward. There was also a substantial cut-out in the leading edge at the junction with the fuselage. The only reason for these features was to improve the view from the rear cockpit.

Following the Skylark 1 and 2, the Eagle used the NACA six-digit wing profiles tapering to an ordinary four-digit profile at the tip, with 3° of washout to control any tip stalling tendencies. Also like the Skylark, the wing was built in three pieces, the outer panels being connected to the centre section with a single vertical steel pin with automatic engagement of very simple front and rear fittings. There was a straightforward pushrod connection for the aileron drive. The centre section, with no dihedral, carried the large Schempp-Hirth-type airbrakes. The outer wing panel mainspars were swept forward enough to produce a straight leading edge at 90° to the centre line, and were set at a slight dihedral angle. A heavy mainspar of I cross-section with spruce flanges and plywood webs took the bending and shear loads. Accurately made wooden ribs were glued fore and aft. Ahead of the spar the wing was skinned with low-density gaboon plywood to resist torsion and preserve accurate contours. The skin was carried back to the auxiliary spar except for the outer wing panels, which were fabric covered. The mass-balanced ailerons were also skinned with plywood.

The Eagle's fuselage was a built-up wooden space frame of rectangular cross-section, covered mostly with fabric but with a rounded turtledeck behind the wing. This type of structure, similar to that of the Skylark 1 and T-21, was light and easily built and repaired although it lacked in aerodynamic refinement. The seats were arranged as close together as possible, and the rear set of rudder pedals were on either side of the front seat, suitably enclosed. The fuselage was widened by about 190mm to make this possible. The cockpit canopy was in two sections, the front portion hinged on the right side, the rear portion hinging to open upwards and backwards. The large, angular tail unit was of orthodox wooden construction, the elevator and rudder being fabric covered and the fixed surfaces skinned with gaboon plywood. Glass reinforced plastic mouldings were used for the nose cap and decking around the cockpits, for the parachute boxes and internal cockpit lining, and for small fairings elsewhere. There was still no attempt to use glass for any stressed components.

In something of a rush, the Eagle was made ready for the 1954 World Championships at Camphill. During their practice flying for this event, Ann and Lorne Welch used it to break the British two-seater distance record with a 248km (154-mile) flight from Lasham to Great Yarmouth, but it was already apparent that the T-42's performance was not coming fully up to expectations, and the rear cockpit was very uncomfortable for long flights. The seating position was such that the pilot sat bolt upright, even having to lean forward slightly. In the contest, which was affected by bad weather so that only four contest days were achieved, the T-42 finished seventh out of nine two-seat entries. The winner was the very refined Yugoslavian Kosava.

The Eagle prototype came into prominence on 14 May 1954, when it was used by Lorne Welch and Frank Irving to make the first crossing of the Channel by a two-seat sailplane. The flight began just after 11 a.m. with an aero-towed launch from Lasham. After a struggle for the first hour, progress improved and a climb was made to 2,400m (8,000ft) near the coast, the sailplane emerging from cloud with slight icing immediately above Dover at about 1.40 p.m. The glide across to France was uneventful, and sufficient height remained to continue soaring. The Eagle passed over Brussels at 840m (2,800ft) and continued in weakening conditions, to land in a field near Louvain at 4.20 p.m. Frank Irving,

whose duties during the flight had been chiefly those of navigation and record keeping, had been so uncomfortable in the rear seat that he was almost unable to stand upright for some time after the landing. The distance covered was 402km (250 miles). The British two-seat distance record had been broken again, and this was only the fourth soaring flight across the Channel.

The prototype Eagle continued in service as a club glider at Lasham. Derek Piggott flew it solo in the 1957 National Championships, and in June 1958 it collided in cloud with a Sky. The pilots of the Eagle saved themselves by parachute, the glider falling in the garden of a house in Lasham village just after a tea party had ended. The Sky lost about 4m (13ft) of one wing, but the pilot was able to retain control and make a safe landing on the aerodrome.

Meanwhile, Slingsby had been working. The obvious cause of the prototype's disappointing performance was the leading-edge cut-out, and the T-42A or Eagle 2 had a much simplified wing with a straight leading edge. This improved the airflow considerably. The slight penalty in terms of pilot view was accepted. The rear seat was redesigned for greater comfort, the centre section was shortened to lighten it for rigging, the tips were lengthened to make up the difference and the brakes were moved outwards.

In 1956 the World Gliding Championships were held at St Yan in France, this being the last occasion on which two-seaters were counted as a separate class. In the usual last-minute rush before a major competition, test flights showed that the controls of the T-42A were not light but they were effective, giving an adequate rate of roll and good harmony between stick and rudder in turns. The stability in pitch was such that some pilots found it excessive, but in a machine intended for cloud flying this was reckoned to be a good fault. The pilots for the Internationals, Nick Goodhart and Frank Foster, did not have a chance to fly the aircraft until they arrived in France.

Compared with the very sleek two-seaters which were entered from other countries the T-42 was considered rather ugly, and various uncomplimentary nicknames, 'mahogany bomber', 'sardine tin' and 'soap box', were applied. Nick Goodhart and Frank Foster astonished everyone by winning after six contest days with a substantial lead. It was pointed out that, despite appearances, the Eagle had a good performance, was not too costly and had many practical advantages including ease of rigging, de-rigging and repair.

The T-42B or Eagle 3 used the same wing and tail unit but the airbrakes were enlarged by 10 per cent. A marked change of trim when the brakes were opened was cured by adding a second elevator trim tab coupled to the brakes so that it moved with them to cancel the trim change. The cockpits were still further improved by lengthening the nose 15cm. In this form the T-42B entered production in 1957. The first customer was Peter Scott, the famous naturalist, who used what he christened his *Sea Eagle* for many excellent flights, including those for his 'Gold C' badge in

1958. Seventeen T-42Bs were built. Most remained in Britain, but three were exported to New Zealand and one to Germany.

A final variation was the T-55 Eagle 4, or Regal Eagle, which was a modification of a standard Eagle 3 done by Slingsby in 1957. This had the centre section extended to give a total span of 20m (65.6ft). It was used by Wally Kahn and John Williamson to break the two-seat goal flight record with a flight from Odiham (towed there from Lasham) to Perranporth in Cornwall, a distance of 312km (193 miles).

The prototype Eagle wing under construction, showing the marked cut-out in the leading edge at the centre. (*Slingsby collection*)

Type 42 Eagle data

Dimensions

Prototypes Eagle 1 & 2

Wingspan	17.86m (58.5ft)
Wing area	21.4m² (230 ft²)
Aspect ratio	14.6
Length o.a.	8.3m (27.25ft)

Eagle 3

Wingspan	17.73m (58.2ft)
Wing area	22.3m² (240 ft²)
Aspect ratio	14.8
Length o.a.	8.5m (27.9ft)
Wing sections	
Root	NACA 63_3618
Mid-span	NACA 63_3618
Tip	NACA 4412

Weights

Tare	372kg (820lb)
Flying	562kg (1,240lb)
Wing loading	26.4kg/m² (5.4lb/ft²)

The original Eagle in flight over Lasham. Various attempts were made to improve the airflow over the centre-section. In this case there appears to be a small turbulator behind the cockpit. (*Charles E. Brown, RAF Museum, Hendon, neg No. 6605-10*)

Another view of the first Eagle in flight. The turbulator is just visible. The emblem on the front of the fuselage came from the owners and sponsors of the aircraft, the *Eagle* children's paper which was popular at the time. (*Charles E. Brown, RAF Museum, Hendon, neg No. 6605-13*)

Ann and Lorne Welch with the Eagle on a typically gloomy day at the 1954 World Championships, held at Camphill in Derbyshire. (*Charles E. Brown, RAF Museum, Hendon, neg No. 6568-13*)

The Eagle 3, much-improved in performance by redesign of the wing. The centre-section cut-out was gone, slightly spoiling the view from the rear seat. (*Slingsby collection*)

An Eagle 3 at Lasham. The airbrakes were now part of the outer wing, instead of being in the centre section. A fixed trim tab on the port aileron indicates that this particular aircraft had a 'one wing low' tendency, probably after repairs.

The prototype Eagle 3 at the Kirbymoorside factory. (*Slingsby collection*)

The cockpits of the Eagle 3. The feet of the rear pilot, on the rudder pedals, were on either side of the front seat, necessitating a wider fuselage. (*Slingsby collection*)

Eagle ZK-GBD in New Zealand. (*P. Layne*)

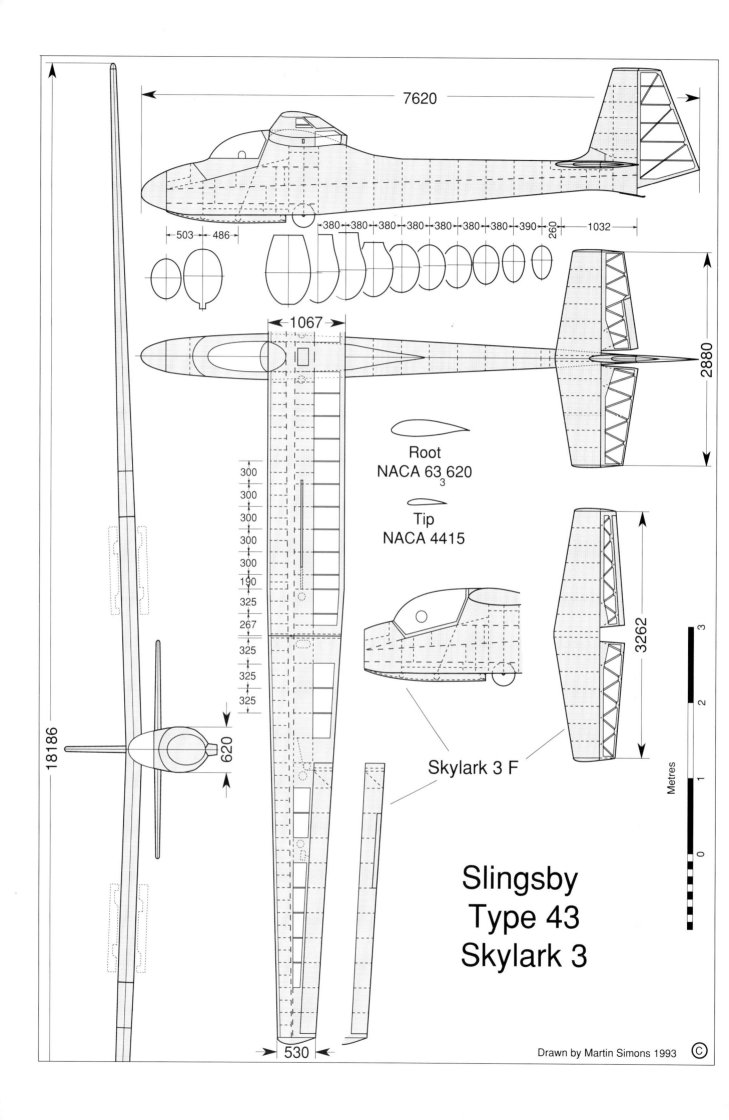

7620

503 486 380 380 380 380 380 380 380 390 260 1032

1067

2880

300
300
300
300
300
190
325
267
325
325
325

Root
NACA 63₃620

Tip
NACA 4415

3262

18186

620

530

Skylark 3 F

Slingsby
Type 43
Skylark 3

Metres

0 1 2 3

Drawn by Martin Simons 1993 ©

Type 43, Skylark 3

The future of the Slingsby Sailplanes Company was in some doubt after the death in April 1955 of J. E. D. Shaw, who, with Fred Slingsby, had founded and supported the company in its early days and was its chairman. His large majority holding of shares had to be sold to defray death duties on his estate and one prospective buyer, an aircraft manufacturer in search of more business, planned to close the Kirbymoorside factory and move its operations to the south of England. To prevent this, Philip Wills, chairman of the BGA, set about forming the Shaw Slingsby Trust to take over the company. There were delays and legal problems, and the threat of eventual closure was not entirely removed.

Operations in Yorkshire continued, and the company was about to achieve its greatest successes. For a few years from 1955 the Type 43, Skylark 3, achieved the kind of prominence that Fred Slingsby must often have dreamed about in the preceding decades. Two sailplane designs dominated this period. In the Standard Class, limited to a 15m wingspan, the Ka 6CR from Germany was outstanding. More of this type were built than any other high-performance sailplane before or since. In the unrestricted or 'open' class the Skylark 3 became the recognised leader, though the number produced in total never reached anything like the figures for the Ka 6.

The Skylark 3 first flew in July 1955. It was basically a simple aircraft, a straightforward development of the successful T-41 Skylark 2, of orthodox structure and sold at a relatively low price. It was not, like most of its immediate international competitors, an expensive 'orchid'. The same materials were used as for its smaller stablemate; spruce spars, longerons, ribs and frames, and low-density gaboon plywood for the stressed skins and glass-polyester resin mouldings for the unstressed front fuselage shell, wingtips and fairings. Skylarks 2 and 3 were in production at the same time in the factory, many of their components being identical.

The most important aerodynamic change was an increase of wingspan from a little under 15m to just over 18m, with a consequent improvement in aspect ratio to 20.5. This was a high figure for a wooden sailplane. Even the remarkable Meteor, a very advanced all-metal prototype from Yugoslavia which flew in the same year, did not quite achieve this figure. Increasing the aspect ratio of a wing is the most important means available of reducing wingtip vortex drag. At low airspeeds, as when a sailplane is circling in a thermal, vortex drag is normally more than half the total drag of the entire aircraft, so any saving here can make a very large improvement in soaring performance. Providing the aspect ratio is high, the inevitable increase in structure weight can be tolerated. A high wing loading is desirable in any case for efficient flight at the other end of the airspeed scale, for penetrating areas of sinking air during the search for more thermals, so the fact that the Skylark 3 without the pilot tipped the scales at 253kg (551lb) did not count against it, except when it came to ground handling, rigging and de-rigging.

To increase the span of a good small sailplane is therefore the most obvious way to improve its performance, but such an exercise is not without difficulties. The stresses in the wing, especially near the root end, increase very greatly and the mainspars have to be much stronger. The three-piece wing of the Skylark simplified the spar design because there was no need for costly metal fittings in the centre. The fuselage could be hung on the wing by the simplest method. The two main cross-frames in the fuselage carried four fittings corresponding with those on the wing spars. Two long steels rods, inserted from the front and passing through the front fittings to engage the rear ones as well, united the wing and fuselage. The airbrakes, suitably enlarged, were built into the centre section. The outer wings were attached by the same type of vertical steel pin as used on the T-41, with automatic engagement of the fore and aft torsion and drag fittings and an ingenious but very simple automatic linkage for the aileron drive. The plywood-skinned ailerons were mass-balanced in the same way as those of the earlier Skylark.

The fuselage was taken almost without change from the Skylark 2. To control such a long and heavy wing, especially in the yawing plane, without lengthening the fuselage, larger vertical and horizontal tail areas were required, and a mass balance for the elevator was fitted. The Skylark 3 was offered on the market with a choice of simple wheeled undercarriage or with skid alone and a droppable wheeled dolly. Very few were ever built without the wheel, and those that were built in this form to begin with were retrospectively modified to incorporate a wheel despite the parasitic drag penalty. At the time, retracting wheels were hardly ever used in gliders, although they had been tried from time to time.

Rigging the Skylark 3 was easy in all respects save one. As with the earlier Skylarks and the Eagle, the centre section had to be lifted into place with the fuselage supported in the upright position. With its very heavy mainspar and the airbrake mechanism the weight was considerable. The fuselage neck was quite high, and getting the wing into the exact position required was tricky. Two men with fully operative back muscles and functioning vertebral discs could manage it, but it was very much better if four were available to lift with an extra person to see that the fittings in the middle were lining up correctly. Some owners devised special equipment to help with this exercise.

In flight, the Skylark 3 came fully up to expectations. The best glide ratio was claimed to be 36:1, although subsequent flight tests by the BGA yielded a figure of 32.5. This was nevertheless very good in a factory production sailplane of the period. (The measured best glide of the Ka 6 was 29:1.) The Skylark 3 was not light on any of the controls, and for some pilots it was too stable, requiring very firm action to change the pitch attitude or to roll into and out of steep turns. Long flights in the usual turbulent air of a good soaring day could be very tiring for wrists and arms. These faults were considered acceptable for the sake of the excellent performance.

After a few had been built and proved successful, the fuselage nose was lengthened by 150mm, moving the seat forward to improve the balance for pilots of different weights. For similar reasons the elevator mass-balance was moved forward to a position just behind the pilot's seat back, whence its action was transmitted to the tail via the control pushrod. In this form the Skylark 3B became the standard production model. A modification kit was supplied to enable some of the earlier examples to be brought to this standard.

Twenty-three 3Bs were built at Kirbymoorside and a kit was sent to Canada. Four specials, known as Skylarks 3C and D, were constructed with stronger wings to meet certain requirements for export to Holland and other countries where airworthiness regulations required it. The Skylark 3E was an experiment with the NACA 64_2 615 profile at the tip and ailerons of reduced chord and curved trailing edges. It proved to have dangerous tip stalling behaviour, and the tip panels were therefore replaced by normal ones after test flying.

Subsequently the Skylark 3F appeared. This version, following suggestions by Frank Irving, had a tailplane and elevator of greater span and smaller chord, greatly reducing the stick forces required, and the trim tab was enlarged. The ailerons were fitted with geared servo-tabs to lighten the stick loads. These were tried on Irving's own Skylark 3B before going into production. The cockpit canopy of the 3F was greatly enlarged to a rather bulbous shape, improving comfort but increasing drag to some extent. Of this model another 25 were built, including five kits, one of which was sent to New Zealand to be assembled by Fred Dunn. The Tull brothers at Dunstable built a Skylark 3F from a kit, incorporating modifications of their own, chief among them being the fitting of a Skylark 4-type cockpit canopy. As usual with amateur constructors, they found that their aircraft was slightly out of date before completion.

In the 1956 World Championships, held at St Yan in France, the British, Argentinian and Dutch teams flew Skylark 3s. Philip Wills and Geoffrey Stephenson achieved 6th and 10th places. It must have been a little chastening for the British that the Spanish pilots L.V. Juez and M. Ara, both flying old Slingsby T-34 Skys, placed second and seventh. Paul MacCready of the USA won this contest in a French Breguet 901.

However disappointing the results on this occasion, the Skylark 3 very soon began to establish a fine reputation. The type was used for most of the British gliding records broken during 1957 and '58, including speed triangles of 100, 200 and 300km by Tony Deane Drummond. It was now well understood that the future of soaring lay in speed flying around large triangular courses, rather than the traditional 'downwind dash'. Deane Drummond won the national championships in 1957 with Nick Goodhart only a few points behind, both flying Skylarks. The Skylark 3 took six of the first ten places.

On 9 June, Alf Warminger achieved a new British height record, climbing to 9,000m (30,000ft) in a thunderstorm. He felt many electric shocks through the control column, but luckily his Skylark 3 was not directly struck by lightning. In New Zealand Dick Georgeson in a Skylark 3B made an out-and-return flight mostly above 6,000m (20,000ft), in lee wave over South Island for a distance of 330km (205 miles). Later he broke the world height gain record, climbing 10,200m (34,000ft) after release from tow. [The absolute height record of 12,630m (42,100ft) was set by W. B. Ivans in the USA in 1950, but this was not a gain of height above release. All previous height records were broken in 1961 by Paul Bikle's flight in a Schweizer 1-23 to 13,880m (46,267ft), with a height gain of 12,690m (42,303ft)].

World women's records were broken during a trip to South Africa by Anne Burns, who achieved 10,200m (34,000ft) height, 434km (270 miles) goal-and-return, 200km and 300km triangle speed records in a Skylark 3. During the height climb in a thundercloud she was struck by lightning which fortunately did not have serious effects, although the aileron and wingtip plywood were damaged. Denis Burns, Anne's husband, broke the goal-and-return record during the same expedition, with 572km (336 miles).

On 11 June 1957 Tony Goodhart soared from Lasham across the Channel in a Skylark 3. This was the fifth cross-Channel soaring flight ever made. Goodhart had not planned a Channel crossing, but on arriving near Dover at 1,500m (5,000ft) he found himself drifted out to sea by a strengthening northerly wind and it became easier to use this to reach France than to struggle back to land on the English side. He found a useful cloud actually over the Channel, using it to climb to 2,550m (8,500ft) before continuing with further cloud climbs to around 3,000m (10,000ft), to touch down after 5¼hr at St Didier, near Arras. In the following year his brother Nick achieved the first flight in Britain to exceed 500km (310 miles) distance. Nick Goodhart placed second in the World Championships at Leszno, Poland, in 1958 against much more costly aircraft.

The peak of the Skylark's achievements came in 1960, when Rolf Hossinger of Argentina won the 1960 World Championships at Butzweiler in Germany. He performed consistently for the six contest days, although he did not win on any one of them. The list of outstanding achievements in Skylark 3s could be much extended.

The Skylark 3 was proved a thoroughly safe and strong sailplane, but there were limits. Under the semi-aerobatic Certificate of Airworthiness, manoeuvres involving inverted flight and rolls were not permitted. This did not prevent someone from attempting them, and a Skylark 3F which was seen to be doing rolls in May 1961 broke up at Fen Ditton, killing the pilot, an RAF flight lieutenant. The tailplane failed first, causing the glider to pitch so severely in the negative sense that the wing broke under downloads.

At the World Championships in Argentina in February 1963, the Dutch pilot Breunissen, flying across the start line in the race with his airspeed indicator needle evidently jammed hard against its upper stop at 200kmh (100kt), had to save himself by parachute when the Skylark 3's starboard wingtip section broke off under downloads, the wreckage falling on the airfield. The maximum permitted or 'red line' speed for this variant, a Skylark 3C which had the stronger wings, was 218kmh (118kt). At high airspeeds it was normal for the tips of the wings of sailplanes to bend down, because the effects of washout, together with some torsional distortion, caused the outer parts of the wing to reach a negative angle of attack.

The total of all Skylark 3s built, including those from kits, was 65. The last to be built at Kirbymoorside was the 3G, which had ailerons of reduced chord and greater span, heralding the final development of the Skylark series, the T-50 Skylark 4, which was to appear in 1961.

Outstandingly successful though it was, the Skylark 3 represented no great technical advance in aerodynamics, materials or structural design. Slingsby pioneered the use of glass cloth and resin mouldings in the Skylark 2 of 1953. In 1957 in Germany the first all glass-plastic sailplane, the Phönix designed by Richard Eppler and Hermann Nägele, appeared and flew with great success. Students in the technical universities in Germany at this time, especially at Darmstadt, were designing and building sailplanes making full use of the new materials, the first results appearing in the air before 1965. During the decade following the first flight of the Skylark 3, the era of Slingsby's greatest successes, an opportunity was allowed to slip by at Kirbymoorside. No further development was done with glass cloth techniques, and no attempt was made to use these materials in load-bearing structures and skins. Glass cloth/epoxy resin laminates were distrusted at this time because of their manifest flexibility, and development in this area stopped. This was to have serious consequences, not only for the Slingsby factory but for British sailplane manufacture generally.

Type 43 Skylark 3B data

Dimensions

Wingspan	18.2m (59.74ft)
Wing area	16.1m² (173ft²)
Aspect ratio	20.5
Length o.a.	7.62m (25ft)
Wing sections	
Root	NACA 63₃620
Mid-span	NACA 63₃620
Tip	NACA 4415

Weights

Tare	253kg (557lb)
Flying	358kg (790lb)
Wing loading	22.2kg/m² (4.56lb/ft²)

A Skylark 3B in flight over Lasham. (*Charles E. Brown, RAF Museum, Hendon, neg No. 6704-9*)

Skylark 3B BGA 739, with no wheel, flown to second place by Nick Goodhart in the 1957 Nationals. A Miles Gemini and two de Havilland Chipmunks are in the background. (*Charles E. Brown, RAF Museum, Hendon, neg No 6271-13*)

Deane Drummond equipped for flight at the National Championships, with the Skylark 3A. The two-wheeled dolly was jettisoned after take-off. (*Charles E. Brown, RAF Museum Hendon, neg No. 6613-9*)

The Tull Brothers' Skylark 3, built from a kit and fitted with the Skylark 4 cockpit canopy, greatly improving the appearance and reducing drag. (*M. Simons*)

Rigging the Skylark. The fuselage is supported upright in a simple cradle. The wing centre section is resting on trestles, ready to be lifted into place. (*M. Simons*)

Dan Smith prepares to take off in the National Championships at Lasham, in a Skylark 3B. The two sailplanes in the background are Elliott Olympia 419s. (*M. Simons*)

A Skylark 3F, showing the enlarged canopy and improved wheel fairing.

The Skylark 3F BGA 980, registered LV-HHO in Argentina, with bulbous canopy, aileron servo-tabs and a tailplane of reduced chord and greater span. (*F. Irving*)

Skylark 3B of the RAF Gliding and Soaring Association, with registration number 259 and contest number 132. This aircraft was subsequently sold to the Korean Air Force.

The penalties of flying too fast. The wreckage of the Skylark 3B from which Arie Breunissen escaped by parachute at Junin in Argentina at the 1963 World Championships. (*F. Irving*)

Philip Wills took his Skylark 3F G-ARBJ to the USA and flew it in the 1960 US National Championships, selling it before returning to Britain. It was registered as N5563V. As shown, it was one of the few with drop-off dolly wheels. He came fourth in the contest. (*R. Storck*)

Philip Wills (left) and Anthony Deane Drummond (right) discuss the Skylark 3 at the Nationals in 1957. Note the small cockpit canopy with clear-vision panel open, and the careful fairing made possible by the glass-plastic moulding. The pitot static tube carries an Irving total energy compensator, a small venturi designed to prevent false readings on the variometer when changing airspeeds. (*Charles E. Brown, RAF museum Hendon, neg No. 6613-5*)

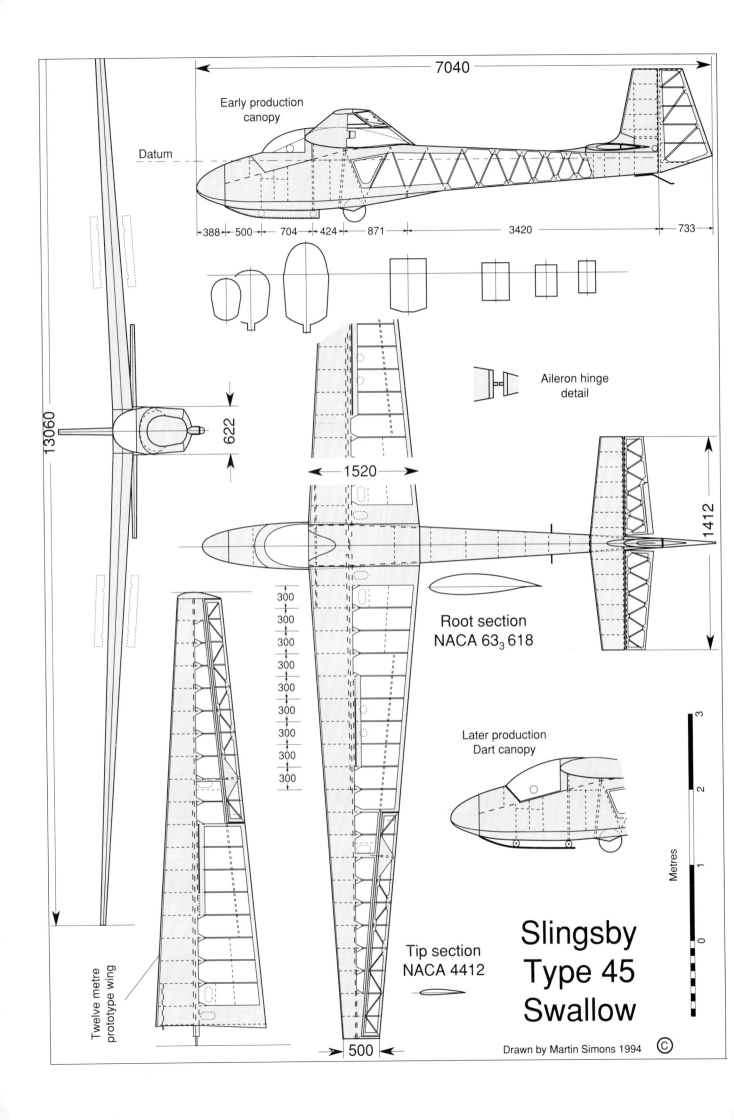

7040

Early production canopy

Datum

388 · 500 · 704 · 424 · 871 · 3420 · 733

13060

622

1520

Aileron hinge detail

1412

Root section
NACA 63₃ 618

300
300
300
300
300
300
300
300
300
300

Later production
Dart canopy

Tip section
NACA 4412

Twelve metre prototype wing

500

Metres

3
2
1
0

Slingsby
Type 45
Swallow

Drawn by Martin Simons 1994 ©

Type 45, Swallow

In the mid-1950s it seemed to many people that there was a demand for a small high-performance sailplane suitable for amateurs to build at home from kits or plans. In the USA the Schweizers had great success with their 1-26 design, which had a span of 12.2m (40ft) and could be bought complete or in kit form. It was small enough to be assembled in an ordinary (American) garage and required no expensive tooling or equipment. In 1955 a regatta was held at Harris Hill, Elmira, New York for this type. The idea was similar to 'one-design' yacht racing and it proved very popular, leading before long to an annual 1-26 competition which still remains on the calendar. The modest performance of the aircraft matters little in contests when everyone flies the same type. The total number of 1-26s produced in kit or complete form reached 689 before production ceased in 1981.

The present author was among those who suggested to Slingsby that something similar might do well on the British and European market. I did some preliminary design work for a small wooden sailplane of 12m span using the NACA 6 series wing profiles, and sent a general-arrangement drawing and some figures to Kirbymoorside. Unknown to me, John Reussner, who had joined Slingsby's company as draughtsman and designer, already had a very similar aircraft on the drawing board. This became the T-45. The prototype flew in October 1957, but unfortunately it was badly broken when Reussner himself flew it into some telephone wires at Sutton Bank. Slingsby, seeing it suspended above the ground, remarked that it had perched like a swallow and the T-45 had its name. (The T-44 was a study for a high-altitude research sailplane with a pressure cabin, designed to a US Air Force specification. It was never built.)

The small span of the Swallow prototype brought the wing loading to a figure considered too high, and Slingsby was prevailed upon to increase the span of the next example. This was done by extending the lines of the wing by 60cm on each side, with a consequent improvement in aspect ratio and soaring ability but a tendency to depart from the original idea of a very

small aircraft for building in confined spaces. In terms of structure weight and size the 13.2m (43.3ft) Swallow was almost back to the original Skylark 1, and possibly this was in Slingsby's mind at the time.

The second prototype T-45 was sent to Lasham for evaluation and certification by the BGA test group there. There was some doubt there as to whether the Swallow was to be regarded as a cross-country sailplane for experienced pilots, or whether it should be for early solo training. There was a pressing need in the clubs for an up-to-date trainer. The old Slingsby Tutors and Prefects still widely used were well out of date, and the new 'laminar' wing profiles coming into general use had different characteristics in flight from the old Göttingen sections. The test group thought that, whatever the manufacturer's original purpose, the Swallow would undoubtedly be used by clubs for training, and hence it had to have very safe handling. In particular, it should not spin too readily even if flown clumsily.

The Swallow, with its strongly tapered wing and only 3° of washout, did spin sharply from a stall in turning flight, and was judged by the test group to be unsafe for beginners. Reluctantly Slingsby increased the washout to 7°, thus tending to spoil the high-speed glide. The test group were still not entirely satisfied with the spinning behaviour. Slingsby therefore introduced a stop in the elevator control circuit which prevented the pilot from pulling the stick back too far. As a result it became very difficult to persuade the Swallow to spin at all. It was found subsequently that the stick restriction tended to reduce the height obtainable on winch launches, the pilot being unable to climb steeply, but in a training aircraft this, too, was not considered a serious defect. A steep climbing attitude taken up too early on the launch could be disastrous if the winch cable should break. At this stage Slingsby suggested he could reduce the washout to what it had been before, relying on the stick restriction to prevent problems, but the test group indicated that the T-45 should be left just as it was. Certification went ahead on this basis. Slingsby was not entirely convinced, but the Swallow entered production, with kits offered as an option.

Structurally, the design followed previous successful types. The wing had a spruce mainspar with stressed skins of gaboon plywood like the Skylark, but the wing was of orthodox two-piece construction. For simplicity the usual intermediate ribs in the leading edge were omitted. The ailerons were fabric covered. Powerful airbrakes, by now considered essential on all sailplanes, were fitted. The rigging system was very simple, being based on that of the old Weihe, which had always been outstandingly good in this respect. A wing was presented to the fuselage and connected to it at the front sub-spar and the mainspar by two steel pins aligned on the same centre. The wingtip could then be rested on the ground and the other wing attached in similar fashion. Then both wingtips were raised and a single pin joined the upper flanges of the main spars.

The fuselage was very similar to that of the T-42 Eagle, being a wooden space frame of rectangular cross-section with plywood skins top and bottom, but the sides mostly covered with fabric and without the refinement of a rounded turtle-decking behind the wing. The cockpit sides were double skinned in plywood. The nose cap and the curved decking ahead of the windscreen were glass-polyester resin mouldings. There was a wheel for landing and a simple ash skid sprung with rubber rings. The tail unit was entirely orthodox, with a trim tab for the elevator.

Following his usual marketing practices, Slingsby sent the Swallow round the clubs for evaluation, and very favourable reports were received and published during 1958. The Swallow did become very popular in Britain, and there were worthwhile export orders. In the clubs Swallows were widely used for first-solo flights and for soaring up to Silver C standard. At least one, in South Africa, achieved a Gold C distance flight of 300km. Later versions were built with improved cockpit canopies and other changes of minor detail.

In 1967 the tobacco firm W. D. & H. O. Wills (no relation to Philip Wills) announced a competition to find the best-trained early solo glider pilots, one in the north of Britain and the other in the south. The prizes were two new Slingsby Swallows to be awarded to the gliding club responsible for training the pupil. Fifty-five clubs entered 235 pilots. The contest involved extensive written tests and practical ground and flying tests. The winners were M. Barker and N. Ellis, of the of the Derby and Lancs and Cornish Gliding Clubs respectively.

Production and sales continued steadily until 1968, a total of 106 being built with more under construction when the main assembly shop at the factory, including the jigs for the T-45, was destroyed by fire. A Mark 3 Swallow was projected but not proceeded with. Many of the type remain in regular service.

Despite the original hopes, not many were assembled from kits. Among the few was the Swallow known as *Penguin*, which was built in 15 months by a syndicate of four young Cambridge University Gliding Club members during 1958-59. With advice from Slingsby himself, the group reduced the wing washout to the figure that had originally been intended, 3°, and omitted the elevator stop. *Penguin* thus came closer to Reussner's notion of a small sailplane for experienced pilots, and it gave excellent service. It was used for various enjoyable expeditions to hill-soaring sites, smaller competitions and rallies, visiting the Long Mynd and Malvern Hills, Clwyd and Snowdonia in North Wales, Sutton Bank in Yorkshire and Portmoak in Scotland, where one of the owners achieved a height climb of 3,450m (11,500ft). Later it was used for a 300-km goal Diamond flight from the Long Mynd to Leiston.

Penguin's greatest achievement was Stuart Waller's flight in the Dunstable Regional competitions in July-August 1983. Twenty-five sailplanes competed, among them several of the best 'open'-class types flown by famous pilots. Waller, who had helped build the aircraft, achieved an ambition by reaching Snowdon in North Wales, where he was able to soar up the face of the mountain in the anabatic thermal from the rock face to reach 1,350m (4,500ft). On his way to Wales he had seen many of his competitors in fields below, and he flew on across the Menai Straits to land in Anglesey, *Penguin* becoming the first sailplane ever to do so. It was a 'Gold C' distance of 305km. Waller won the day, but unfortunately an accident to the trailer prevented *Penguin* from getting back to Dunstable in time to compete next morning, so after scoring 1,000 points one day there was zero for the next. At the end of the week the modified Swallow nevertheless placed seventh.

The prototype T-45, which had crashed into the wires, was taken away by John Reussner and rebuilt with a wingspan of 15m and a lengthened fuselage. In this form, known as the Swift, it matched the Standard Class specifications and proved quite successful until written off in an accident in 1963, when its pilot suffered a heart attack in flight.

The second prototype Swallow posed for a photograph. Slingsby (far left) adjusts his camera. (Slingsby collection)

Type 45 Swallow data

Prototype

Dimensions
Wingspan	12m (39.37ft)
Wing area	12.88m^2 (139ft^2)
Aspect ratio	11.18
Length o.a.	7.315m (23.67ft)
Wing sections	
Root	NACA 63$_3$ 618
Tip	NACA 4412 (modified)

Weights
Tare	190.5kg (420lb)
Flying	317.5kg (700lb)
Wing loading	24.6kg/m^2 (5.0lb/ft^2)

Production model

Dimensions
Wingspan	13.2m (43.3ft)
Wing area	13.55m^2 (145.9ft^2)
Aspect ratio	12.6
Length o.a.	7.06m (23.2ft)

Weights
Tare	195.4kg (431lb)
Flying	317.5kg (700lb)
Wing loading	23.4kg/m^2 (4.8lb/ft^2)

Bel Ami, a typical Swallow built for a gliding club, in flight. The photograph was used to illustrate the Slingsby brochure on the T-45. The skid was more often left open without the canvas fairing. (Slingsby collection)

Although here carrying a competition number, the Swallow was not often flown in serious contests. (Slingsby collection)

Building from a kit. Anthony Edwards, Stuart Waller and John Griffiths bring the fuselage of their Swallow out of the workshop in Cambridge. (A. Edwards)

The Penguin at a late stage in construction, assembled in the garden of Anthony Edwards's home. (A. Edwards)

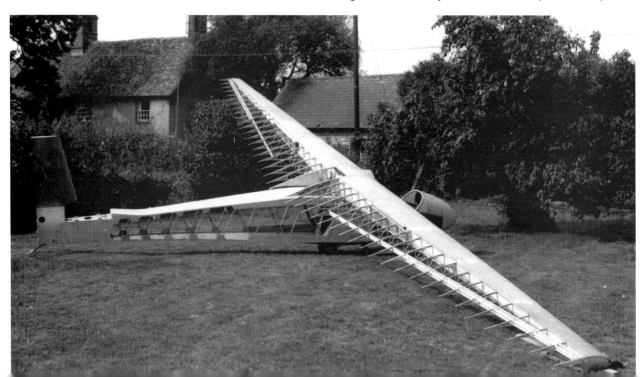

Rigging the Swallow. With both wings attached to the fuse-lage by two steel pins, the tips are raised together to allow the upper main spar connection to be made. (A. Edwards)

Swallows on safari in the Lake District in 1989. Small, light and easily transported, the T-45 still finds favour with small groups in search of adventure. (A. Edwards)

Anthony Edwards, who in 1959 was one of the four who built Penguin, now owns another Swallow. He is shown here flying it in May 1989 over Grisedale Pike in the Lake District. (A. Edwards)

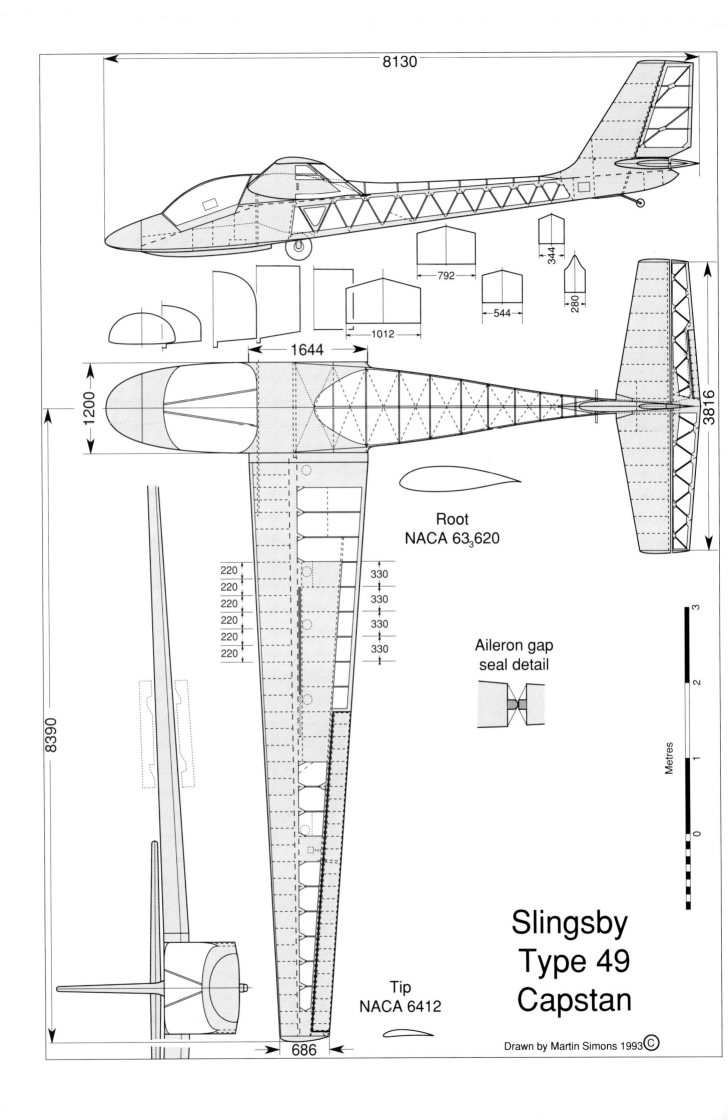

8130

344

792

280

544

1012

1644

1200

3816

Root
NACA 63₃620

8390

220
220
220
220
220
220

330
330
330
330

Aileron gap
seal detail

Tip
NACA 6412

686

Metres

0   1   2   3

Slingsby
Type 49
Capstan

Drawn by Martin Simons 1993 ©

Type 49, Capstan

The T-43 Skylark 3 and the T-45 Swallow were in full production and sales were going well. Slingsby's attention turned again to two-seater training sailplanes. In civilian clubs the T-21B was still widely used, and the ATC had a fleet of T-31s, but these aircraft were aging. The T-42 Eagle was expensive, large and heavy, good for cross-country flying and for aero-towed launching instruction, but not for primary training.

The market was becoming highly competitive. In Germany the Rhönschwalbe from Schleicher and the Specht of Egon Scheibe were successful basic trainers, a few of which found their way into British clubs, but these were not much superior to the T-31 and not what seemed to be needed now. There were several excellent two-seat sailplanes from European factories, notably the Ka 7, which was produced in quantity after 1959 by Alexander Schleicher. A few were appearing in Britain, usually being imported by private syndicates for cross-country flying. The Ka 7 had wooden wings and tail, but the fuselage was a built-up frame of welded steel tubing, fabric covered. The all-metal Blanik from Czechoslovakia, by the standards of the time highly complex with large Fowler flaps and a semi-retractable wheel, was also available at a relatively low price from the state-owned and subsidised LET factory. It did not seem to Slingsby that these types were suitable for *ab initio* training, and British gliding clubs were quite unfamiliar with metal structures, whether aluminium alloy or steel tubing.

Some thought had been given to an improved version of the T-21, and the outcome in 1957 was the T-21C, later renumbered to become the T-46. This had practically the same wing as the T-21B, but a new fuselage and tail unit. The tall wing pylon was done away with and the wings, still with strut bracing, were mounted directly on the fuselage, the wingspan thus being increased to 17.22m (56ft). There was an enclosed cockpit and the tail unit was enlarged and simplified. The performance and handling were a little better than the T-21, but the cost of production was quite high. Only one was built. (It remains in service still.)

If the Swallow was to become the standard first-solo sailplane, a two-seater which had similar performance and handling was required. It might best be imagined as a two-seat Swallow using similar NACA wing profiles. It had to be of simple wooden construction for easy maintenance and repair in the clubs, had to have a fully enclosed cockpit and, while being suitable for primary instruction, should also perform well enough for teaching students cross-country flying and navigation.

In Britain, instructors accustomed to the T-21 still tended to prefer side-by-side seating. The instructor could watch the students' facial expressions and see where they looked and how the controls were held, and conversations could be natural and instructions given in a normal voice. The disadvantage of the side-by-side layout was the increased fuselage drag, but this was not a serious problem in a training aircraft. The penalty could be reduced by reclining the seats slightly, allowing the fuselage depth to be less. For solo flying, simple and easily accessible fitments should be built in to allow ballast to be carried, ensuring a safe c.g. position. Slingsby probably also thought that, while everyone else in the northern hemisphere was building tandem two-seaters, he might find a good market for something different.

By the end of 1960 work on the design of the T-49 was proceeding and Slingsby was ready to accept advanced orders. (The T-47 was a projected 20m-span Skylark which was never built, and the T-48 a delta-winged research aircraft design study which was transferred to Handley Page Ltd to emerge as the HP 115.)

The T-49 wing plan was similar to that of the Swallow, with well-marked taper. The section changed from the thick root profile NACA 63_3 620 to the NACA 6412 at the tip. The increase of camber to 6 per cent, as indicated by the first digit of the tip profile's number, was intended to delay stalling there by increasing the available lift coefficient. Some geometric washout was built in so that the outer wing would not reach the stalling angle before the root. Large Schempp-Hirth airbrakes were fitted.

The structural methods followed the already well established practices at Slingsby. The wing had spruce spars and gaboon plywood stressed skins, the open-framed portions aft of the mainspar being fabric covered. The ailerons were plywood skinned and mass balanced. As in the Swallow the fuselage was a built-up space frame of wood with cross-frames in highly stressed areas, fabric covered except on the underside, where there was a plywood skin. Three-dimensionally-curved shells around the cockpit, not stressed, were moulded in glass reinforced plastics which were also used for fairings and wingtips. The very broad transparent cockpit canopy, hinged at the back to lift upwards, was made in three sections rather than being moulded in one piece, so that if one section cracked or was otherwise damaged it was not necessary to replace the whole unit. By careful attention to balance and moments the pilots could be placed entirely in front of the wing, instead of being underneath it as in the T-21. The field of view from the cockpit was extremely good. The wing was attached to the fuselage by three horizontal steel pins with a fairing to close the gap at the root. The undercarriage was a simple wheel and skid arrangement with a small tailwheel.

The tail unit was a departure from normal as far as Slingsby was concerned. The plywood skinned tailplane was mounted behind the fin on a fuselage extension, with the rudder above it. The entire vertical tail was raked back, probably more for reasons of style than to gain any important aerodynamic advantage, although the effect of the sweep was to increase the moment arm of the surface slightly. The elevator was fitted with a large tab. With the reduced fuselage height and the swept fin the sailplane had a pleasing appearance in side view.

While the T-49 was still on the drawing board Walter Kahn, a well-known and influential sailplane pilot and member of the BGA council, met a representative from the firm of W. D. & H. O. Wills, whose most widely advertised trade mark was a capstan. The possibility of the cigarette manufacturers supporting gliding as they supported other sports was discussed, and the outcome was that W. D. & H. O. Wills agreed to provide a two-seater for the BGA, to be used for training and checking gliding instructors. The BGA had established an instructors' panel whose responsibilities included visiting gliding clubs regularly to ensure that training standards were being well maintained. The possibility of the BGA employing a full-time coach was being considered, and if a suitable two-seat sailplane could be provided the prospects seemed very good. Slingsby was persuaded without much difficulty to name his new two-seater Capstan. The first flights were made in November 1961, and the Capstan was sent to Lasham for the usual testing and certification procedure by the BGA Test Group.

Now the kind of problems which had haunted Slingsby most of his life reappeared. The stalling and spinning characteristics of the prototype T-49 were unsatisfactory. On stalling it would behave quite nor-mally on most occasions, the nose pitching down moderately and the sailplane picking up speed again in the ensuing recovery. On other occasions, unpredict-ably, one wing or the other would drop very sharply and the T-49 would enter an incipient spin and lose height rapidly. Such behaviour in a basic trainer was unacceptable. The fault could not always be demon-strated, and Slingsby's own test pilot had not discov-ered it. The Capstan behaved perfectly most of the time, but every now and then it would 'bite' severely. This inconsistency made the aircraft more dangerous than if it had always reacted in the same way. It may be that the wing was unusually sensitive to slight amounts of yaw or sideslip at the stall, so that it would only mis-behave if flown a little clumsily. Such clumsiness was only too likely to occur with a student pilot.

Slingsby's first response was one of disbelief, since the problem had not shown up before. A second opinion was sought, and it took further trials before the peculiarity manifested itself and everyone was con-vinced. To try to establish the cause of these difficul-ties, tests were made with wool tufts on the wings. A helicopter took station alongside the glider as it was flown at various speeds, and an observer attempted to see what the airflow was doing. For various reasons the results were not very helpful. The Capstan was returned to Kirbymoorside and the wings were mod-ified to increase the washout. This tended to degrade the performance but had to be accepted.

Further tests ensued and more difficulties emerged. With the c.g. approaching the designed rearward limit corresponding to two fairly light pilots in the cockpit, the T-49 had two distinct spinning modes. One was normal, with easy recovery. The other was a very dangerous flat spin with a very slow recovery and great loss of height. As before, this characteristic showed itself only occasionally. The obvious solution was to restrict the c.g. to a safe forward position by fixing some ballast permanently in the nose.

The repeated testing and modifications delayed progress. A year after the new type had been announced and the first provisional orders accepted, Slingsby's advertisements early in 1962 stated that this was the training two-seater for the next decade, but none had yet been sold. Still more delays followed. The T-49 was criticised for having a rudder that required hard work for little effect, the stalling behaviour with c.g. aft was still somewhat alarming, and when the pilots were out of the cockpit the weight on the tail lifting bar was too great for easy ground handling. When it was finally approved for certification the Capstan had a taller fin and rudder and the wheel posi-tion was moved aft to take weight off the tail. The T-49 became ready for regular service only towards the end of 1962.

With additional grants from the Central Council of Physical Recreation and the Ministry of Education the BGA could pay for a National Coach, and John Everitt was appointed to this position. A programme of Coach and Capstan tours was set up as soon as the two-seater became available, handicapped at first by the worst winter weather ever experienced. Once the snows melted in 1963 the tours continued with hardly a break. Apart from visits to some 22 clubs during the year, Everitt flew *hors concours* in the National Championships in late May and early June, and in the Northern Regionals a month later, to give competition cross-country experience to selected club instructors who had not had the chance to do such flying before.

One effect of this programme was that club pilots all over Britain had the opportunity to fly the T-49A and to see how it might fit in to their operations. Everitt himself was very pleased with the aircraft. He liked the side-by-side seating and the excellent view, but made it clear in his writings that any club which relied on low-powered launching apparatus, as many still did, would find the Capstan unsuitable. Compared with the old, slow T-21 the T-49 would not climb well on a feeble winch launch. It weighed about 90kg (198lb) more than the T-21, and had a stalling speed of 32kt instead of 28. Even compared with the Eagle, the Capstan had a higher wing loading and a greater all-up weight. For clubs which had powerful winches and sites with ample space to lay out long cables, and especially if aero-towed launches were available, the Capstan was eminently suitable, and it was excellent for teaching map reading and navigation on cross-country flights.

With further minor modifications the T-49B entered production in July 1963, the first aircraft off the production line going in September to the Lasham Gliding Centre. Sponsored by the brewers, Watney's, it was christened *Red Barrel*, and was followed soon afterwards by two more. Thirty-two Capstans were built and sold, which was a moderate success, but the objective of replacing all the old T-21 and T-31 trainers was never achieved. Many clubs continued to use the T-21 for another decade or more.

In 1962, in an article in *Sailplane and Gliding*, Derek Piggott suggested that training methods for glider pilots should in future rely on simple self-launching two-seaters which would have motors for take-off and taxying but which would be flown as gliders for the majority of their time in the air. He worked out the likely costs and illustrated the article with a photograph of a model Capstan with the engine mounted on a pylon behind the cockpit. A McCulloch four-cylinder two-stroke motor of 72bhp was suggested. He returned to the basic idea two years later, and serious efforts were made to launch a company to produce such an aircraft. A revised drawing showed a Capstan with a motor in the nose and an orthodox undercarriage. Slingsby's were interested and took over the project. The powered Capstan T-49C, with a 45hp Nelson motor, made its first flights in February 1968. The engine was mounted on a pylon, as in Piggott's original scheme. The thrust line of the propeller was high, the motor was not very powerful for a total flying weight with two pilots of 612kg (1,350lb), and the standard undercarriage of a single wheel and forward skid was retained. The necessary development work proceeded

slowly. Only one T-49C was built, and this prototype, together with the last ordinary Capstan on the production line, was destroyed in the factory fire of November 1968.

The Capstan never did become the standard club training aircraft in Britain, and it was not very popular overseas. Two T-49 kits were exported to New Zealand for assembly there, five went to Burma and one to Pakistan. As an indication of the kind of market of which Slingsby's share was so small, production of the contemporary Ka 7 in Germany reached 511 between 1957 and 1966, and examples appeared all over the world. The Ka 7 was replaced by the Ka 13, of which 585 were sold before 1977. (Some have been built more recently under licence.) Simultaneously there was very large production of Blaniks; 100 being sold in Australia alone. Other successful two-seaters came from other factories and other countries, the Schweizer 2-22 in the USA, the French Bijave, the Polish Bocian, and so on.

Type 49 Capstan data

Dimensions

Wingspan	16.78m (55.05ft)
Wing area	20.43m^2 (220ft^2)
Aspect ratio	13.78
Length o.a.	8.13m (26.67ft)
Wing sections	
Root	NACA 63$_3$ 620
Tip	NACA 6412 (modified)

Weights

Tare	345kg (761lb)
Flying	567kg (1,250lb)
Wing loading	27.7kg/m^2 (5.7lb/ft^2)

The prototype Capstan at the factory, showing the original, smaller, vertical tail. (*Slingsby collection*)

The Capstan being prepared for a test flight. The large transparent canopy, hinged at the back, was thought at first to be vulnerable to damage, but proved quite serviceable in practice. (*Slingsby collection.*)

A Capstan approaching to land at the 1992 vintage glider rally at Terlet in the Netherlands. (*M. Simons.*)

With two pilots on board, the Capstan rested on its wheel and front skid. On landing, once flying speed was lost the skid acted as a brake, but the wheel was also equipped with a brake, allowing very short landing run.

The prototype Capstan flown solo at Sutton Bank during the preliminary test flight programme. (*Slingsby collection.*)

A Capstan on the ground at Dunstable. (*M. Simons.*)

The tail unit of the Capstan was unusual for a Slingsby aircraft, with the tailplane mounted behind the fin and the rudder above it. This may have contributed to the spin recovery problem in the prototype, but caused no difficulties with the T-49B. (*M. Simons.*)

In side view the Capstan was quite elegant, and the additional drag caused by the wide cockpit was not a serious fault. The cockpit was entirely ahead of the wing, allowing an exceptionally good field of vision. (*M. Simons.*)

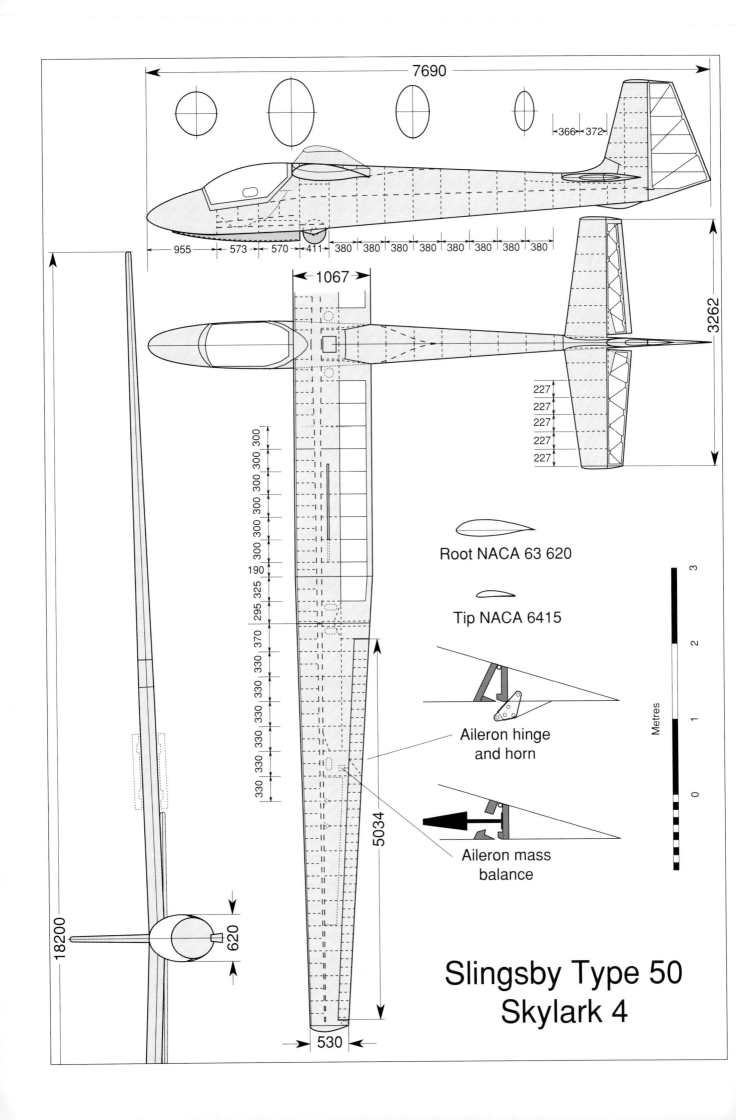

7690

366 372

955 573 570 411 380 380 380 380 380 380 380 380

1067

3262

227
227
227
227
227

300 300 300 300
300 300 300
190
295 325
370
330 330 330 330 330 330 330

5034

530

18200

620

Root NACA 63 620

Tip NACA 6415

Aileron hinge
and horn

Aileron mass
balance

Metres

0 1 2 3

Slingsby Type 50
Skylark 4

Type 50, Skylark 4

The date of the first flight of the Skylark 4 is given in several references as February 1961, but the first public announcement of the new type's existence was in February 1962. In May of that year the Skylark 4 began to appear on the BGA register, and the earliest report on its flying characteristics was published in June, when production began in earnest. None of the workshop plans on which the accompanying three-view drawing is based is dated earlier than 1962, except where components from the Skylark 3 were used.

Aerodynamically and structurally, the Skylark 4 was a straightforward development from later versions of the T-43 Skylark 3. The wing, still of the three-piece type, was mounted on the fuselage in the same way, two long pins inserted from the front connecting both front and rear wing fittings to the main frames. The centre section was almost unchanged, with the normal type of parallel-ruler airbrakes. The 20 per cent thick NACA six-digit section had the advantage of a wide operating range of low drag, and the great thickness of the wing at the root allowed a deep spruce spar to be used without the need for special reinforcement. The materials used on the earlier Skylarks were retained; gaboon plywood for the skin, with a machined spruce leading edge carefully faired to preserve the laminar boundary layer over the forward third of the chord. The tip panels carried the long-span ailerons of narrow chord which had been proved on the Skylark 3G.

The only important aerodynamic change to the wing was the use of the NACA 6415 aerofoil section, 6 per cent cambered and 15 per cent thick, at the tip. For a modern sailplane this was a very strongly cambered section. At airspeeds above 90kt the outer wing of the Skylark 3, with 3° of aerodynamic washout and the 4 per cent cambered NACA 4415 profile, began to bend down, indicating that the tips were forced to operate at negative angles of attack. Considerable loss of glide ratio at these speeds resulted. The new tip section allowed the T-50 to fly at 108kt without any reversal of the tip loads, and a noticeable improvement in the ability to fly fast between thermals. The higher maximum lift coefficient of the strongly cambered profile prevented tip stalling at low speeds without any aerodynamic washout.

The fuselage of the T-50 was a great improvement on the earlier design. Instead of the fairly high neck which had been a feature of all Slingsby high-performance sailplanes since the Gull 4, the new fuselage was a simple streamlined form of oval cross-section throughout, with a reclined seating position for the pilot. The height and cross-sectional area of the fuselage were much reduced, which had the additional advantage that the ground crew did not have to lift the heavy wing centre-section so high when assembling the aircraft. The cockpit canopy, accurately moulded over a male form rather than being blown, improved the airflow over the nose considerably compared with the rather bulbous shape of the earlier type, although Slingsby did not return to the fully contoured shape that had been used long ago for the T-12 Gull. Visibility from the cockpit of the Skylark 4 was exceptionally good. As before, the sailplane was offered with or without a wheel, though hardly any without the wheel were produced. The tail unit was taken without change from the Skylark 3G, and there was no greater use of glassfibre reinforced plastic components than in the earlier type.

The T-50 handled well and was lighter on all the controls than the earlier models of the Skylark 3, and had a noticeable edge in performance. Slingsby's advertisements stated that it was the most advanced 18m contest sailplane available as a standard production aircraft. Although this was strictly true, it did not necessarily imply that it was the most advanced sailplane available from any factory. In Poland the Zefir 2, under development since 1960, was in production. Plastic foam and plywood sandwich skins were used together with glassfibre shells. The pilot lay supine rather than sitting in the cockpit, giving the fuselage a very refined aerodynamic form with a retracting wheel. The wings carried Fowler flaps. A parachute airbrake, normally stowed in a tailcone, was standard. This was technically a much more advanced sailplane than anything Slingsby had produced. It spanned 17m rather than

18m which allowed Slingsby to make the above claim. Indeed, to most ordinary glider pilots the Zefir seemed too complex, but it pointed the way ahead, whereas the Skylark 4 marked the end of a series.

The advantage the British aircraft retained lay in price. Like its predecessors, the Skylark 4 was simple in design, used no costly materials or complicated methods of construction, was robust and easily repaired and it did perform well. When a reliable polar curve became available from flight tests by Dick Johnson in the USA, the best glide figure was 36.3, a worthwhile improvement over the Skylark 3F, though the glide at high speeds was not as good as the figures claimed by the factory. It was also widely believed that Johnson had done a lot of work on his Skylark, cleaning up details and sealing small gaps to achieve the figures he reported.

The Skylark 4 was never regarded as particularly fast, having a modest wing loading of 23.35kg/m^2 (4.56lb/ft^2). It was designed for British pilots accustomed to using rather weak thermals. Elsewhere, sailplanes with higher wing loadings were appearing. The Zefir's figure was 28.9kg/m^2 (5.9lb/ft^2). In the USA the all-metal Sisu had a wing loading of 32.05kg/m^2 (6.57lb/ft^2), and the HP 11, also metal, was equipped to carry water ballast for a maximum wing loading of 39kg/m^2 (8lb/ft^2). The attitude of most British pilots in 1962 was that these 'hot ships' or 'lead sleds' were all very fine for soaring in the strong thermals of Texas or Eastern Europe on record-setting days, but they would never survive long in humid British air. It was believed that the Skylark would score consistently in competitions, winning the difficult days and doing well enough on the occasional very good day, and so heading the list at the end of a competition week.

The first real test of the Skylark 4 in competition came at the 1963 World Championships at Junin in Argentina. Many lessons were learned. The weather was mixed, some days being relatively poor and similar to English conditions. There were some great thunderstorms which a few pilots used to climb, surrounded by lightning, to 6,000m (20,000ft) only to have the subsequent glide spoilt by heavy icing and navigation made impossible. On other days strong thermals were ideal for heavy, fast sailplanes. After seven days Skylark 4s were placed 8th, 9th, 10th and 11th in the 'Open Class', Zefirs 1st, 2nd and 5th, the HP 11 from the USA was 3rd and the Sisu 4th. It was a triumph for the 'hot ships'. The SB-7, an 'all-glass' sailplane built by the students of Akaflieg Braunschweig, did not do particularly well.

After the contest the British team spoke with almost a single voice. The Skylarks could survive in poor weather, but they did not always win even then. The 'lead sleds' could usually keep up or overtake. They used their good glides at high airspeeds to search larger volumes of air, and could find the few better thermals which existed even on these difficult days. A Skylark might be climbing steadily but slowly in weak lift which an experienced Zefir or Sisu pilot would fly through without turning. The Skylarks lingered in bad patches which the fast aircraft ignored altogether or flew round. Stronger lift could usually be discovered a few kilometres further on. If the better thermal was not there after all, the heavier sailplane might have to struggle or land out, but with flaps deployed and plenty of skill a heavy sailplane could nearly always surpass the Skylark's cross-country-speed. On the really good days, the Skylark pilots became used to seeing the competition disappearing rapidly into the distance, and they had no chance of catching them. Frank Irving, in cautious retrospect wrote: 'It is just possible that, even in England, a bit more wing loading would be a good idea, but we may have to relearn how to soar'.

Soon afterwards, in May 1963, Dick Johnson seemed to give the lie to these new beliefs when he won the US Nationals at Elmira in New York State. Perhaps because of this result several more Skylarks were exported to the USA during the next few months. Johnson, however, was one of the most experienced sailplane pilots in the world, and his win was thought to be due to his greater skill rather than to his aircraft. He had a long string of previous wins to his credit. He followed his success with another win in the following year at McCook in Nebraska, where it was expected that the heavy, fast sailplanes would do particularly well. The weather was untypical, favouring light sailplanes. The Ka 6CR filled four of the top six places and a Sisu flown by A. J. Smith came third. The other two Skylarks in this competition placed 23rd and 37th.

At about this time, George Moffatt, a future World Champion, wrote of the Skylark 4 that although it handled very well and was comfortable, its performance was disappointing, very little superior to the Ka 6, and he found fault with the finish and detail design. The price advantage remained. Philip Wills had described the Skylark 4 as 'among the most lovely aircraft of all time', and took delivery of one of the first off the production line. Others in Britain followed his example, and three kits went to New Zealand and several others were exported. Production reached 66, one more than the entire output of all versions of the Skylark 3. The total of all marks of Skylark including the two little Skylark 1s of 1953, was just short of 200.

Meanwhile, things were not developing happily at Kirbymoorside. Fred Slingsby himself was ageing, and after 1962 was in poor health. He had some heart trouble and retired at the age of 70 in 1964. For complex legal reasons the Shaw Slingsby Trust which had been established after the death of J. E. D. Shaw in 1955 had to be wound up, and the majority shareholdings which the Trust held had to be placed on the market. It was not even certain that production of gliders at Slingsby would continue under the new ownership.

Type 50 Skylark 4 data

Dimensions
Wingspan   18.2m (59.7ft)
Wing area   16.1m^2 (173.3ft^2)
Aspect ratio   20.57
Length o.a.   7.69m (25.23ft)
Wing sections
  Root   NACA 63$_3$ 620
  Tip   NACA 6415

Weights
Tare   256kg (564lb)
Flying   376kg (829lb)
Wing loading   23.35kg/m^2 (4.56lb/ft^2)

The Skylark 4 destined for Philip Wills in flight over Hampshire in 1962. (*Charles E. Brown, RAF Museum, Hendon, neg No. P100736*)

Geoffrey Stephenson's Skylark 4 at Dunstable. (*M. Simons*)

A much modified Skylark 4 in Australia. The cockpit canopy was altered to improve the contours, and a retractable wheel was fitted. (*M. Simons*)

In the USA, Dick Johnson took delivery in May 1963 and twice won the National Championships in his Skylark 4, registered N7997A. (*R. J. Johnson*)

Wills's Skylark 4 at Dunstable. In the background is a
Slingsby T-34 Sky. (*M. Simons*)

Charles Benson flew a Skylark 4 in Britain until it was sold to
Australia in 1967, when it was registered VH-GTB.
(*M. Simons*)

Skylark 4 N74876 in the USA . (*N. Ellison*)

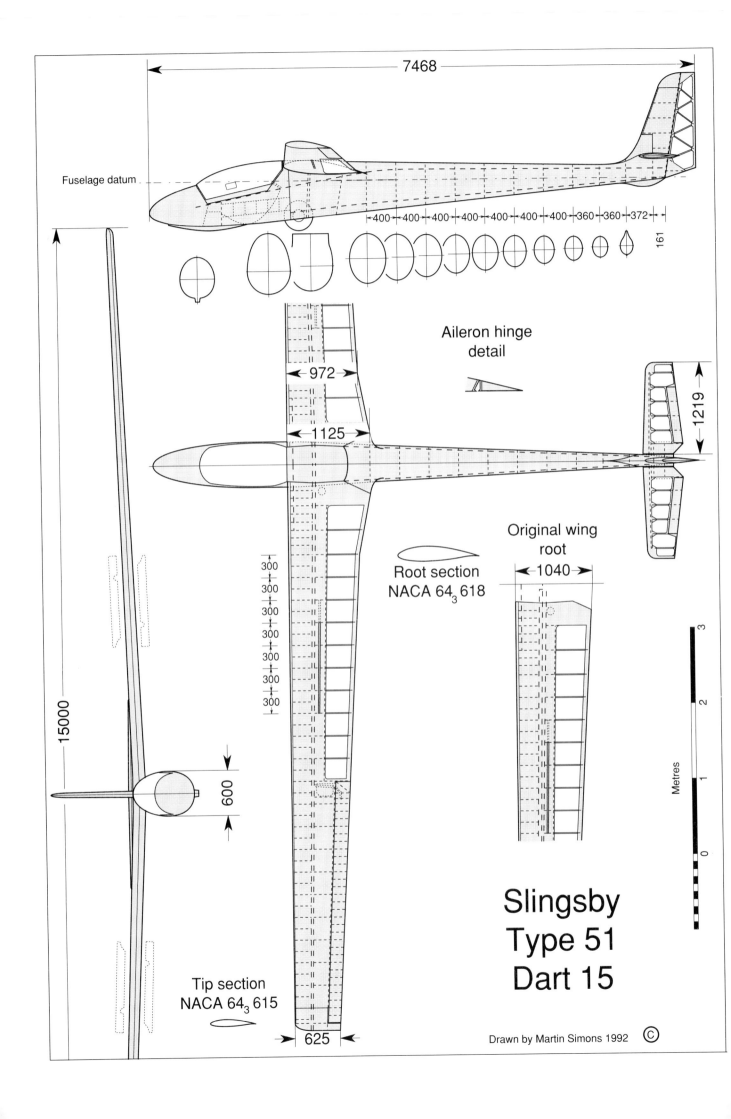

7468

Fuselage datum

400 400 400 400 400 400 400 360 360 372

161

Aileron hinge
detail

972

1125

1219

Original wing
root

1040

300
300
300
300
300
300
300

Root section
NACA 64₃ 618

Root section
NACA 64$_3$ 618

15000

600

Tip section
NACA 64$_3$ 615

625

Metres

3
2
1
0

Slingsby
Type 51
Dart 15

Drawn by Martin Simons 1992 ©

Type 51, Dart 15 & 17R

The British had been disappointed when the Skylark 2 failed to win the International Standard Class design prize in 1956, but there was little doubt that the Ka 6 designed by Rudolf Kaiser deserved the award. Since then, no serious attention had been paid at Kirbymoorside to the Standard Class. The prize was won in 1960 by the V-tailed Standard Austria and in 1963 by the Finnish Vasama. A writer in the French magazine *Aviasport* suggested that the Ka 6 should really have won every time, but it had not been entered in the competition again after the first occasion.

According to Bill Slater, who soon afterwards became managing director at Slingsby, in 1963 the company faced a serious sales problem. The Skylark 4 was in production at the rate of about one per week and Capstans and Swallows were being built, but few new orders were coming in. No significant improvements could be envisaged for the Skylark series. It was therefore decided early in 1963 to tackle the problem of producing a Standard Class sailplane and to aim for the design award in 1965, when the World Championships were to be held in England. The senior staff of the company were more enthusiastic about the new project than Slingsby, but following reconstruction of the board he was no longer in a controlling position and about to retire, approaching 70 years of age.

Following the dissolution of the Shaw Slingsby Trust, the company was bought by Jack W. Bradley, whose chief interests were in building mass-produced houses. A fire in one of Bradley's York factories in 1964 had necessitated a reorganisation. The Kirbymoorside company was split into two, Slingsby Joinery Ltd and Slingsby Aircraft Ltd, with Bradley himself as chairman of both and of a holding company. New workshops were erected at Kirbymoorside to prefabricate window frames and other parts for houses. Glass-plastic technology was used to produce bathroom ware, including a magnificent two-seat bathtub advertised as the Gemini.

There could be no point in producing a machine that was not superior to the Ka 6, so it was decided to undertake considerable research before any of the main design features were settled. For the first time, so far as anyone knew, computers were used to arrive at the best compromise. The necessary program was written and the calculations carried out at Cambridge University by Anthony Edwards, well known as a pilot and writer of statistical articles about cross-country soaring in Britain. Some additional computing capacity was called on from an Italian university. To achieve the performance to match the computed figures required the sailplane to have accurately built 'laminar flow' wing profiles and to come out close to the expected flying weight. Wind tunnel tests were carried out at Imperial College in London under the supervision of Frank Irving, also well known for his technical articles and his advisory position with the BGA. Once the basic aerodynamic configuration had been worked out, the engineering began and construction started on the Type 51 in May 1963.

The wing was very straightforward, and reverted to the usual two-piece design joining on the centreline. A relatively high aspect ratio of 18 for the fixed 15m span was chosen and NACA '64 series' profiles were used. As indicated by the second digit, a 40 per cent laminar boundary layer was aimed for. To prevent the wingtips being forced to operate at very small Reynolds numbers (narrow chords and low airspeeds), at which the performance of these low-drag aerofoil sections was thought to deteriorate, the taper ratio was small. The root of the wing was 20 per cent of the chord thick to provide sufficient depth for the mainspar. A short distance outboard it was thinned to 18 per cent. The mainspar was of spruce, and to achieve the necessary strength it had to be twinned over about half the total span. It was heavy.

The use of gaboon ply was now abandoned. Except for a fabric covered area inboard of the ailerons, the wing was skinned with birch plywood. This was thicker than necessary for the loads it had to carry, but it was hoped it would retain a wave-free form to preserve the low-drag contours. It was supported with ribs and auxiliary ribs ahead of the mainspar. To overcome the difficulties of forming the skin around the leading edge, which had a fairly small nose radius, the method worked out for the Skylark series was used

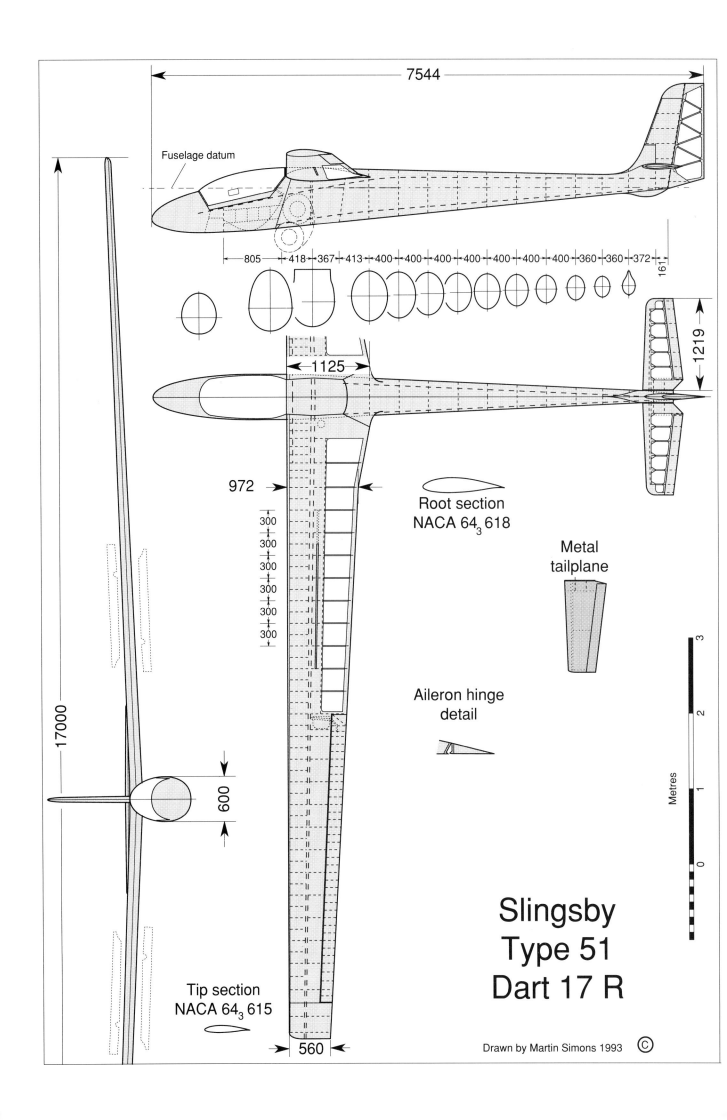

Fuselage datum

7544

805 418 367 413 400 400 400 400 400 400 400 360 360 372 161

1219

1125

972

17000

300
300
300
300
300
300

Root section
NACA 64₃ 618

Metal
tailplane

Aileron hinge
detail

600

Tip section
NACA 64₃ 615

560

Slingsby
Type 51
Dart 17 R

Metres

3
2
1
0

Drawn by Martin Simons 1993 ©

again. A light front spar provided gluing area for the ply to be laid in separate panels, top and bottom. An accurately machined hollow leading-edge member was glued on to form an accurate entry for the profile. This structure was not particularly light.

Ailerons of small chord, plywood skinned, proved fully adequate and required no mass-balancing. The brakes, as required by the Standard Class specification, were large enough to limit the airspeed in a dive to less than the safe maximum. The rigging system was similar to that of the T-45 Swallow, which in turn had been modelled on that of the old German Weihe. Each wing was attached to the fuselage with two pins in line, a large one at the mainspar and a smaller one at the leading edge. Then both wings could be raised together for the upper spar flanges to be united with a fifth, large pin. For wooden sailplanes this method of rigging has never been surpassed.

Much effort was put into reducing the cross-sectional area of the fuselage. Designers everywhere had been much impressed by the Polish Foka which had been entered in the 1963 design contest. It did not win because it was considered too extreme, with the pilot supine in the cockpit and very limited visibility directly ahead. But by following this example to some extent and running all the controls along the sides of the fuselage instead of beneath the seat, the fuselage height of the T-51 was reduced by about 10cm compared with the Skylark 4. Yet the reclined seating position was very comfortable, with an excellent view through an accurately moulded canopy.

The company's approach to new materials was still extremely cautious despite ten years' experience with GRP. Polyester resins were still used. The front fuselage around the cockpit and the extreme nose were GRP, as was the central wing fairing, put in place after rigging. Otherwise the fuselage was orthodox, oval in cross-section and skinned with birch plywood. The landing wheel was fitted forward of the balance point so that the nose would not go down when the pilot climbed into the cockpit. A small nose skid was fitted to protect the fuselage when landing on rough ground. The vertical tail was stylishly raked back and faired carefully to the fuselage with large moulded GRP panels. The horizontal tail was of the all-moving type, but anti-balance tabs were fitted to ensure that the pilot should have some positive feel in the elevator. The all-moving tailplane was skinned with GRP ahead of the spar, with expanded polystyrene foam taking the place of ribs. This was the first time the company had used glass for a load-bearing component. Gussets and trailing-edge stiffeners were also made from GRP.

In general appearance, with its long rear fuselage and a small tail unit, the T-51, now christened Dart, was stylish and attractive. Its proportions were very different from the Skylarks and there was much interest among likely customers. However, the prototype turned out to be quite a lot heavier than intended. Perhaps despite themselves the Slingsby team had produced a rather fast, heavily loaded sailplane which

could not be expected to scratch about and climb in weak thermals. The careful computer studies that preceded the detailed work were partly vitiated.

The first flight was made on 26 November 1963. There was no doubt in anyone's mind after these early tests that the Dart was exceptionally pleasant to fly. It was light on all the controls and very responsive without being unstable or tricky to handle. It had an excellent rate of roll, very helpful in centring thermals, and its performance at high speeds seemed impressive. It would drop a wing and spin if clumsily handled, but this was true of many sailplanes. The company announced that it expected to produce a batch by March 1964, in time for several to be entered in the National Championships.

Four were indeed entered for the competitions held at Lasham in May. In one of the outstanding flights of the competition, John Williamson in the Dart reached Sunderland, 262km (162 miles) from his take-off, after a flight involving some very tricky scratching in weak lift to reach better weather further north, followed by some cloud flying. The one pilot who exceed this distance by a couple of kilometres, Brennig James, was in a Skylark 3 with 18m span, and he took nearly an hour longer to make the distance. Williamson reported circling at 45 or even 50kt, at least 10kt faster than the larger aircraft, but, providing thermals yielding climb rates better than 2 or 3kt could be found, the Dart left the others behind. The Darts were placed 2nd, 4th, 6th and 8th in the Standard Class, a mixed result and not what Slingsby had wished. It was especially annoying that the first and third places went to Ka 6CRs flown by pilots who had a good deal less competition flying experience than those who flew Darts.

Tests followed at Slingsby, and it was established that the low-speed performance was not as good as expected. Airflow separation around the wing roots was thought to be part of the cause. The 20 per cent locally thickened root section was perhaps to blame. After some hesitation the section was reduced to 18 per cent like the rest of the wing. The wing roots were widened by adding an extension, producing an unusual re-entrant tapered planform but smoothing the flow over the roots and slightly increasing the total area.

A more significant change was the introduction of aluminium alloy reinforcement for the mainspar flanges, which reduced the weight by 20kg (44lb) compared with the original spruce spar. This limited use of metal in what remained essentially a wooden structure was not entirely new, having been introduced in 1953 on the Orao designed by Boris Cijan and built in Yugoslavia. For the Dart the spar reinforcements, after machining to size, were sent away to have a veneer of wood bonded on to them by the Redux process and then returned to Kirbymoorside to be inserted in the wing jigs and glued up virtually as if they were wooden members.

With these changes it was considered that the Dart had almost achieved the performance expected of it. With the additional wing area and reduced weight the low-speed situation was acceptable. Nonetheless, work had already begun on a version with larger span. An early move in this direction was a 15m Dart convertible to 17m by the addition of interchangeable extra-long tip sections. One was built in this form, but because the ailerons did not extend to the tips of the 17m version there was some loss of roll rate.

The Dart 17 prototype first flew in November 1964. It was essentially a Dart 15 with the wings stretched to 17m. The rudder was subsequently enlarged to aid control of the extended wing in yaw. In April 1965 this aircraft was used by Nick Goodhart to win the Inter Services Competition, in preparation for the World Championships. He was very pleased with it, praising especially the good cockpit, visibility and handling. The performance of both the 15 and 17m versions in international competition remained to be discovered. The World Championships took place at South Cerney in 1965, and the Slingsby team was delighted when the Dart 15 won the design prize. This had been the objective from the beginning. Might sales now equal those of the Ka 6?

The results of the soaring competition were less exciting. Only one Dart 15, flown by George Burton, was entered. The other British entry in Standard Class was the Olympia 465 from Slingsby's rival, Elliotts of Newbury. Burton was placed 5th, the first four places being taken by the French Edelweiss, the Swiss Standard Elfe and two Polish Foka 4s. As designs, none of these was considered suitable for general club use, so the Dart had done well, but a Ka 6CR was very close behind in sixth place. Also competing were the all-glass Phoebus from Germany and the all-metal HP 12 from the USA.

What was more surprising at these competitions was that the Open Class was won outright by a Standard Class Foka 4 flown by Wroblewski, with Makula 4th in another Foka.. This probably said more about the Polish pilots' well practised techniques of team flying than their aircraft, but it did show that good 15m manoeuvreable sailplanes well flown could still compete with much larger and costlier machines. Second place in Open Class was taken by the most extraordinary aircraft of all, the D-36 Circe, which on paper was by far the best-performing sailplane in the world. It was entirely built of GRP, and because of its manifest flexibility was nicknamed *gummiflügel* (rubber wing) by the German team. Three Akaflieg students, Klaus Holighaus, Gerhard Waibel and Wolf Lemke, had designed and built it at Darmstadt Technical University.

The SHK, a 17m development of the Standard Austria, was placed third, and even those who believed the future might still lie with wooden aircraft found this aircraft more impressive than the Dart 17. The SHK had entered production at Schempp-Hirth in Germany during 1965 with new wing profiles developed by Richard Eppler at Stuttgart University. A radically different wooden structure with accurate surfaces enabled full advantage to be taken of these. It had a retracting wheel. It did not handle so well in the air, was less easy to rig and derig and was structurally

heavier, although it had the same maximum weight in flight and a lower wing loading. These disadvantages were not enough to offset the fact of its superior soaring and cross-country racing performance. Nick Goodhart came 7th in the Dart 17; a good result, but not what had been hoped for.

The exposed landing wheel created some additional drag in itself, and a fairing was added to the production aircraft, but there was a less obvious, more important penalty. In order to take-off and land safely with the wheel more than half-buried in the fuselage, the rigging angle of incidence of the wing had to be large to produce a reasonable angle of attack during the ground run. In the air this mattered very little at low airspeeds but during fast glides between thermals the wing operated at low angles of attack. This forced the fuselage into a distinctly nose-down attitude, across the general flow, and created a good deal of unwanted parasitic drag. Philip Wills took the 15/17m interchangeable-tips Dart to Texas and made some informal comparisons there with the Austria SH and the world-record-breaking all-metal Sisu. According to Wills, at inter-thermal airspeeds the Sisu fuselage was horizontal, the SH fuselage slightly nose-down and the Dart markedly nose-down. The other aircraft left him far behind in strong conditions.

George Moffat, the most influential pilot and commentator in the USA, after these comparisons and after flying the aircraft himself, expressed disappointment with the detail and profile accuracy. 'The Dart is a beauty as long as you stand far enough away to miss the amateur paint job and the protruding ribs,' he wrote. He admired the handling and comfort. Of the 15m version he remarked that it was probably a little better than the Ka 6CR, which was very faint praise. The Ka 6E was by now on the market, itself already a little better than the Ka 6CR.

Making the wheel fully retractable allowed the Dart 17R to take a safe attitude on the ground with the wing incidence reduced by 5°. The nose skid was not necessary and was removed. The high speed glide was better. A retracting wheel was also fitted to some Dart 15s. At a late stage in the production an all-metal tailplane was introduced. The final version of the Dart was thus a composite of wood, metal and glass, but the most important component, the mainplane, was skinned with plywood over ribs in the old tradition.

Of the Standard Class version of the Dart, 30 were built at the factory and another five from kits, four of these in New Zealand. Forty-four Dart 17Rs were built by Slingsby, and two more from kits in New Zealand. Production ended early in 1967.

It had to be faced. The Dart 17R was not as good, even in British weather, as the rival SHK. But by the end of 1966 the SHK, too, was beginning to look old-fashioned.

It was very apparent that the type of wooden structure hitherto employed at Slingsby was now inadequate for high-performance sailplanes, and the NACA six-digit wing profiles were also superseded. The required accuracy of wing surface for new sections coming from the university researchers could not be achieved with wood, and a bump where the skin passed over the mainspar.

In Germany and Switzerland, glass/plastic techniques were well established. The aeroelastic problems that had beset the early prototypes had been solved or were well on the way to solution. Messerschmitt-Bolkow were selling their Phoebus, Eugen and Ursula Hänle established Glasflügel and produced the H 301 Libelle and engineers from Zürich University co-operated with Hänle and Rudolf Kaiser to produce the Diamant. Klaus Holighaus, one of the students responsible for the D - 36 *gümmiflugel,* joined the Schempp-Hirth Company in 1965, Gerhard Waibel went to Schleichers and Wolf Lemke joined the Rolladen-Schneider Company.

The final Dart development came in 1968. F. X. Wortmann in Stuttgart, pursuing rather different lines of theoretical argument from Eppler, had produced a range of new wing profiles that, given a wave-free wing surface, could yield considerable advantages. For the 1968 World Championships, to be held at Leszno in Poland, Slingsby undertook to build two Standard Class Darts using these new profiles. The general outlines of what the team pilots thought they needed were sketched informally at a conference with Bill Slater. These ideas included a new cockpit canopy with a fully faired nose instead of the slightly less efficient stepped form, and air for ventilation ducted from intakes beneath the wing root. Slater, it seems, took the rough sketches to the factory for production with little further draughting work being done on them.

There was a considerable rush to get the two new sailplanes ready, along with two HP 14C all-metal sailplanes for the Open Class contest, and the team went to Poland with inadequate time for preparation. The results were disappointing. The Dart 15W flown by John Williamson came 22nd in the Standard Class Championships. Williamson was greatly frustrated when he was joined in a thermal by the Swedish pilot Persson flying one of the new all-glass H 201 Standard Libelles. It out-climbed the Dart 15W with ease, and in the glides also left him far behind. Persson finished in second place. Towards the end of the competition Williamson escaped death by a fraction when, caught by a violent windshear from nearby storms, he was forced into a dangerous downwind landing and hit some hidden steel wires. One of the wires sliced through the cockpit canopy and cut deeply into the headrest, but he somehow escaped injury. The Dart was repaired overnight and flew in the contest next day.

Afterwards, Frank Irving wrote of these special aircraft:

They were, in fact, sawn down Dart 17Rs with a fixed wheel picking up on the attachments intended for retracting undercarriages. In the event the promised performance gain at low speeds did not seem to have been entirely achieved and they were just outclassed.

The long canopies also looked surprisingly bulky compared with those of the opposition . . . bodging front fuselage lines doesn't work.'

Subsequently these two special aircraft were converted to 17m span, but they never made a great impression. The one Williamson flew still exists. (The owners never replaced the headrest.)

Dart production tapered off in 1967. About the only thing that seemed clear was that traditional wooden sailplane construction had a very limited future. The reconstructed Slingsby Aircraft Company faced serious problems.

Type 51 Dart data

Dart 15

Dimensions

Wingspan	15m (49.21ft)
Wing area	12.5m^2 (12.63ft^2)
Aspect ratio	18 (17.8)
Length o.a.	7.47m (24.51ft)
Wing sections	
Root	NACA 64$_3$ 618
Tip	NACA 64$_3$ 615

Weights (wooden spar, original wing)

Tare	242.6kg (535lb)
Flying	331.1kg (730lb)
Wing loading	26.48kg/m^2 (5.42lb/ft^2)

Weights (metal spar)

Tare	222kg (490lb)
Flying	331kg (750lb)
Wing loading	26.21kg/m^2 (5.37lb/ft^2)

Dart 17 R

Dimensions

Wingspan	17m (55.77ft)
Wing area	13.87m^2 (149.3ft^2)
Aspect ratio	20.4
Length o.a.	7.54m (24.6ft)
Wing sections as Dart 15	

Weights

Tare	225.9kg (480lb)
Flying	340kg (750lb)
Wing loading	22.8kg/m^2 (4.67lb/ft^2)

Dart 15 W

Dimensions

Wingspan	15m (49.21ft)
Wing area	12.63m^2 (135.89ft^2)
Aspect ratio	17.8
Length o.a.	7.47m (24.51ft)
Wing sections:	
Root	Wortmann FX 61-180
Tip	Wortmann FX 61-163

Weights

Tare	250.7kg (555lb)
Flying	381kg (840lb)
Wing loading	3.05kg/m^2 (6.25lb/ft^2)

The Dart 17 in which Nick Goodhart competed in the 1965 World Championships at South Cerney. The wheel was not retractable, and the wing incidence relative to the fuselage was high. The rudder was subsequently enlarged. (*Charles E. Brown, RAF Museum, Hendon, neg No 6874-4*)

The Dart 15 flown by George Burton in the 1964 British National Championships. The original wing planform is shown. Behind the Dart is the Olympia 460B prototype (Contest No. 54), which was produced by Elliotts in competition with the Dart as a Standard Class sailplane. (*G. Bailey-Woods*)

A Dart 15 about to take a winch launch at Dunstable in 1965. The wheel is now faired. (*M. Simons*)

Nick Goodhart in the Dart 17 at the British Nationals in 1966. Note the small ground clearance, necessitating a high angle of incidence for the wing. Behind the Dart 17 is Peter Scott's EON Olympia 419X. (*M. Simons*)

A Dart 17R with the author and wife, crew chief, preparing for aero-tow launch at Dunstable in 1967. Note the greatly improved ground clearance, allowing a lower angle of incidence. (*E. A. Hull*)

The Dart prototype soon after its public debut in red and white colour scheme. The main wheel was not faired. (*Slingsby collection*)

The tail unit of the Dart 15, showing the anti-balance tab on the all-moving tailplane. The wheel being ahead of the c.g. made lifting the tail of the empty aircraft for ground handling quite difficult. The T-shaped lifting handle was removed before flight. (*G. Bailey-Woods*)

The wing rigging system of the Dart. Two steel pins, aligned on the same centre, attach each wing to the fuselage frames. A fifth pin then joins the upper flanges of the main spars. (*M. Simons*)

A Dart 17R at Dunstable. A beauty providing you stand a little distance off, wrote George Moffat unkindly. (*M. Simons*)

Construction of the Dart 15 at the factory. Note the templates used to check the ribs for accuracy, and the very heavy twin spruce spar on this early production aircraft. (*Slingsby collection*)

Traditional methods were no longer good enough. The plywood wing skin of the Dart, grain laid diagonally, was held to the ribs and spar during gluing by the old method of tacking strips. (*Slingsby collection*)

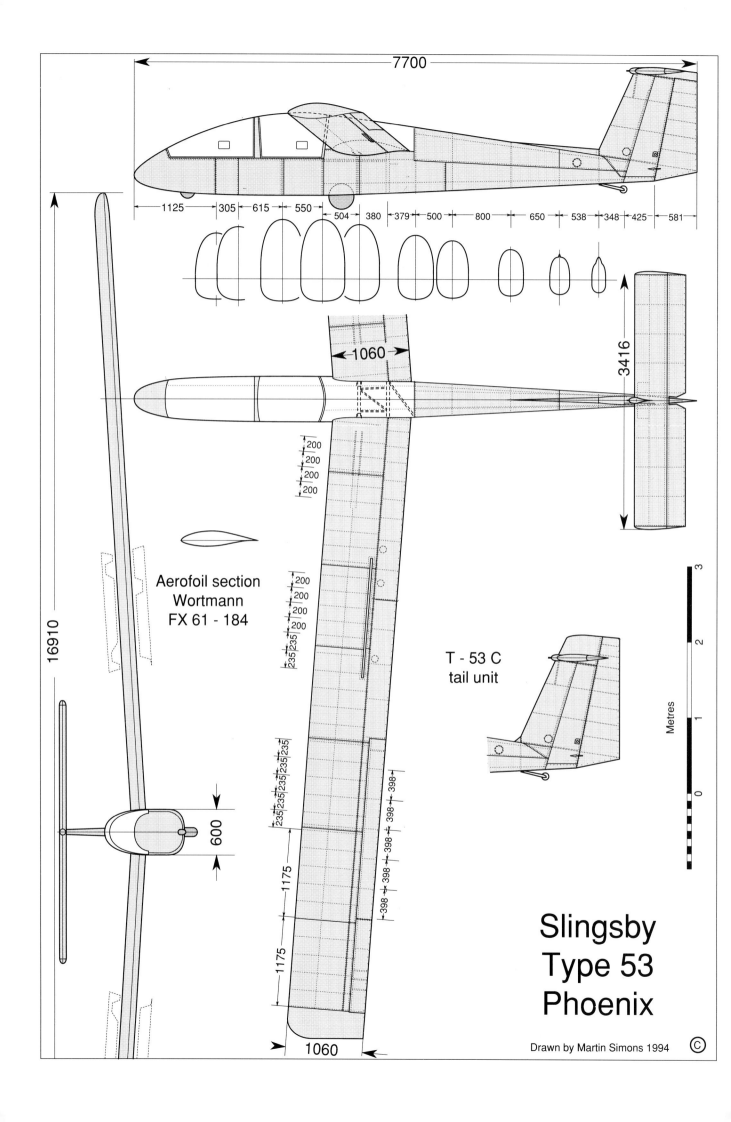

7700

1125 | 305 | 615 | 550 | 504 | 380 | 379 | 500 | 800 | 650 | 538 | 348 | 425 | 581

1060

3416

16910

200
200
200
200

200
200
200
200

235 | 235

Aerofoil section
Wortmann
FX 61 - 184

T - 53 C
tail unit

600

235 | 235 | 235 | 235

398 | 398 | 398

1175

398 | 398 | 398

1175

3

2

Metres

1

0

1060

Slingsby
Type 53
Phoenix

Drawn by Martin Simons 1994 ©

Type 53, Phoenix

It was apparent after the 1965 World Soaring Championships that high-performance sailplanes built in wood had reached their limit. Glass-reinforced epoxy resin aircraft were entering production in Germany and Switzerland, and their performance advantages were quite evident.

In Britain many competent aeronautical engineers still distrusted GRP. There were doubts about stiffness, maintenance and repair, the likely effects of weather, and fatigue. There had been bad experiences with some of the earlier composite materials, such as those proposed for the Kendall K 1 two-seater which was to have been built by the Miles Aircraft Company. The experimental laminations had seemed very promising, but deteriorated chemically over a period and disintegrated. The new GRP wings flexed alarmingly in flight, and most of the early glass sailplanes had flutter problems. There were worries about temperature control for curing epoxy resins if repairs had to be done in ordinary, draughty club workshops, and doubts were expressed about the effects of high temperatures in tropical and semi-tropical countries. (A Swiss Diamant sailplane imported to Australia in 1968 had a thermometer built into the main wing spar near the root to allow the pilot to check before take-off that the structure was not beginning to soften in the sun.)

It did not take long for everyone to realise that all of these problems were soluble, but it was far from clear at first that GRP was the way ahead. The sad thing is that no real advantage had been taken of the experience gained at Slingsby during the years immediately after the introduction of glass-polyester moulded sub-components on the Skylark 2 in 1953. Even a very modest research programme started at this time would have found the company in a much stronger and better-informed position ten years later. In Germany most of the development work was done not by vast organisations with huge financial resources, but by tiny groups of enthusiastic students in academic flying groups attached to technical universities. They were provided with workshop facilities and advice by their colleges, but had to seek financial support elsewhere or manage with none. In Britain nobody did anything at all along these lines at the crucial time.

There was ample experience in the aircraft industry with metal. Stiffness and resistance to weathering, maintenance and repair techniques were all well understood. Aluminium alloy sailplanes had long been customary in the USA. The Schweizer Aircraft Company had been building metal gliders since the late 1930s, and there were homebuilders all over that country using metal. As late as August 1969 Schweizers still argued that metal construction of sailplanes was preferable, not perhaps in terms of outright performance, but in economy of labour, unit cost for small production runs and other factors. It was stated that Schweizers produced a metal sailplane of modest performance in about 500 man-hours. The labour required for a glass sailplane was three times greater.

Some comparative flying of the Dart against the world-record-breaking metal Sisu, designed and built in limited numbers by Leonard Niemi, suggested that a metal wing skin suitably filled and smoothed could be sufficiently free from waviness. With a simple structure the assembly of a metal aircraft was demonstrably easier than that of a wooden one, once the jigging and tooling had been set up. The necessary techniques were not hard to learn. In 1966 Slingsby Aircraft Ltd made the decision to change over to metal.

The accumulated woodworking skills among the local labour force would not be wasted. Older aircraft would often come back to the factory for repairs. Sales of some training types such as the T-45 Swallow and T-49 Capstan were expected to continue, and the Dart would remain in production for a while. In the spring of 1966 Slingsby's only serious rival in Britain, Elliotts of Newbury, gave up sailplane manufacture and concluded an agreement which saw all servicing, spares and any future manufacturing rights of the EON Olympia 463 sailplanes (of mainly wooden structure) handed over to Kirbymoorside. There were prospects for licence production of light wooden aircraft such as the Tipsy Nipper and replica aircraft for the film industry. The powered version of the Capstan, the T-49C, was also being tested and might prove popular.

No doubt the decision was also influenced by preparatory discussions which led to the Sigma project, which was started early in 1966. A group of distinguished British engineers and sailplane pilots formed a small company to design and build a world-beating sailplane, aiming to have it ready for the World Championships in about 1968 or 70. It was intended to bring to bear all available knowledge in the one aircraft, hence the name Sigma, the Greek letter signifying the total sum in mathematics. The Sigma group were thinking of extremely large span (by the standards of the time) and a very high aspect ratio wing with large and complicated area- and camber-changing flaps. Glass plastic materials seemed out of the question, and metal was the only alternative. It was agreed that the design work and construction would be done in space leased by the company at Kirbymoorside, although Sigma was not a Slingsby project.

At about the same time, Slingsby undertook under contract the construction of a gigantic aerial advertising hoarding known as the Camco V-Liner. This was an enormous, though very light, girder-like space frame built up from sub-components rather like a huge Meccano set in fabricated aluminium alloy tubing, with a tandem arrangement of lifting surfaces, multiple power units and a control cabin. It was meant to carry advertising signs over the skies of Los Angeles and other American cities, a role hitherto reserved for airships.

John Sellars joined the company as chief engineer in 1966. The first sailplane study he made for the company was the T-52, a proposed 14.63m (48ft) span two-seater with tandem seating, intended for the ATC to replace the old fleet of T-31 Cadet Mk. 3 and T-21 Sedbergh two-seaters. The T-52 was not built, but the design was developed and enlarged to become the T-53, which flew as a prototype in March 1967. Some wind tunnel testing of a one-tenth scale model was done at Imperial College in London. Much depended on official approval of the design for the Cadets. It was hoped to sell the type to civilian clubs too, but a bulk order from ATC was the main hope.

The T-53 had a span of 16.76m (55ft) and a swept-forward cantilever wing of constant chord with flaps and airbrakes. The wing profile was one of the relatively new Wortmann sections, FX 61-184. The structure was kept as simple as possible, with pressed alloy ribs, a substantial mainspar and a light rear spar carrying the flaps and ailerons. The whole was metal skinned. Flush rivets were used to preserve the laminar boundary layer as far as possible over the forward parts of the wing, but round-headed rivets and ordinary pop rivets were used elsewhere. The airbrakes were housed in separate boxes above and below the wing, preventing leakage of air through from the lower surface to the upper, a common fault with previous sailplanes, even when the brakes were fully closed.

The fuselage, of oval cross-section, was relatively short with the two-seats in tandem. The skins were pop-riveted to the frames. The transparent canopy was moulded in two sections, fore and aft, but fitted to a one-piece frame which was lifted off as a whole to allow the pilots into and out of the cockpit. The field of vision from both seats was good, the forward sweep allowing the rear pilot to be seated close to the c.g. in flight but entirely ahead of the wing root. Behind the cockpit, the fairing over the centre section of the wing was also transparent, further improving the view. A two-wheeled tandem main undercarriage was used, the main wheel being sprung. With the crew in the cockpit the nose went down on to the front wheel, and it was easy to hold the aircraft straight during the early, slow phases of launching before full rudder control was available. With the seats empty the centre of balance was behind the main wheel, so the aircraft rested on its tailskid. A T-tail unit layout was used, taking the tailplane out of the wing wake and keeping it well clear of the ground, where it was not vulnerable to damage in rough landing fields. The tailplane was of orthodox type, with a hinged elevator. There was no dorsal fin extension on this prototype. Glassfibre reinforced plastic mouldings were used for the nose cap, the wing and tailplane tips and some fairings.

The new aircraft, known subsequently as the T-53A, first flew on 3 March 1967 in bare metal finish. At this time John Sellars left to work for the Sigma group, and his place as Slingsby's chief engineer was taken by Pat Monk, who also left soon to go to New Zealand and was replaced by James S. Tucker.

The ATC were very interested in the new two-seater, and about August 1967 a provisional contract for 40 aircraft was placed, subject to some alterations and a revised specification. The new requirements included provision for flying the aircraft with open cockpits, which required an alternative canopy arrangement with windscreens. On test this proved quite satisfactory. Directional stability was actually improved because of the reduction of fuselage side area forward of the wing, but a demonstration flight in a sudden snowstorm caused the ATC officer concerned to recommend deletion of the open cockpit requirement. It was also supposed at first that, to fit in with ATC operations, the T-53 would often be flown with the airbrakes locked in a partly open position. This would reduce the performance, and hence the time in the air from each winch launch, to a level comparable with the Cadets Marks 1 and 2 still used by the ATC for solo flights. Camber-changing flaps would not be needed. It was pointed out at the time that such a specification, including open cockpits, could have been more easily met if the ATC had simply reordered the Slingsby T-31 Cadet Mk. 3. It was also envisaged that, to save time between launches at the gliding schools, the T-53 would be retrieved after each flight by being towed or pushed backwards over the ground. This necessitated a tailwheel.

Construction of a second prototype was begun. The structure was further simplified by deleting the flaps. The nose was lengthened to increase the range of pilot weights allowed in the front cockpit, and to satisfy the

ATC the nosewheel was temporarily replaced by a small skid. A spring trim, rather than a trim tab, was fitted to save weight and complication, and there were other minor changes. The T-53B flew first at the end of March 1968, a full year after the original prototype. After initial flight trials a small dorsal fin was added to improve the directional stability, which was not good.

The company was very busy with other projects: the V-Liner, half-a-dozen replica S.E. 5A biplanes for filming, and the construction under licence of the HP 14 metal sailplane designed in the USA by Dick Schreder, and a Slingsby derivative of it, the HP 14C.

It was remarked soon after the T-53B had been flown and exhibited that, while it was not beautiful, it had a look of purpose and character. The handling characteristics were adequate and safe, but no one ever described them as very pleasant. The constant-chord wing and forward sweep combined with the rather short rear fuselage resulted in considerable adverse yaw when banking to initiate a turn. Firm use of the rudder in co-ordination with the ailerons was very necessary. Twenty or even ten years previously this would have drawn little criticism, since almost all of the older gliders had similar feel, but modern sailplanes, including those from the Slingsby factory, had led pilots to expect something much better. The rate of roll was good for a two-seater, but the ailerons were heavy at maximum deflection. The stall was docile and lateral control was retained throughout. Spinning behaviour was normal and recovery, even after five full turns was very quick. A good performance was claimed, the best glide ratio being stated as 29:1. This was probably optimistic, but whatever the true figure it was more than satisfactory for a training aircraft. In weak thermals with two pilots aboard, the T-53B did not climb well, although it made good progress at high speeds to penetrate sinking air. Flown solo from the front seat it soared very much better.

The T-53B prototype was painted in Service colours with roundels and fin flashes, the obligatory yellow bands and the words 'AIR CADETS' in black capitals on the front fuselage. It left the factory in May 1968 for evaluation by the ATC, bearing the military serial XV 951.

Production began. The civil version was equipped again with the nose-wheel undercarriage, and the tailwheel became standard. Only one was bought by an English gliding club at this time, but Reading University engaged in meteorological research, also bought a T-53B and equipped it with special instrumentation. The rest of this early batch were exported, several going to the USA, two to New Zealand for the Air Cadet League there, and others singly to Australia, Switzerland and Israel. Soon after its arrival in Australia, the T-53B w/n 1686 was found to be seriously out of trim, the tailplane being set some 5° from its correct incidence and requiring full forward stick to prevent a dangerous nose-up pitch. How this occurred was never explained, but after correction at Schneider's factory the aircraft was satisfactory.

Then disaster struck at Ings Lane. In the early morning of Monday 18 November 1968, after the weekend and long before any workers arrived, the aircraft factory, including the assembly, fitting and machining shops, the stores and the planning department, was destroyed by fire. The Piper Tri-Pacer belonging to Jack Bradley, his private yacht and other costly items of property which had been parked in the factory during the previous week, were destroyed. The partly-built Sigma prototype and nearly all records and plans of this project were lost. (The Sigma was later completed and flown elsewhere.) The V-Liner was destroyed, never to be heard of again, and so were several other aircraft of various types, complete or under construction or repair, including four T-53Bs. Two partly completed T-53s were saved, but all of the production jigs and tools were destroyed.

The cause of the fire could not be established. The Slingsby Aircraft Company as an entity never fully recovered, although immense efforts were made to rebuild. The two surviving T-53Bs were used to aid reconstruction of the jigs and tooling, and these two aircraft were then completed and sold. Production of new aircraft began again slowly, with some sales at home and a few exports. The name adopted for the type was appropriately Phoenix, after the bird that rose from the ashes, but this nomenclature never seems to have caught on.

The ATC called for further modifications, and a T-53C was envisaged to accommodate these, but the expected bulk order never came. The first T-53B remained in use at two ATC gliding centres, and was taken by the Ministry of Technology for a time in 1969-70, for Service acceptance trials at Boscombe Down, before being returned to the ATC. It was badly damaged and struck off charge in 1972, although parts were salvaged (see below). The original T-53A was never registered and was scrapped in 1969. Altogether 18 T-53Bs were completed by Slingsby. Some of them went into store in the post-fire months to be sold several years later.

Some defects were discovered in service. The tailplane incidence was increased by nearly 2° on all aircraft, perhaps influenced by reports from Australia and following extensive flight tests at the factory. Modifications were required to the steel tube centre-section, where cracks developed in some aircraft.

Some work was done on the T-53C proposal. The most important change was reduced forward wing sweep, a new mainspar design and centre-section structure, and an increased all-up flying weight. Other changes included the addition of servo-tabs to the ailerons and a fin and rudder extension attached above the tailplane, with deletion of the dorsal fin extension. Some refinements in the cockpit included moulded glassfibre seats and an improved instrument panel and trimmer system. No complete T-53C to the new design was ever built, but a T-53B, works number 1721, was taken off the production line and modified to produce an interim type as a demonstrator. The wing was not altered except for the aileron tabs. Development went no further at Kirbymoorside. Subsequently, w/n 1718 was similarly modified and test-flown before sale.

By 1969 the Slingsby Aircraft Division was in severe financial difficulties. Bradley, the managing director, facing some legal problems, had resigned, and there were many staff redundancies. The entire Bradley group of companies was placed in receivership in July 1969. For a period of several months all aircraft production ceased.

The story of the T-53 does not quite end at this point. Yorkshire Sailplanes Ltd, a small company based near Ripon which had hitherto been engaged in glider repair and maintenance and trading in sailplanes, was able in 1972 to buy the design from the revived Slingsby company, together with the tooling and jigs. The interim T-53C demonstrator, w/n 1721, was taken over as part of the deal and became the prototype of what was subsequently announced as the YS-53 Sovereign. This aircraft with some modifications, including removal of the dorsal fin strake, made its initial test flight on 10 February 1973. It was re-registered.

Another YS-53 was constructed partly from the wreckage of the prototype T-53B, ex-ATC. Only the belly of the fuselage was useable. New wings were built, solid-riveted throughout except for the aft lower wing skin, where no internal access was possible to back up the rivet setting process. Other modifications were introduced, including a change to the aileron gearing. This aircraft, which flew in July 1973, was the first true YS-53. One more was nearly completed when Yorkshire Sailplanes in their turn went into receivership. The third, incomplete, Sovereign went to Slingsby in settlement of a debt. It was finished privately under contract by Geoff Bailey-Woods, flown by him at Wombleton in June 1974, and sold.

A few T-53s survive, though not many are still flying. In the USA Michael Eacock almost singlehandedly rebuilt a damaged T-53B, incorporating all the modifications which had been introduced in the interim T-53C demonstrator. The single Australian example remains in regular use in Queensland and is popular with some pilots there. It is used to give inexperienced solo pilots the feel of an older type of aircraft with somewhat idiosyncratic controls. Several in the USA have been restored and are flying. One of the two that were sold in New Zealand survives, and after passing through several hands is once again operating with cadets. In Britain at the time of writing only one survives in airworthy condition, w/n 1718, which was modified to the interim T-53C standard. Several others are still extant and capable of restoration or repair.

Type 53 data

T-53 A

Dimensions

Wingspan	16.76m (55ft)
Wing area	18.95m² (204 ft²)
Aspect ratio	15.2
Length o.a.	7.62m (25ft)

Wing sections

Root	Wortmann FX 61-184
Tip	Wortmann FX 61-184

Camber Flaps 5° up, 15° down.

Weights

Tare	362kg (798lb)
Flying	544kg (1,200lb)
Wing loading	28.75kg/m² (5.98lb/ft²)

T-53 B

Dimensions

Wingspan	16.91m (55.5ft)
Wing area	19.02m² (194ft²)
Aspect ratio	15.9
Length o.a.	7.80m (25.6ft)

Wing sections as for T-53 A; no flaps.

Weights

Tare	353kg (780lb)
Flying	526kg (1,160lb)
Wing loading	29.3kg/m² (6lb/ft²)

The T-53A prototype after completion at the Slingsby factory. The aircraft, after test flying, was stored, eventually being scrapped in 1969. (*N. Ellison*)

The T-53A prototype about to be launched for its first flight, with Geoff Bailey-Woods in the front cockpit. (*G. Bailey-Woods*)

The T-53A airborne on the first flight over the Vale of Pickering in Yorkshire. (*G. Bailey-Woods*)

The American T-53B/C taking a winch launch. (*M. Eacock*)

The interim T-53B/C demonstrator soon after completion of the alterations. The dorsal fin remains at this stage. Servo-tabs on the ailerons are just visible. (*Vickers-Slingsby via G. Bailey-Woods*)

Two examples of the T-53B were exported to New Zealand, registered ZK-GFQ and 'GFW. 'GFQ, seen here in smart livery, is still in service with Air League cadets. (*R. Burns*)

The first T-53B, XV951, in Air Cadet livery, showing the nose skid instead of the wheel. This aircraft remained in service for several years but was scrapped after a very heavy landing at Cranwell in 1972. (*N. Ellison*)

The T-53B was said to 'have a look of purpose and character'. An American author unkindly remarked, in the magazine *Soaring,* that 'one gets the impression that a ghastly mistake has been made at the Boeing factory. The ship looks like a small Boeing 727 that has been assembled with the wings on backwards.' (*M. Simons*)

One of very few T-53Bs still in regular service. Completed before the factory fire, this aircraft was displayed at the Farnborough Air Show in 1968, and soon afterwards was exported to Western Australia, where it was flying early in 1969 registered as VH-GUB. It is now operated in Queensland by the Boonah Gliding Club. (*M. Simons*)

In the USA, several T-53Bs are still in existence, although not all are flying. This example, N1578, was one of the earliest batch, built in 1968. It has been damaged many times, extensively repaired and partly rebuilt. Finished now in imitation of British colours, it flies in Wyoming with new owners. (*D. Carswell*)

The T-53B cockpits gave an exceptionally good field of view to the instructor in the rear seat. (*M. Simons*)

The prototype Yorkshire Sailplanes YS-53 Sovereign at Dishforth. (*N. Ellison*)

A T-53B was taken off the production line for modification to produce a demonstrator for the proposed T-53C. The vertical tail was increased in height. The small dorsal fin remained on this prototype. (*N. Ellison*)

Michael Eacock in New England almost single-handedly restored this T-53B and incorporated the modifications to transform it to the T-53 interim C standard. (*M. Eacock*)

Yorkshire Sailplanes YS-53, number 2, built using some parts from the ex ATC T-53B. G. Bailey-Woods is in the front seat. (*G. Bailey-Woods*)

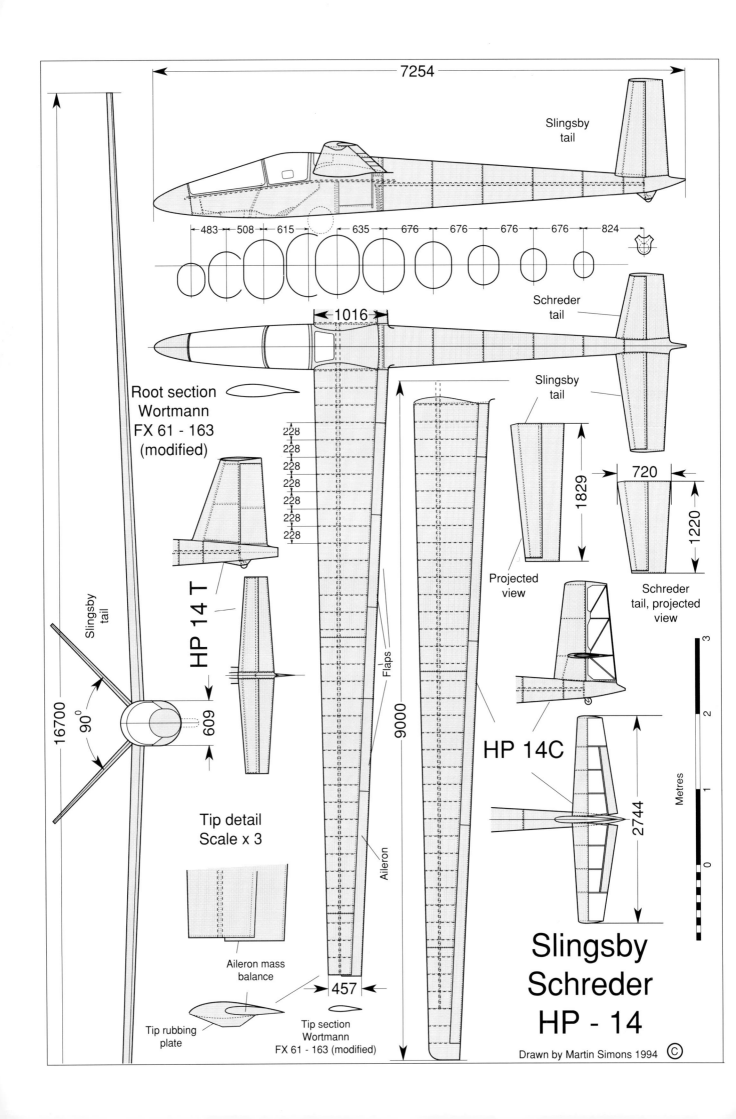

7254

483 — 508 — 615 — 635 — 676 — 676 — 676 — 676 — 824

Slingsby tail

Schreder tail

1016

Root section
Wortmann
FX 61 - 163
(modified)

Slingsby tail

Projected view

720

1829

1220

Schreder tail, projected view

228
228
228
228
228
228
228

9000

HP 14 T

609

Flaps

Aileron

Slingsby tail

16700

90°

HP 14C

2744

Tip detail
Scale x 3

Aileron mass
balance

457

Tip rubbing
plate

Tip section
Wortmann
FX 61 - 163 (modified)

3

2

Metres

1

0

Slingsby
Schreder
HP - 14

Drawn by Martin Simons 1994 ©

Slingsby Schreder HP-14

In 1966 Richard Schreder won the US National Soaring Championships at Reno, Nevada, in his new sailplane, the all-metal HP-14. Schreder had designed and built light powered aircraft at Bryan, Ohio, before he competed in his first US National Soaring Championships in 1956, flying a Schweizer 1-23D. By the next year he had built and was flying his own design of sailplane, the HP-7, and he was soon rated one of the top ten pilots in the USA. With his HP-8 he won the Nationals at Bishop, California, in 1958, and in the following year broke three world records for speed round triangular courses. As a member of the US team at the 1960 World Championships, held near Cologne, he landed the HP-8 on the eastern side of what was then the Iron Curtain. He spent a night in jail, but was not ill-treated and rejoined the competition a day later. New sailplane designs now began to emerge from Schreder's small factory at the rate of about one per year, each an improvement on the last. The HP-9, HP-10, HP-11 and HP-11A appeared, kits for home constructors being marketed under the liberal American regulations for amateur building of aircraft. A British writer said: 'For simplicity and effectiveness, Dick Schreder's HP-12 is the most superbly engineered aircraft that I have ever seen'. The HP-13 followed. Another commentator remarked on the American's ability 'to knock up a superb metal glider in no time at all, or, more precisely, in six months or a year. . . . The whole process shows a degree of initiative which we might well emulate in the UK.'

Advanced details of the HP-14 were published in *Sailplane and Gliding* in December 1965. It was said that several American amateurs had started construction from kits supplied by Schreder even before he himself had flown the prototype. The anticipated best glide ratio was claimed as over 40:1, compared with the 36:1 of the 17m Slingsby Dart (still in production) and 38:1 of the German SHK. Schreder's 1966 US Nationals result with the HP-14 was added confirmation of the excellence of his design. Handling was good, the aircraft having no serious vices, although the ailerons were less effective than desirable because of stretch-

ing in the cable-driven controls. A significant point in British eyes was that the HP-14 had been designed with a larger wingspan and lower wing loading than Schreder's previous sailplanes. He said he now recognised that competitions were won or lost not on the best days, when everyone did well, but on the 'scratchy' days of weak thermals when the heavy, fast aircraft, so-called 'lead sleds', had to struggle to keep up while the lighter gliders made better progress across-country. Even so, by British standards the HP-14 was not a lightweight. The wing loading of 28kg/m² (5.75lb/ft²) was 20 per cent more than that of the Dart 17. The trend towards higher loadings with better wing profiles was becoming accepted, and the new Schreder design looked like a good compromise.

Slingsby had decided to build metal sailplanes. With its simple structure and ease of construction, it seemed they could hardly do better than to undertake the manufacture of the HP-14 under licence using, in the first instance, kits supplied from America. It would give them in the shortest possible time a product that would be competitive in price and performance with German, Swiss and Polish sailplanes, and they would gain valuable experience with metal structures. It was anticipated that, after the first few aircraft, all the necessary components would be made in England.

An agreement was reached with Schreder and the first two kits arrived at Kirbymoorside early in 1967, Schreder himself coming too, to advise and supervise the early stages of assembly. At the same time a third kit went to Ken Fripp's Southdown Aero Services at Lasham. The intention was to have the two Slingsby aircraft completed in time for the British Nationals at the end of May, Schreder to fly one *hors concours* and John Williamson the other. The Southdown example was being built for Peter Scott. No Slingsby type number was allocated.

The HP-14 with a span of 16.7m (54.8ft), had a simple tapered wing, using the Wortmann FX 61-163 profile with a slight modification at the trailing edge as explained below. A 16.3 per cent-thick wing, compared with the 18 and even 20 per cent-thick profiles seen in previous Slingsby products, was claimed to be an important advantage made possible only because of the metal structure. The mainspar flanges were cut from ¼ inch thick 2024 T6 alloy. The large metal plates were rolled to produce a slight chordwise curve conforming to the wing profile. They then required cutting longitudinally to produce the spar flanges, whereupon the metal tended to spring into a curve. Straightening required careful hand work with a ball pane hammer. The pressed ribs were riveted in front and behind to the spar webs. There was a light rear spar of C section. The ailerons were hinged to the top flange of this spar, the flaps to the bottom. The whole wing was skinned in sheet metal with countersunk rivets. The 3.6m(12ft) wide metal sheets for the skin had to be bent to conform to the leading-edge radius. This was done by a band of five or six persons with one edge of the sheet under their feet (protected), pulling the other edge up and over to make the initial bend. Then, with the aid of a long, heavy plank of wood they stood or even jumped up and down to tighten the bend until it was close enough to the correct radius. Unlikely as it sounds, this worked quite well.

To the British pilots the most unusual feature of the wing was that, instead of parallel ruler-type airbrakes, flaps along the entire trailing edge of the wing inboard of the ailerons were made to hinge down to 90°. For landing, such flaps proved excellent. Having chosen a field, the pilot could lower the flaps fully at a suitable height on the final approach. The increase in drag was very great. Airspeed was maintained by adopting a steep attitude, about 45° nose-down to maintain 50kt. On rounding out, the speed rapidly decayed and a very short landing run was the result. The proviso was that, if the pilot was undershooting, it was dangerous to raise the flaps suddenly to the neutral position because this precipitated a sudden loss of lift and a very high rate of descent. It was shown, however, that between about 70° and full deflection the wing lift coefficient hardly changed, whereas the drag varied considerably, so a badly judged approach could be adjusted by moving the flaps between 70° and 90°. In practice it was easier to land an HP-14 in a small field than almost any other comparable sailplane. By using flaps of this kind the complications of housing airbrakes inside the wing, with all the required cut-outs, seals, rods and bellcranks to drive them, were avoided.

For thermalling, the flaps could be lowered from neutral slightly, allowing tighter turns, and for high-speed 'penetrating' dashes through sinking air to the next thermal they could be raised 10° to reduce drag. They were not interconnected with the ailerons, so these remained in their normal position as the flaps went up or down.

Strictly, the 61-163 profile has a slight concave cusp on the underside at the rear, but to form this accurately while preserving structural simplicity in the flaps and ailerons was difficult. Schreder made the last few per cent of the profile flat underneath. The control surfaces could then be made in the easiest possible

manner by twice folding appropriately sized metal sheets and riveting the extreme trailing edges together to form a triangular-section tube, with small riblets at each end. The loss of performance was very slight. The mainspars were joined on the aircraft centreline with two large horizontal pins through inter-digitating aluminium alloy fittings, and the fuselage was attached by four further pins at the main and rear spars. The flaps were driven from the extreme root end by a torque tube carrying a triangular arm extension which engaged inside the root of the flap as the wings were rigged.

The wings were attached at shoulder level to the fuselage, which was very simple in outline, the only double curvature in the skins being in the nose. The rest was a conical metal tube of oval cross-section with pressed formers and flush-riveted skins. The cockpit canopy was also very simple, the most forward portion being a curved sheet of transparent plastic. The rear section, hinged at the side for access, was a simple moulding. There was a large retracting main wheel and a steerable tailwheel linked to the rudder pedals. The control column was orthodox. The flaps were driven by a rack and pinion with a large handle. Several full turns of the handle were required to lower the flaps fully, but all the necessary adjustments during the landing approach could be done within one turn.

Because of the very successful Austria and SHK sailplanes, V tails were already familiar, but the standard HP-14 tail areas looked very small by comparison with the surfaces of the SHK. Recovery from inadvertent spins had proved difficult in a few V-tailed gliders, and the effectiveness of the small tail areas in a cross-wind take-off also worried some pilots. Schreder was entirely confident of his aircraft, but the first one from Slingsby's after test flights was given much larger tail surfaces. Linkage of the ruddervators with the controls was, supposedly, automatic. For carriage by road the two elements of the V tail, after disconnecting the lower spar flanges from the fuselage cross-frame, were raised to the vertical position and strapped together. The elevator control linkage did not disengage when this was done, so to rig the tail it was necessary only to lower each surface and insert the bottom pins.

The Slingsby aircraft had a powerful hydraulic wheel brake operated by pushing with both feet together on the rudder pedals. Also on the first Slingsby HP-14, for various reasons, the flap rack and pinion drive was not used, a simple lever being adopted. With this arrangement the full 90° flap deflection was not possible, and a 'one-shot' tail parachute was fitted for landing. (The parachute was a standard item of equipment from a Folland Gnat jet aircraft.) This prevented the installation of the steering tail-wheel. Schreder himself retained the original arrangement for the second Slingsby example.

The first flight in Yorkshire was made in May 1967, and John Williamson flew the HP-14 for the first time only three days before he was due to use it in the National Championships. Schreder's aircraft arrived even later. After flying Schreder's machine the day before the competition began, Williamson had his flaps hurriedly modified overnight to the standard rack-and-pinion drive, and the tail parachute was removed. As a result of this alteration, which required an all-night working session by Geoff Bailey-Woods, there was a desperate rush to get the HP-14 into its front-row position on the starting grid for the first competition take-off. The crew were actually still rigging the V tail as the aircraft was being towed out to the launch point. This almost precipitated a serious accident. When the tail surfaces were in the vertical position the controls did not disengage, but as the HP-14 was rolling along, rocking slightly from side to side and being rigged at the same time, one of the surfaces was allowed to move beyond the usual 'at rest' vertical alignment. The ruddervator linkage became disengaged and did not re-engage as the surface was lowered and locked in flying position. The standard cockpit check just before take-off did not reveal the disconnection because the surface moved normally, resting by its own weight against the drive though it was not actually being driven.

Williamson, on tow, had no control and experienced a wild ground loop, finding himself airborne and travelling sideways before skidding for 10m (30ft) along the ground. It was a thoroughly ignominious and dangerous start to the British contest career of the HP-14. Fortunately only slight damage was done, the wingtip skid plate being ripped off and a dent being made in the nose. With the plate pop-riveted on again, the HP-14 was able to fly after all in the first contest task. After this Williamson was very pleased with it. The weather was not particularly good, only four days being scored in the whole Championships. Williamson, by now getting used to the sailplane, won the last day, but placed 10th overall against the wooden opposition. Schreder, *hors concours*, was placed 18th in the unfamiliar British conditions.

Later in the year Peter Scott took delivery of his own HP-14 from Lasham and flew it competitively for the first time at the London Regionals in August. In this contest he came fourth, being beaten by some wooden sailplanes (including Carr Withall's Skylark 4, Alf Warminger's Dart 17 and a Ka 6E flown by the author). The absolute performances were somewhat obscured because handicapping factors were applied to the aircraft, but the HP-14 did not impress the assembled pilots greatly. The ground crew found it troublesome to rig and christened it the 'Iron Lady'. Scott won the Western Regionals with his HP-14 in June the following year.

Problems now emerged with certification. To permit an experimental aircraft to be flown in competitions by experienced pilots was one thing, but to issue a general type approval was another matter. By the end of 1967 the BGA Technical Committee reported not that the certification was imminent, but that: 'This type is now being developed into a definitive version and we will soon be concerned with the certification'. No one

doubted that the HP-14 was structurally sound and strong, but this had to be proved, which meant there had to be a good deal of calculation and paperwork. Schreder himself relied mainly on experience and had almost no figures to show. Both of the HP-14s built from Schreder's kits were sent for sale to the USA, where they were readily accepted under the official 'experimental' category there. The tail surfaces of Williamson's example were replaced by the normal smaller ones.

Slingsby's aircraft division was now extremely busy and perhaps overloaded. Production of the T-53 two-seater and the Camco V-Liner aerial hoarding were proceeding. Tipsy Nipper light aeroplanes were being built and kits for them sold. Replica S.E.5As were being made for filming, the Swallow sailplane was in production, the motorised Capstan was being developed and two special versions of the Standard Class Dart 15, with Wortmann wing profiles, were being built for the next World Championships, scheduled for Poland in June 1968. Alongside there was production of polyester/glass components for bathrooms.

Also for Poland, Slingsby was committed to the production of two advanced sailplanes for the Open Class. As most of the other pilots in this category would be flying large glass sailplanes, the most obvious expedient was to improve the performance of the HP-14 by stretching the span to 18m. This could be achieved by adding three extra rib bays to each tip, extending the metal skins and adding glass-polyester wingtip mouldings. This entailed removal of the aileron mass-balances, which, on Schreder's original, had been attached at the outermost end of the control surface, outboard of the tip skid plate. To improve handling with the larger span, the tail unit was redesigned with a large vertical fin and rudder and an all-moving tailplane. Changes to the rest of the aircraft were kept to the minimum. Schreder actually fitted a pair of the 18m wings to his original HP-14 for this World Championships.

In Britain, unlike some other countries, it was legal to fly in cloud providing the sailplane was suitably certificated. Loss of control in blind flight was a well recognised danger, the usual outcome being an increasingly steep spiral dive with rapidly rising airspeed, very high g forces and serious structural collapse. It had been decided long before that a sailplane approved for cloud flying must have airbrakes which, when fully open, would restrict the airspeed to the maximum permitted in rough air. It would be very difficult to sell the HP-14C on the home market without a cloud-flying airworthiness certificate. The flaps certainly limited the speed once they were fully down, as Williamson proved in his own test flying, but, if the airspeed was already high and rising, the effort required from the pilot to get the flaps down to $90°$ was too great. If the sailplane was genuinely going out of control in cloud, the flap brakes would be useless.

During the next months Slingsby worked on the HP-14C to surmount this problem. Various expedients were tried, the addition of a simple bungee spring proving very effective in reducing the loads for normal approach and landing. To achieve full flap at high airspeeds a compressed-air system was devised. This relied on a high-pressure air bottle which had to be pumped up before take-off, and pneumatic jacks to drive the flaps down against the aerodynamic resistance. When the flaps were needed in an emergency the pilot could release air to the jacks and the flaps would go fully down at once. Enough pressure was put into the bottle before take-off to allow this to be done twice or thrice during any one flight. Checking the pressure gauge was added to the pre-flight checklist. Unfortunately, forcing the flaps down in this way at high airspeeds proved too much for the light secondary spar structure, and strengthening this member involved more complications.

The HP-14Cs were barely ready in time for Poland, and the first one out of the workshop was found to be virtually unflyable, unstable fore and aft and so touchy in pitch that it required the pilot's constant attention to prevent dangerous oscillations. It had to be rushed back to the factory for modifications. What had been a splendidly simple and easily maintained sailplane of modest wingspan threatened now to become something of a monster. The nose was lengthened and a geared anti-balance tab was added to the elevator. This increased the stick force per g enough to make the aircraft steady in high-speed flight, although the stick loads could not be fully trimmed out at low speeds. Nick Goodhart, the chosen pilot, made only one cross-country flight in it before the first contest day. His comments in print before the competition started were guarded. The HP-14C, he said, had a very reasonable performance, which was faint praise. The ailerons were heavier than he liked, the rate of roll only adequate. With Goodhart's weight in the cockpit the sailplane was now neutrally stable in pitch. There was, he pointed out, a good deal of development work still to be done. Many adjustments had to be made in Poland in the urgent days just before the competition started. The other British entrant in this class, George Burton, decided not to fly the HP-14C provided for him, competing in a wooden SHK and coming a very creditable 7th. Goodhart struggled on to 16th place, which was very good in the circumstances but not good enough. Schreder came 21st.

It was accepted that the performance of the 18m aircraft in relation to its price was good, but the technical conclusions after this contest made sorrowful reading. Frank Irving wrote: 'The moral for Slingsby's is that the production aircraft must have better finishes and improved details. . . . compressed air for operating the flaps at high speeds is simply not acceptable'. It was becoming, said team manager Ann Welch, 'sadly obvious that no longer could we fly British if we wanted to have any chance of winning'.

As well as some of Schreder's own kits shipped directly or through Slingsby as agent, sales of several HP-14C kits had been made in advance of test flying.

One went to Joe Provins in Yorkshire. The small Sydney Soaring Club, a long-standing customer for Slingsby products, and another group in New South Wales ordered and paid for two HP-14C kits. There were long, unexplained delays. Enough parts arrived at last to enable construction to begin, but many necessary components were not delivered. When ordering his kit, Provins had required a written assurance that a BGA type approval and Certificate of Airworthiness for the sailplane would be forthcoming. It was also the rule in Australia that an imported sailplane could be accepted by the Department of Civil Aviation (as it was then called) only if type approval was granted in the country of origin. Little progress towards certification had been made. Having already been told after the Polish experience that the type was not acceptable, Slingsby were now legally required to bring the HP-14C up to the necessary standard. Using the ex-Goodhart aircraft, Geoff Bailey-Woods was given *carte blanche* to do whatever was necessary. He removed the compressed-air system, redesigned the trimmer and airbrake drives and installed a drag parachute, carrying out the test flights during October and November 1968.

On Monday 18 November 1968 came the factory fire described in the previous chapter. The HP-14C which had been intended for George Burton to fly in Poland was destroyed. All of the jigs and tooling and parts for several more HP-14s were lost. The newly modified aircraft however, had been de-rigged and put in its trailer outside the factory on the Saturday afternoon. After flying it during the day, Bailey-Woods found the available space rather scarce with the chairman's yacht and private aeroplane inside, so countermanded the instructions that had been given to the factory crew and left it outside. It therefore survived.

Provins continued work, but still lacked some parts of his kit. The company cut up the remaining HP-14C to obtain the missing components. Provins's aircraft was completed and test flown by Bailey-Woods in June 1969, eventually being accepted by the BGA and registered.

Not so the two in Australia. The subsequent bankruptcy of the company left these customers without many vital parts for wings and tails and no prospect of the rest of the kits ever being delivered. They were never recompensed. The two sailplanes were eventually fitted with Schreder's own design of T-tail, the required materials and parts being bought directly from Ohio. The full 18m-span Slingsby wingtips were retained. Permits to fly were eventually obtained after long bureaucratic procedures.

The New South Wales group's 18m span HP-14T broke up in clear air at 2,400m (8,000ft) during the Australian National Championships on 5 January 1972. The pilot, Jan Coolhaas, who had been flying at a moderate airspeed, saved himself by parachute. He had heard a loud bang, and the HP-14 entered a steepening spiral dive which he could not correct. After official investigation the cause was attributed to wing-aileron flutter which led quickly to fracture of the main fittings, loss of control and complete disintegration of the wing. The fittings that failed, forged by another company under contract to Slingsby, were of a different design from Schreder's and may have been defective. Presumably the deletion of the aileron mass balance, about which Schreder had never been happy, was also partly responsible. The Sydney Soaring Club's HP-14T also experienced flutter on a subsequent occasion, but did not break up. This 18m aircraft was then cut down to the original 16.7m span and the mass balances were restored, after which it proved very satisfactory. This machine and several other HP-14s in the USA and others in Australia, some built from Schreder's kits or, in one case, entirely from scratch, remain in service.

As all of the homebuilders discovered, by the time their sailplanes were finished and approved for flying they were out of date and no longer competitive with glass/plastic aircraft. The original HP-14 did not achieve the claimed 40:1 glide ratio. Flight measurements published in the USA showed that a well-built and carefully maintained HP-14T, even with slightly extended wingspan of 17.4m, achieved a best glide ratio of 1:36.3. This figure was exactly the same as best glide measured for the old wooden Skylark 4, although the metal aircraft achieved the figure at an 8kt faster airspeed and was appreciably better than the Skylark at speeds above 70kt. The 15m glass Libelle was better than both of them.

HP-14 data

HP-14

Dimensions
Wingspan	16.7m (54ft 9½in)
Wing area	12.85m² (138.3ft²)
Aspect ratio	21.6
Length o.a.	7.254m (23ft 9½in)

Wing sections:
Root	Wortmann FX 61-163 (modified)
Tip	Wortmann FX 61-163 (modified)

Weights
Tare	245kg (539lb)
Flying	362.9kg (800lb)
Wing loading	28.1kg/m² (5.75lb/ft²)

HP-14C

Dimensions
Wingspan	18m (59ft 0½in)
Wing area	13.58m² (146.21ft²)
Aspect ratio	23.9
Length o.a.	7.28m (23ft 10½in)

Wing sections, as for HP-14

Weights
Tare	290.3kg (640lb)
Flying	381kg (840lb)
Wing loading	28.1kg/m² (5.75lb/ft²)

The 18m-span HP-14C built from a Slingsby kit in New South Wales. The parts for the T-tail had to be supplied by Schreder in the USA. This flight was its last. The wing failed and broke up in the air. (*T. Neuman*)

The cockpit of the HP-14C. On the left is the pressure gauge for the pneumatic flap operating system and the necessary plumbing. The flap operating lever carried a button on the top which, when depressed, released air to the rams. (*G. Bailey-Woods*)

Building an HP-14 was not as easy as it appeared, although, as this picture shows, the wing structure was very simple. This example was built entirely from scratch in Adelaide by Harry and David Bache. (*H. Bache*)

Geoff Bailey-Woods prepares for take-off in the first Slingsby-built HP-14. At this stage there seemed to be no serious problems. (*G. Bailey-Woods*)

The HP-14C under test with Bailey-Woods in the cockpit. The aircraft proved a disappointment and production did not proceed. (*G. Bailey-Woods*)

The prototype Slingsby HP-14, built from a kit supplied by Schreder. Here it has the original small V-tail. (*G. Bailey-Woods*)

The enlarged tail unit of the HP-14 as flown by John Williamson in the National Championships. Incorrect rigging caused a spectacular ground loop on the first attempted take-off. (*M. Simons*)

The instrument panel and cockpit of the second Australian Slingsby HP-14C, from an incomplete kit. This was later cut down to the original span after a wing flutter incident. (*T. Neuman*)

The Slingsby HP-14 at the British National Championships, being towed out to the take-off point at Lasham. The tail surfaces are greatly enlarged. (*M. Simons*)

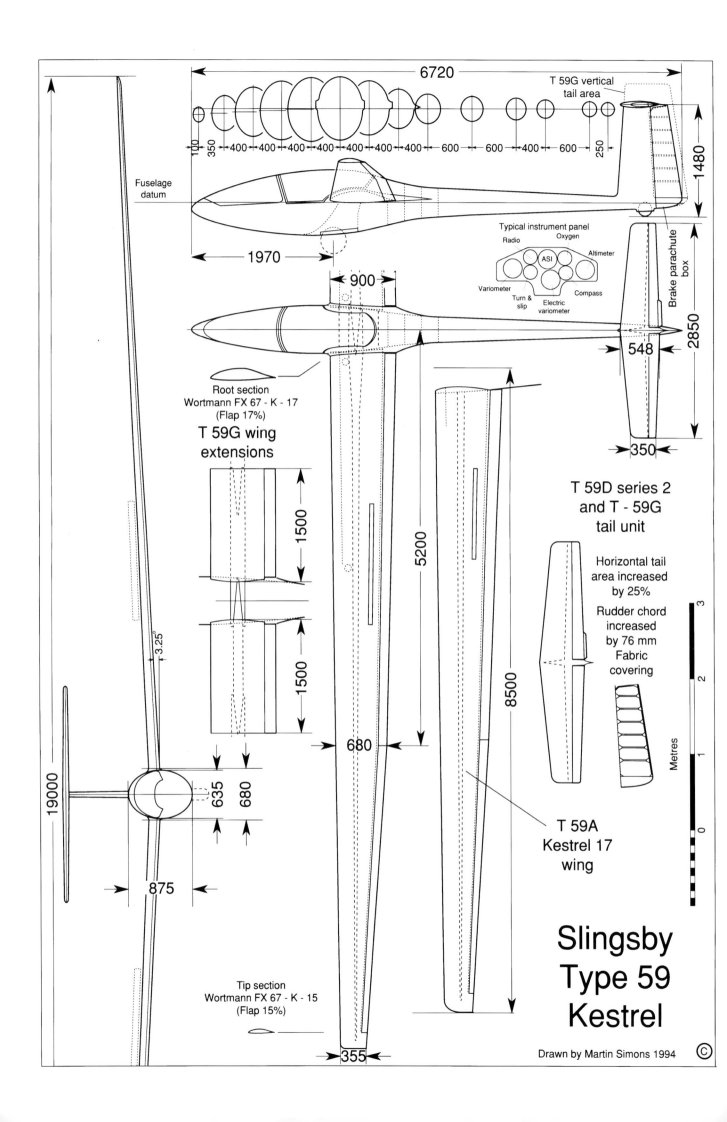

6720

T 59G vertical tail area

100 350 400 400 400 400 400 400 400 600 600 400 600 250

1480

Fuselage datum

1970

900

2850

548

350

Typical instrument panel

Radio Oxygen
Altimeter
ASI
Variometer
Turn & slip Electric variometer Compass

Brake parachute box

Root section
Wortmann FX 67 - K - 17
(Flap 17%)

T 59G wing extensions

1500

1500

5200

680

635 680

19000

3.25°

875

T 59D series 2
and T - 59G
tail unit

Horizontal tail
area increased
by 25%

Rudder chord
increased
by 76 mm
Fabric
covering

8500

T 59A
Kestrel 17
wing

Tip section
Wortmann FX 67 - K - 15
(Flap 15%)

355

3

2

1

0

Metres

Slingsby
Type 59
Kestrel

Drawn by Martin Simons 1994 ©

Type 59, Kestrel

The financial collapse in 1969, a few months after the fire at the Slingsby factory, seemed likely to bring aircraft production at Kirbymoorside to an end. In receivership for months, the factory was closed except for a few maintenance staff.

Sir Leonard Redshaw, chairman of the Vickers Shipbuilding group based at Barrow-in-Furness, was a keen glider pilot, and he had recognised that new materials were likely to be important in shipbuilding as well as in aviation. The Vickers Company, with a long tradition of building submarines, had already made some enquiries about the possibility of using GRP for pressure hulls. In Britain very little research had been done. There was no support from the Ministry of Defence, and some very limited experience reported from North America was discouraging. In aviation there was nothing at any British university or technical college that could be compared with the German Akafliegs (Academic Flying Groups), whose theoretical design studies and research results were translated into actual aircraft.

Redshaw met Peter Scott, then Chairman of the BGA, at Lasham. Scott had discarded the disappointing all-metal HP-14 and was flying a German glass sailplane, the 18m BS-1 originally designed by Björn Stender of the Brunswick Akaflieg, now in production and marketed by the Glasflügel factory at Schlattstall in Germany. In the Open Class British National Championships that year most of the competitors flew imported sailplanes, many of them of GRP construction. Any aspiring champion was forced to look overseas for a competitive aircraft, which Scott greatly regretted.

By now, experience with imported glass aircraft had convinced British pilots and engineers that their earlier hesitations over composite materials were unjustified, providing the new aircraft were flown with discretion. GRP sailplanes picked up speed very quickly with small nose-down changes of trim, or if camber-changing flaps were slightly raised there might be no perceptible nose-down pitch at all. The glide remained comparatively flat. This was a great advantage in cross-country racing but required care in monitoring airspeeds. With much higher wing loadings and the wing tanks or bags full of water ballast, on a good soaring day the most efficient speed for flying through sinking air to reach the next thermal might easily be faster than the critical flutter speed.

Out of the informal talk at Lasham came a meeting later in the same week between Slingsby and Redshaw. The Slingsby company records for the previous five years were scrutinised. Among the papers Redshaw came across a recent offer from Eugen Hänle, proprietor and chief engineer of the Glasflügel Company, for Slingsby to take on the manufacture of his Kestrel under licence. Hänle had been one of the engineers primarily responsible for designing and building the very first glass sailplane, the Phönix, in 1957, and the Kestrel was in production and proving very successful. (The author, living now in Australia, took delivery of the 18th off the production line late in 1969.) With Slingsby in receivership the offer could not be taken up when it was first made, but Redshaw saw the possibility of combining his two interests, submarines and sailplanes, bringing both shipbuilding and glider construction into the age of composite materials.

After discussion, the Slingsby factory and all of its assets were bought by Vickers. Redshaw took Bill Slater, Jim Tucker and George Burton with him to see Hänle. It was agreed after negotiation that if Slingsby were to continue building gliders under Vickers ownership and control, Hänle would train some of the workforce in glass-plastic methods of construction and either the Kestrel or the highly popular Standard Libelle could be built at Kirbymoorside. One of the conditions laid down by Hänle was that the Slingsby works must be managed by a competition glider pilot of international standing. Despite some success in regional contests, Redshaw was not in this category. Slingsby's would also be appointed agents for the importation and sale in Britain of other Glasflügel sailplanes.

Few people in Britain were qualified both as champion glider pilots and aircraft engineers, but George

Burton had won the nationals, had a secure place in the British International Team and had an honours degree in physics with flight research experience at Farnborough and years in the electronics industry. It seemed to Redshaw that he was ideal for the job, and he was persuaded, at the age of 38, to change career and become managing director of the new company, now to be known once again as Slingsby Sailplanes Ltd. Burton was already familiar with the Libelle, but flew the Kestrel at Schlattstall. The Kestrel seemed to have the better prospects for development and sales. It was agreed that a core group of craftsmen from the Slingsby factory should spend three months at the Glasflügel works to learn the basic techniques. The agreement was signed in November 1969, and a few weeks later the selected team travelled to Germany. They succeeded in learning the necessary skills and picked up some especially useful German phrases, too.

Redshaw realised from the beginning that sailplane manufacture could be only a part of the operation. Research and eventually production of submarines with glass-plastic pressure hulls, and other marine applications of composite materials, had a high priority. (This led to the development of two-person submersible craft for work with oil drilling rigs and in deep-sea exploration, as well as other applications and devices including marine oil spill cleaning systems.)

The learning process began. How much sailplanes had advanced became instantly apparent to anyone who compared a Skylark 4, new in 1962, with the Kestrel which first flew six years later. The Skylark was a simple wooden aircraft with plywood skins, fabric covering and a painted finish. Stick and rudder, airbrakes, elevator trimmer and tow release were the only controls the pilot had to bother about. The modern glass sailplane was a different proposition.

The Kestrel was a complex 17m-span aircraft with Wortmann wing sections and an aspect ratio of 25. It was known that departures from the correct wing profile of one or two tenths of a millimetre (5-6 thousandths of an inch) were enough to disturb the boundary layer and cause a disproportionate increase in profile drag. The wing was built from the outside inwards, beginning in effect with the paint. Large female moulds for the upper and lower skins had first to be constructed to a degree of accuracy far beyond anything in the old Slingsby company's experience. Making the moulds themselves, from accurate forms or 'plugs', was a time-consuming and expensive operation. The moulds, one for the upper wing skin and one for the lower, were highly polished and suitably treated with parting agents before a white gel coat was applied to make the outermost surface of the aircraft. White was the preferred external colour, to reduce heat absorption from the sun on hot days. With the gel coat still soft, layers of alkali-free glass cloth of selected weave and orientation, with the minimum required amounts of epoxy resin were laid up by hand with rollers or brushes. The resin and glass were in measured proportions of 40 of resin to 60 of glass. Too

much resin did not increase strength and added a lot of weight. Too little resulted in dry spots and weaknesses in the laminations. The flanges of unidirectional glass rovings for the very substantial mainspar and auxiliary spars were laid in place, the rovings being wound round the metal fittings at the root end to ensure structural continuity. The outer skin in front of and behind the spar was then overlaid by a layer of balsa wood 6mm thick in planks 75mm wide, lightly grooved longitudinally to permit them to bend to the aerofoil section. (Later, expanded plastic foam or honeycomb material was used for all glass sailplanes.)

The filling layer was followed by more glass cloth, completing the sandwich. A simple vacuum bag system was used to ensure good bonding during the subsequent curing process. There were very few crosswise ribs in the wings. The spar webs and any necessary internal brackets, bearings and control pushrods, and the boxes for the airbrakes, were built-in after curing at this stage. The upper and lower shells were then brought together and joined, the resulting wing being virtually hollow with a mainspar and a light rear spar to carry the flaps and ailerons. Temperature and humidity were controlled throughout the laying-up and the resin curing time. Post-cure tempering at 50°C added a further 20 per cent to the compression strength of the material. Some cleaning-up along the glue lines, particularly along the leading edge of the wing, was necessary, but otherwise the wings emerged from the moulds ready for flight. Ailerons and flaps were constructed in the same general fashion, and were required to fit accurately with the minimum of gaps and leakages at hinge lines.

The Kestrel fuselage was also a shell made in female moulds. It was of the pod and boom or 'club' shape. Steel cross-tubes with spigots to fit into the wings were bound into the glass structure. Laminar flow was preserved as far as possible over the nose, but after transition the cross-section contracted to reduce the area of skin exposed to the ensuing turbulent boundary layer. The cockpit canopy was a transparent moulding cut into two pieces, the forward part secured to the fuselage and the rear part removable and with a frame of glass rovings. It had to fit very accurately and conform to the aerodynamic contour. The fin was built as part of the fuselage shell. The main landing wheel was retractable, but the tailwheel was not. The T tailplane, built in much the same way as the rest, gained efficiency because of its high position clear of the wing wake.

Flaps were coupled to the ailerons to change the wing camber for slow and high airspeeds. By means of a separate handle, the flaps drooped to 35° independently of the ailerons for landing. Airbrakes were operated by the usual lever, but a drogue parachute housed in a compartment at the base of the rudder could be deployed as well. Inside the wing leading edge there were large bags to carry water ballast, with a knob in the cockpit behind the pilot's head, reached by some mild contortions, for jettisoning the water before landing or when the thermals became weak. To reduce the likelihood of pilot-induced oscillations at high speeds, the stick worked with a parallel action linkage giving a fore and aft motion. A particularly good feature was the elevator trim control, which was mounted on the stick with a self-adjusting spring. The pilot needed only to hold the stick in the desired position, press a small button with a finger, and the trim was set.

Rigging the Kestrel was easy, although the wings were heavy. The system was based on that of the Libelle. One wing had a forked spar end which the other undivided spar fitted into, steel spigot extensions mating with self-aligning sockets in the opposite wing. As the wings were pulled together, using an ingenious but very simple lever, they simultaneously picked up the spigots on the tubular steel fuselage cross-members. The assembly was completed by inserting a horizontal locking pin which passed right through the spar fork on the centreline. Brake and flap linkages were automatic as the wings went on, but the ailerons had to be connected and checked by hand. The tailplane was slotted into place, picking up elevator control spigots automatically, and locked on with a spring-loaded pin set into the fin leading edge.

Joining up the plumbing and filling with ballast became a normal ritual unless the weather was obviously very poor. The drogue parachute was supposed to be repacked before each flight. Small cameras loaded with fresh film for photographing turning points in competition races, badge flights or record attempts were fastened to a small bracket on the cockpit side and arranged so that the wingtip would always appear in the picture.

Before getting into the cockpit it was wise to make sure the wings were clean, as the crushed bodies of insects on the leading edge caused a very noticeable loss of performance. Nothing could be done about insects picked up during flight. (In-flight wing wipers had not yet been invented. They do exist now.) Raindrops on the wing had an effect like opening small airbrakes. Rudder pedals could be adjusted and the seat back repositioned in flight, and cushions under the thighs could be inflated or deflated by small hand-pumps. Depending on the type of instrumentation and radio, and whether oxygen breathing equipment was carried, the pilot might be confronted by some 20 or 30 items of varying importance to be checked before take-off. Written checklists became necessary rather than the simple mnemonics used hitherto.

During the take-off roll it was best to set the flaps to a slight negative position which improved aileron response at low speeds while the tailwheel was still on the ground to keep straight. As full control became available, lowering the flaps slightly allowed the sailplane to lift off. Handling in the air was good. The Kestrel was stable in pitch and there was no tendency to drop a wing in a stall or slow turn. Continuous spins were possible only at the aft c.g. limit with ailerons held into the spin, recovery requiring less than a full turn. Spinning deliberately was not encouraged, as the airspeed during the recovery might exceed the safe

maximum and the airbrakes were not large enough to keep the airspeed within limits in a dive, especially if the tanks were full of water. The parachute brake would have been sufficiently effective, but once deployed could not be retracted. It was possible to jettison it, but this would probably result in losing it entirely. Control forces were relatively light, although the rate of roll was not high. Aerobatics were not approved because of the danger of a badly executed manoeuvre causing excess airspeed.

Getting such an aircraft safely down in an outlanding required good standards of airmanship and judgement. The retractable wheel had to be lowered and the ballast dumped. Landing with the water still on board was not advisable because of the likelihood of greater shock loads on the undercarriage and the extended ground run after touchdown, though it could be done with care on a smooth surface. When dumping the water it poured out through the wheel well, taking a little less than 2min to empty completely. With full flap and even without the drogue, touchdown airspeed was about 35kt, slow enough to land in quite small spaces.

The best glide ratio was measured at 1:41, compared with the Skylark's 36. Much more importantly, with flaps slightly raised it was reasonable to fly the Kestrel between thermals at airspeeds above 80kt, at which speed the glide ratio was still about 1:25. This glide ratio at high airspeed was superior to the maximum achieved by many of the better 'pre-laminar-flow' sailplanes at half the speed. In the final stages of a race with some margin of height to spare, the Kestrel could be flown safely at 110kt or even up to 135kt, which was the permitted maximum. Such fast finishes with the water streaming out and leaving a visible trail behind were not at all unusual.

From the beginning the Kestrel was criticised by some pilots because it was said not to climb very well in weak thermals. The most influential of these critics was George Moffat in the USA, who carried out some comparative flying of one of the early Glasflügel Kestrels against his own Cirrus. In a widely-read article in the magazine *Soaring*, early in 1970, he complained that the Kestrel was too heavy and that the rate of roll was too slow. Other pilots disagreed, although it was true that in flight at low airspeeds the pilot could hear noise suggestive of airflow separation behind the cockpit. It seemed that the contraction of the fuselage cross-section might have been overdone slightly, but in competition the Kestrel climbed well enough, even with full ballast. Some damage was done to sales prospects by these reports even before Slingsby's products came on to the market.

In August 1970 the first Kestrel built at Slingsby emerged to fly, followed by the second early in December. These were in most respects identical to the Glasflügel product. Hänle had changed the cockpit canopy to hinge just behind the pilot's head and lift up. (The original canopy was longer and lifted off completely for access to the cockpit and wing roots.) A matt black shield was added in front of the instrument console to prevent internal reflections on the front canopy. When the aircraft, works number 1722, had passed its preliminary test flights, a camera which could be operated from the cockpit was fitted to the fin. Its field of view included the wing root junction with the fuselage. Wool tufts were fixed all over this area and Geoff Bailey-Woods, the company test pilot, was instructed to fly at low speeds and take photographs. The results were surprising. The wool tufts indicated an area extending from the fuselage junction for about a metre outwards along the span in which the air on the surface was proceeding in a circle, some of the tufts pointing in a direction opposite to that of the main stream. Glasflügel were informed at once, and technical departments in both factories tried to work out a solution. Hänle had the advantage of having Dr F. X. Wortmann of Stuttgart University as a consultant, and most modern sailplanes at this time used Wortmann wing profiles. With access to a research wind tunnel, Wortmann and his colleague Dieter Althaus developed a large fillet at the wing root junction which, by reducing the rate at which the combined cross-sectional area of the wing/fuselage was reduced, effectively cured the problem.

The airbrakes, which in the Glasflügel version had opened above and below the wing, were changed to emerge from the top surface only. Some other small improvements were made in the cockpit, in particular the addition of a removable tray covering the spar junction under the rear of the canopy. On this was mounted an adjustable headrest, radio and batteries, and extra instruments, such as a barograph. The original type of lift-off extended canopy was reintroduced. The flaps were coupled to the ailerons to improve the rate of roll (as well as the ailerons being coupled to the flaps for camber changing). The company now felt confident enough to begin production, and the first five 17m Slingsby Kestrels were ready in April 1971.

Yet before these first few Kestrels were being finished at Kirbymoorside even better sailplanes had appeared. George Burton took an experimental 19m version, the T-59B, to the World Championships at Marfa, Texas, in June 1970. This was an ordinary Glasflügel Kestrel with an extra metre of wing spliced on to each tip. It was permitted to fly under experimental licence in the USA. Burton came fourth. The Glasflügel Kestrel 604, a 22m development, was there too, and so was the prototype 22m Nimbus from Schempp-Hirth, with which which George Moffat won the contest despite some serious handling difficulties. As Slingsby himself had said years before, there is no substitute for span, and these new aircraft had a 5m advantage. Good though the Kestrel 17 was, it could not compete with this new generation of monsters. Development would not stand still. It was announced that after the first five, no more of the 17m Kestrels would be produced at Kirbymoorside. Hänle was therefore free to reintroduce Kestrel 17 production in Germany, which he did. A total of 129 were built, plus 601 of the Standard Libelles.

Work on a 19m Slingsby Kestrel had already begun,

and it was intended that production would be under way by the end of 1971. The span was extended by adding half a metre at the root and half a metre at the tip of each wing. After a good deal of research and testing under Tucker's direction, a carbonfibre spar was made and used in the wing of the prototype Kestrel 19, the T-59C. This flew in May 1971, only three weeks before Burton was to compete with it in the British National Championships. He came second, and in the Coupe d'Europe at Angers in France in July he took third place, beaten by a Kestrel 17 and an ASW 12, partly because the flaps of the T-59 were not yet properly adjusted and various other minor problems had been discovered.

So far as known, this was the first time any aircraft in the world had used carbonfibre for an important structural member. It was an important step. The new spar was much stiffer and stronger than the glass one, although it was very much more expensive. For a time it appeared that Slingsby had not only caught up with developments in their field but had begun once again to lead the way, although other sailplane manufacturers were not far behind. A consequence of the carbon spar was that the greatly increased wing stiffness in bending gave the pilot a much harder ride in rough air. This also created problems with the root end fittings, which began to show signs of metal fatigue and had to be replaced. Cost prevented the immediate adoption of carbon for production 19m Kestrels.

The T-59C was used for development and test work during the rest of the summer. Some longitudinal stability problems were overcome by introducing a small, sharp cusp on the trailing edge of the elevator. An inescapable increase in stick forces was only partly alleviated by the use of stronger springs in the trimmer control circuit. Production did not start until this and other minor difficulties had been sorted out.

The prototype Kestrel 19 with glass spars did not fly until September 1971, and it was the end of the year before Slingsby was able to advertise that 'after three years of development, all the bugs are out of it and its performance is the equal of any super ship on the market'. Support for this claim came with summer in the southern hemisphere, when a Kestrel 19 flown by Ingo Renner won the Australian National Championships held over the New Year period.

Depending on whether the Certificate of Airworthiness was issued by the BGA or the Civil Aviation Authority (both bodies were empowered to issue the certificate), the Kestrel 19 was known as either the T-59D (BGA) or T-59E (CAA).

The wings of the original 17m Kestrel were heavy. The 19m wings weighed 93kg (205lb) each, totalling 60 per cent of the bare structural weight. With maximum load, instruments, batteries, pilot and water ballast the gross weight was 472kg (1,040lb). The old Skylark 4, with an all-up weight of 376kg (830lb), had a maximum wing loading of 23.35kg/m^2 (4.56lb/ft^2). The Kestrel 19 fully laden reached 36.9kg/m^2 (7.5lb/ft^2) and was already beginning to seem too light for good soaring weather.

By the time of the British National Championships in May-June 1972, Kestrel 19s were coming out of the factory regularly. Six were flown in the championships, John Delafield flying one to win after six hard days.

Other minor changes were introduced at various stages during production. An anti-balance tab was included on the elevator to allow removal of the cusp and reduce stick forces. A 10 per cent larger, lighter rudder was required to help control of the extended wing in yaw. The weight reduction was achieved by cutting away much of the glass cloth skin and covering with fabric. Rudders on 'Open Class' sailplanes with their huge spans and short fuselages have never been adequate, and in this respect the Kestrel 19 was no different from the rest.

Eight Slingsby Kestrel 19s, including Burton's with the carbon spar, flew at the World Championships in Yugoslavia in July 1972. As well as the British, the Australian, Czech, Canadian, New Zealand and Japanese pilots flew the T-59. They met competition from the latest Nimbus (which won, flown by Goran Ax of Sweden), the ASW 17 and the Polish Jantar 2. Nick Goodhart came 4th and Burton 6th. This championship was greatly affected by a series of very bad thunderstorms. A Hungarian pilot was killed by a lightning strike in cloud, a Canadian in a bad weather landing accident, and there was a mid-air collision from which the pilots saved themselves by parachute. An Australian pilot was arrested by a village policeman after landing too close to the Albanian border, and several others had cameras, parachutes and other equipment stolen from their cockpits.

In September 1972, Dick Georgeson in New Zealand broke the world out-and-return record in his Kestrel 19, flying in lee waves generated by a north west wind over the Southern Alps. The total distance was 1001.94km (623 miles). It was the first time a sailplane had flown more than 1,000 km round a predeclared task. (The record was broken a month later in the USA, and again there two days later.)

In May 1973 Fred Slingsby died, aged nearly 80. He was greatly mourned. Although he had little active role in the company after his retirement in 1964, he had never lost interest. In 40 years he saw gliding progress from the days of crude primary training gliders and the strut and wire braced open cockpit British Falcon, built in his Scarborough furniture factory, to an era of giant spans, water ballast, sophisticated aerodynamics, complicated electronic instruments, extraordinary new materials and methods of construction. He was instrumental in reviving the company when it had seemed doomed in 1969.

When the performance of the Kestrel 19 was measured by an independent test group the best glide was found to be 1:44. New, bigger German production sailplanes by this time were getting close to and even exceeding 1:50. They had the advantage of extra span but they also achieved better standards of accuracy in the wing surfaces.

It was recognised internationally that the trend to huge spans in the unrestricted or 'Open' class was getting out of hand. A 29m two-seat sailplane, the Brunswick Akaflieg SB-10, was already flying in 1972 with a best glide of 1:53. It broke world records in the following year. (The SB-10 was not the largest sailplane ever built. The *Austria* of 1931, flown by Robert Kronfeld, spanned 30m.) In an attempt to check rising costs, it was announced that at the next World Championships, to be held at Waikerie in Australia in January 1974, a special cup would be awarded for the best score by a sailplane of 19m span or less. This, it was hoped, would give manufacturers something to aim for which would not be financially crippling for pilots, although it was soon pointed out that a 19m sailplane made entirely from carbon would cost more than a larger aircraft using glass. The Kestrel 19 flown by the Austrian pilot Hämmerle won the cup when the time came, but it was almost by default. His position overall was 9th. There was only one other modern sailplane design of 19m span contending, the Polish Jantar 1. Interest in the 19m cup faded.

The 1975 British Championships in May/June were dominated by Kestrels, eight coming in the top ten and George Lee winning. The run of excellent competition results continued through the season, but by June 1975 all outstanding orders for the T-59 had been met and the company announced that it would wait for at least five more orders before re-establishing production of the type. It seems that the five orders never materialised. In 1975 Hänle was killed in a light aeroplane accident and his company was absorbed by Schempp-Hirth. There were no prospects of any new agreements in that quarter.

The Kestrel 19 had been successful, with exports all over the world, including Italy and South Africa. Three had even gone to Germany, nine to the USA, three to New Zealand and six to Australia. More than 90 were built, one being sold incomplete for finishing by the owner. More than 40 were still registered in Britain in 1994. But in the end there was no apparent financial profit. What had been gained was experience in the use of composite materials.

At Waikerie, George Burton had announced the development of a 22m Kestrel, the T-59G. This was to be achieved ingeniously by adding a 1.5m root extension piece on each side, producing a four-piece wing. Owners would be able to buy a conversion kit. The root sections would plug into the existing fuselage, and would in turn accept the old 19m wings without any alteration. A 25 per cent bigger tailplane was required, but no further changes would be necessary. It proved less easy than expected to make the conversion. The undercarriage had to be strengthened, the rear fuselage skins required extra laminations of glass cloth, and the area of the vertical tail had to be increased by 35 per cent. This was done by adding 75mm of chord to the rudder and extending the fin area above the tailplane.

When it came to test flights, the handling of the T-59G was fairly satisfactory, but no one seemed interested in what pilots probably thought of as a 22m sailplane cobbled together. The wing stubs and fin extension were scrapped and the aircraft was sold as a 19m Kestrel. The increased rudder and tailplane areas and stronger rear fuselage were incorporated in the last few Kestrel 19s off the production line.

It was now decided to develop an entirely new 22m Kestrel, the T-59H. This, advertised late in 1975, had the wing in four pieces, but the division now came outboard of the airbrakes. A carbon spar was used. The fuselage was extended behind the main wing junction by 750mm, allowing the standard tail to be retained. A stronger landing gear was incorporated. A first batch of three was planned, but problems arose when the prototype was test-flown. The company test pilot was now Norrie Grove, an ex-RAF pilot. All went well until the time came to prove the aircraft to a flight speed up to 169kt. This was to allow a reasonable safety margin over and above the permitted maximum speed which would be placarded in the cockpit. When Grove reached 140kt he reported that something drastic happened which prevented him from going faster.

The Kestrel was taken to Lasham for further tests. George Burton, who had flown for five years at the RAE had no idea what was wrong and decided, without any extra instrumentation or preliminary calculations, to do the tests himself. After a tow to 1,800m (6,000ft) he rashly accelerated in a steep dive. At 140kt the wing fluttered so violently that he had difficulty holding the stick, but he succeeded in gradually pulling out of the dive and, with everything still apparently working, flew gingerly back to Lasham to land safely. Inspection revealed considerable damage to the flaps, and the glider was hurriedly de-rigged and taken back to the factory.

Two 22m Kestrels were taken to the 1976 World Championships, one, registered G-BDWZ, to be flown carefully in the contest by the Irish pilot Jeremy Bryson. The other, G-BDZG, delayed by the repair work, arrived late in the fortnight for demonstration and flying by prospective customers. A safe limiting speed was imposed, but an over-exuberant pilot allowed the Kestrel demonstrator to exceed the limit in a fast run over the aerodrome. At about 135m(450ft) there was a loud noise and the alarmed watchers on the ground saw the wings vibrating so violently that they seemed to disappear in a blur. The pilot managed to slow down and land safely, white-faced and severely shaken.

The RAE was consulted by Slingsby's technical department. The flutter, which involved wingtip deflections of about 30cm up and down, was symmetrical and had two nodes. That is, the fuselage and the inner wing moved up and down violently as the tip panels, out of phase, moved down and up with, at some point along the wing between root and tip, a node or crossover point which moved neither up nor down as the wing distorted on either side of it. (The Akaflieg students at Brunswick in 1970 had already researched and filmed spectacular, continuous but damped asymmet-

ric flutter in their 22m SB 9. They went on to extend the span to 29m in the SB 10.)

The problem with the T-59H was lack of torsional stiffness in the wing. At the time carbonfibre cloth was not available, so the wing skin was of conventional glass cloth and foam sandwich. This did not give sufficient torsional rigidity to match the bending stiffness of the carbon spar. The two completed 22m Kestrels were given a severely restricted maximum speed of 105kt and were sold at reduced price. No attempt was made to build any more.

The only Slingsby product competing at the World Championships in Finland in 1976 was the lone Irish pilot Bryson's Kestrel 22. He had taken delivery of this unproven aircraft only two days before leaving for the contest, and did not do well. (On return to Ireland he and his syndicate partners made some outstanding height climbs in this aircraft.) Ironically, George Lee, the Kestrel 19 British champion of 1975, won the 1976 World Championships flying a German ASW 17 from Schleichers. George Burton, chosen by the BGA to compete in the 15m Standard Class, had no suitable British sailplane to fly and selected a Finnish Pik 20 to take third place.

Both of the Kestrel 22s survive and in 1994 were flown regularly: Bryson's aircraft, BGA 2470, is based at Cambridge after changes of ownership and the other, BGA 2481, is at Crowland. Tests by the owners, among whom is Peter Bisgood, an experienced test pilot, have demonstrated flutter-free airspeeds up to 135kt. The maximum permitted speed was therefore raised to 125kt. The rate of roll of these large aircraft is relatively slow, but they perform well and have given good service. The total of all marks of Kestrel built at Kirbymoorside was 105, including the five original Kestrel 17s and the Kestrel 22s.

The development costs of the Kestrel 22 were carried by Vickers Shipbuilding division as a research project. Under Sir Leonard Redshaw's protection, the true financial situation of the aeronautical part of the business was not made immediately obvious to the parent company's accountants, but at the end of 1975 Vickers had regrouped and Slingsby Sailplanes became Vickers-Slingsby, a division of Vickers Offshore Engineering. What the future held was again very doubtful. It was advertised that Slingsby's involvement in gliding would continue, but it now represented a much smaller part of the business. How much smaller soon became apparent. For months the company's advertisements offered only gliding instruments and accessories from stock. Sailplane production ceased, and it was uncertain that it would ever begin again.

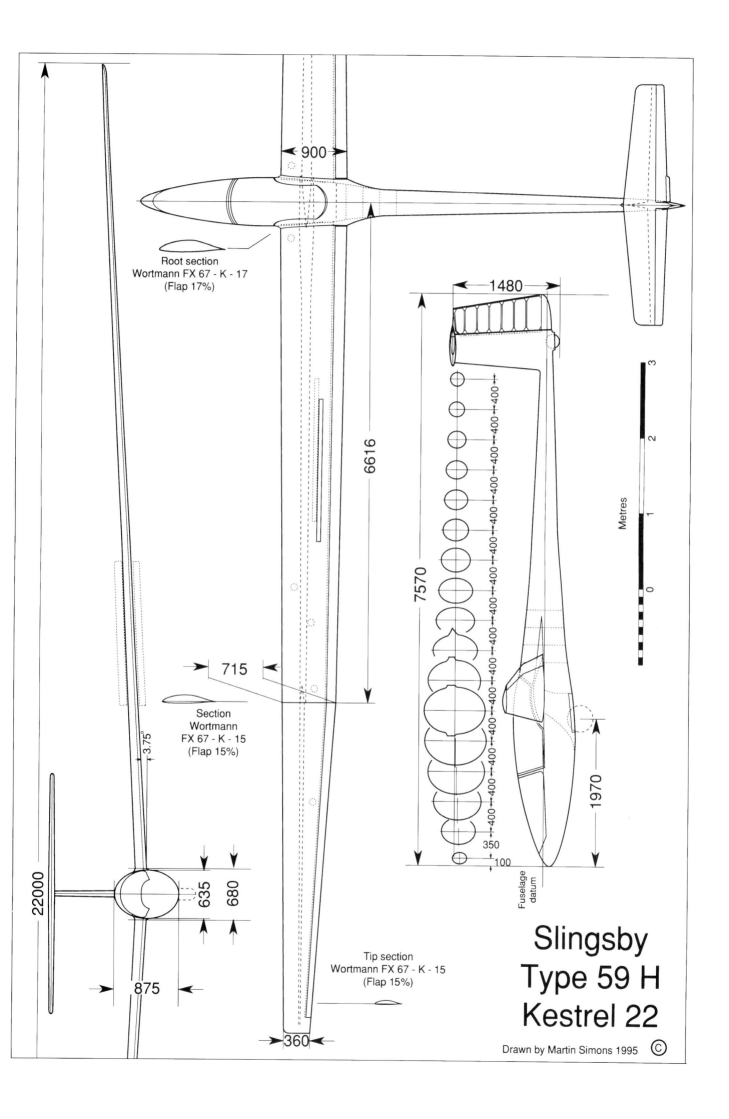

900

Root section
Wortmann FX 67 - K - 17
(Flap 17%)

1480

6616

7570

400

350

100

Metres

715

Section
Wortmann
FX 67 - K - 15
(Flap 15%)

3.75°

1970

Fuselage
datum

22000

635

680

875

Tip section
Wortmann FX 67 - K - 15
(Flap 15%)

360

Slingsby
Type 59 H
Kestrel 22

Drawn by Martin Simons 1995 ©

The first T-59A 17m Kestrel built by Slingsby prepares for take-off with Geoff Bailey-Woods as test pilot. The short canopy, with rear hinge, was introduced by Glasflügel but was changed to the older, long canopy on the Slingsby Kestrel 19. (*G. Bailey-Woods*)

Type 59 Kestrel 17 data

Dimensions

Wingspan	17.00m (55.78ft)
Wing area	11.6m^2 (123.8ft^2)
Aspect ratio	25.1
Length o.a.	6.72m (22ft)

Wing sections

Root	Wortmann FX 67-K-17 (17 per cent flap)
Tip	Wortmann FX 67-K-15 (15 per cent flap)

Weights

Tare	210kg (463lb)
Flying	350kg (772lb)
Ballasted	400kg (882lb)
Wing loading	30.3kg/m^2 (6.2lb/ft^2) to 36.8kg/m^2 (7.54lb/ft^2)

Flap movement: up max 8°, down (normal) 12°, (landing) 35°.

The instrument panel and cockpit of the T-59A, 17m Kestrel. On the left side of the cockpit are the flap and airbrake levers, the canopy latch, ventilator and drogue parachute deploy handle. On the right cockpit wall are the under-carriage retracting handle, seat back adjustment, canopy latch and ventilator. On the central console, left to right are the tow release below the landing flap handle, canopy de-mister and drogue jettison handle, with rudder pedal adjust-ment below. On the stick are the radio transmit button, elevator trimmer and wheel brake. On the seat, hand pumps for inflatable seat cushion. The water ballast tap is behind the pilot's head. (*G. Bailey-Woods*)

T-59D Kestrel 19

Dimensions

Wingspan	19m (55.5ft)
Wing area	12.80m^2 (138.5ft^2)
Aspect ratio	28.2
Length o.a.	6.72m (22ft)
Wing sections, as for T-59	

Weights

Tare	295kg (650lb)
Flying	400kg (880lb)
Ballasted	426kg (940lb)
Wing loading (max)	33kg/m^2 (6.78lb/ft^2)

T-59H Kestrel 22

Dimensions

Wingspan	22m (72.18ft)
Wing area	15.44m^2 (166.2ft^2)
Aspect ratio	31.35
Length o.a.	7.80m (25.6ft)
Wing sections, as for T-59	

Weights

Tare	390kg (860lb)
Flying	559kg (1,232lb)
Ballasted	659kg (1,450lb)
Wing loading (max)	42.65kg/m^2 (8.74lb/ft^2)

George Burton releasing water ballast in the Kestrel 19 at the World Championships at Waikerie in 1974. (*M. Simons*)

The smooth front lines of the Kestrel were designed to preserve the laminar boundary layer as far as possible. (*G. Bailey-Woods*)

Canadian pilot Richard Mamini in a Kestrel 19 landing at the World Championships, Waikerie in 1974 (*M. Simons*)

Wool-tuft tests on the Kestrel 17 revealed serious flow separation on the fuselage and wing roots at low flight speeds. Apart from general turbulence close to the fuselage, the tufts show a definite circular pattern over the wing, extending for about a metre. Pilots could hear the disturbance from the cockpit. At higher airspeeds the problem vanished. (*G. Burton*)

The central fittings of the Kestrel 17, showing the interlocking spars and one of the tubular steel cross-members picking up on the wing roots. The ballast tap and plumbing are also visible. (*M. Simons*)

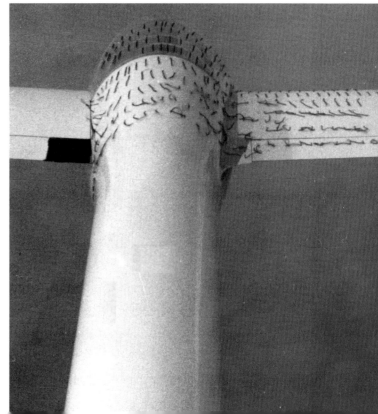

George Burton flying the prototype Slingsby Kestrel 17 with
the new wing root fairings

The Kestrel 19 showing the wing-root fairing developed to
cure the low-speed flow problem. (*M. Simons*)

A Kestrel 19 showing the tray mounted over the wing roots to
carry batteries and barograph. (*M. Simons*)

The Austrian pilot, Hämmerle, won the 19m World Cup in his
Kestrel 19 at Waikerie in 1974. (*M. Simons*)

The Glasflügel 604, a 22m version of the Kestrel, flown by
Bert Zegels at the 1974 World Championships at Waikerie.
(*M. Simons*)

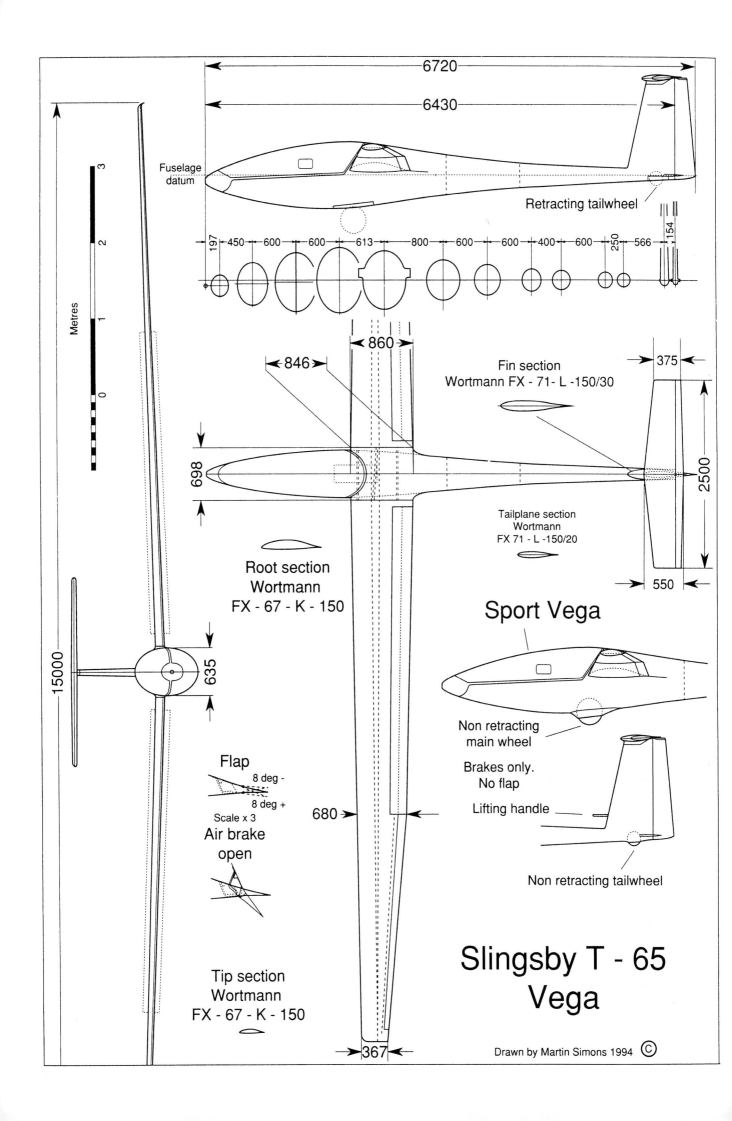

Metres

6720
6430

Fuselage datum

Retracting tailwheel

197 450 600 600 613 800 600 600 400 600 250 566 154

860

846

Fin section
Wortmann FX - 71- L -150/30

375

698

2500

Tailplane section
Wortmann
FX 71 - L -150/20

550

Root section
Wortmann
FX - 67 - K - 150

Sport Vega

15000

635

Non retracting
main wheel

Brakes only.
No flap

Lifting handle

Flap

8 deg -
8 deg +
Scale x 3

Air brake
open

680

Non retracting tailwheel

Tip section
Wortmann
FX - 67 - K - 150

367

Slingsby T - 65 Vega

Drawn by Martin Simons 1994 ©

T-65, Vega

'The Standard Class is dead,' wrote Mogens Petersén, a former chairman of the Danish Gliding Union, late in 1975. Though his opinion proved false in the long run, it was shared by many in the gliding movement at the time. The Standard Class of competition sailplanes had been established by the CIVV (gliding commission of the Fédération Aéronautique Internationale) in the 1950s. The original formula was straightforward. The span was limited to 15m, and there had to be speed-limiting airbrakes, a non-retractable landing wheel, no wing flaps, no water ballast tanks and no complications. The outstanding exemplar was Rudolf Kaiser's design, the Ka 6. No other sailplane since the old Grunau Baby has ever been produced in such quantities.

Bit by bit the rules were eroded. To save drag, undercarriages in some designs were so deeply buried in the belly of the fuselage that they caused poor take-off behaviour and gave inadequate protection from damage in field landings on rough ground. Retracting wheels were safer, caused less drag and were only a little more expensive. The Standard Class specification was changed. Such aircraft as the Standard Libelle and the Standard Cirrus resulted; glass-plastic aircraft with excellent performance, cheaper than the huge Open Class types and very popular. Then water ballast was permitted. Existing sailplanes could be adapted without too much cost, and the advantages in operational flexibility were worthwhile. There were few protests.

The next relaxation came close to destroying the Standard Class concept altogether. It was argued vigorously by some designers that simple trailing-edge flaps that could be lowered to 90°, as used on Richard Schreder's HP-14, were simpler and cheaper than airbrakes. This was true. Housing the usual vertical parallel-ruler type of brakes in the wings created many structural difficulties. Brake boxes and skin discontinuities in the wings created stress concentrations. Opening, closing and locking brakes shut required quite complicated mechanism, and sealing them properly against air leakages when closed was

difficult. When the brakes were open the lift load distribution changed markedly, throwing more load on to the outer wing panels. The CIVV changed the rules again to permit flaps, providing they were not coupled with the ailerons to change the camber across the whole wingspan. The idea was that they should be used only as brakes, but there was no way the Commission could prevent a pilot using the flaps to vary the wing camber in flight, gaining some aerodynamic advantage both in the climb and in high-speed glides.

In the 1974 World Championships, held at Waikerie in Australia, Helmut Reichmann of Germany flew the LS-2 with flaps conforming to the new rules. In this sailplane the ailerons were truncated to a bare minimum, allowing the flaps to extend over most of the span. The rules had nothing to say about this. Handling during the slow phases of take-off and landing verged on dangerous, and the rate of roll was poor, but Reichmann won the championship by a small margin over Ingo Renner in a Standard Cirrus. Ironically, on the 11th and last day, at the start of which Renner was leading, the Cirrus developed a problem with its airbrakes, which would not lock closed properly. This delayed and slowed Renner down enough to let Reichmann and the LS-2 take the title.

It seemed that all of the older Standard Class sailplanes were now uncompetitive. Aspiring champions would have to replace their aircraft with brutes like the LS-2. There were even suggestions that ailerons could be dispensed with altogether, to be replaced by wingtip spoilers for lateral control. Flaps then could extend from root to tip. The whole idea of the Standard Class originally was to produce a safe, practical and relatively inexpensive sailplane with a good enough performance for distance flights and competitions with other aircraft of similar performance. Reichmann himself made the point that the repeated rule changes had done serious harm.

The CIVV thought again. At the delegates' meeting in March 1975 the Standard Class rules were put back to where they had been, but at the same time an entirely new class, the unrestricted 15m or, as it was immediately termed in illogical popular parlance, the Racing Class, was announced. (Illogical because all modern gliding competitions are races.) It was believed that the unrestricted 15m class would become most popular, surpassing even the Open Class in prestige. What might emerge in the way of complications and expensive machinery remained to be seen. The new rules were to take effect after the next World Championships in June 1976.

George Burton was full of enthusiasm for the new class. In the 1976 World Championships he flew the Finnish designed Pik 20 (with flaps as permitted under the 1974 rules) to third place in the Standard Class, and beat many of the large Open Class sailplanes when flying against them on the same courses. He broke the world record for distance over a triangular course with a flight of 720km (446 miles). Immediately after returning from Finland he made a proposal to his chairman, Sir Leonard Redshaw, for the design of a new 15m sailplane using a carbonfibre spar and new combined flap airbrakes which he had outlined in talks with the Glasflügel company the previous year. (This ingenious flap design was incorporated in the Glasflügel Mosquito.) The fuselage would be based on the Kestrel, but without the excessive waisting which had caused so much aerodynamic trouble. Redshaw, now in his last year before retirement, agreed funding of £250,000 for the project. The technical department estimated the aircraft would be ready for test flying within one year.

Slingsby's accordingly announced the Type-65 Vega. Deliveries were promised for June 1977. More capital was invested in tooling than for any other British sailplane, in an effort to keep the labour costs down.

During 1976 a whole new crop of 15m Racing Class sailplanes appeared. They were based on the old breed, often using the same fuselages and tail units but with new wing profiles and flaps, ailerons coupled. The Mosquito and LS-3 (a much more sensible design than the LS-2) were German, and from Finland came the PIK 20D, which had a carbon fibre spar. All of these were available before the end of the year. The ASW 20 from Schleicher came on the market in 1977, and the Grob Speed Astir, the Glaser-Dirks DG 200 and the Schempp-Hirth Mini Nimbus soon followed.

The Slingsby Vega was the first sailplane ever to be designed from the outset for a carbonfibre main wing spar, stronger and stiffer yet lighter than glass. The PIK 20D had inherited a 17 per cent thick wing root from the 20B, so was not taking full advantage of the new material. The Vega wing was 15 per cent thick throughout. The Wortmann profiles were similar to those of the Kestrel and all the other contest sailplanes of the period. Balsa wood was no longer used for the filling of the sandwich skins, having been replaced by plastic foam. There were, of course, flaps with ailerons coupled to vary the camber across the whole span.

For landing, the entire trailing edge inboard of the ailerons, carrying the flaps, pivoted to present nearly vertical airbrake surfaces both above and below the wing. In normal flight the flaps could be moved independently for slow and fast flying. Burton had his own ideas about the mechanism, but had long arguments with the company's technical director and was finally convinced that the loads did not have balanced paths through the structure. An acceptable solution was found but it was complicated and seemed likely to create maintenance problems in the future.

Pilots were used to having two separate levers; one for the flap, another for the brakes. In the Vega one lever operated both controls. In the forward position the flaps could be drooped or raised as required for general flying. For landing, the lever was brought back through a gate and the full brake was available. The system gave some trouble in the prototype and was modified several times. In the final arrangement the flap settings were varied by moving the lever in a rotary sense, a spring-loaded latch holding them in any desired position. For opening the brakes the lever was pulled fully back. From the pilot's viewpoint the system worked well.

An interesting point was that the glass skin on the upper side of the flap-brake was continuous, forming a perfect seal. As the flaps were moved up or down through their range of 8° either side of central, the glass skin adjacent to the hinges flexed. The only visible discontinuity in the wing surface was at the forward edge of the brakes.

Provision was made for 100kg (220lb) of water ballast in plastic bags inside the wings, as had become normal practice. The amount of ballast permitted in the Vega was subsequently increased to 160kg (352lb), about the weight of two extra pilots.

The fuselage front end and cockpit were based closely on the Kestrel. Indeed, the moulds were made from the same plug, but the somewhat too sudden contraction of the cross-section aft was smoothed out, avoiding flow separation. The canopy was in one piece, pivoted at the front and held open, when required, by a gas strut. An inflatable pneumatic seal, pumped up with a small hand bellows after closing the canopy, was provided. The landing wheel was large, also coming from the Kestrel and giving more ground clearance and a higher ground angle of attack than any of the other 15m sailplanes. The fin and T tailplane used the latest rather thick but low-drag symmetrical profiles developed by Wortmann for such applications. The tailplane junction with the fin was particularly neat, a small section of the fin being permanently attached and faired to the tailplane so that there was no gap or leakage at the junction. A neat fairing closed the place at the top of the rudder where, on most other sailplanes, there was an awkward air trap. A little drag was saved by making the tailwheel retractable.

There were many other good features of detail. George Burton wrote and said on many occasions that there could be no vast margin in performance over the rival racing class aircraft, all of which were using similar wings, similar fuselages and of course had the same span. The combined effect of all the small improvements would make the difference. At the same time the cockpit was slightly larger and the tailplane a little greater in area, so the Vega would be more comfortable to sit in for long flights and more stable.

'Vega is cleana', 'safa', 'lighta', a 'betta glida', the advertisements said. Everything about the new sailplane looked good, and about 50 were ordered even before the prototype had flown. Vega was 'a generation ahead of its competitors', or was expected to be so when in production. The first flight took place early in June 1977, the month in which customers had originally been led to expect delivery.

Sir Leonard Redshaw retired and a new chairman took charge of Vickers-Slingsby.

Flight certification had to be completed and a lot remained to be done after the preliminary air tests. At the most forward position of the c.g. elevator authority was lacking. Further modifications of the flap-brake system proved necessary. Burton felt that everything must be completely right before he could deliver sailplanes to waiting customers, but the technical department of the company was greatly preoccupied and there were delays. The first production batch, it was now said, would be ready in the spring of 1978.

Most of the work going on at Vickers-Slingsby at this time was to do with marine engineering. The last of four miniature glass-plastic submarines was approaching completion, a one-man deep-sea diving apparatus was under development, and there was much going on in associated electronics. Equipment for naval minesweepers ranging from washbasins to engine mountings was being made. A gondola for a small airship was built and an order for 15 wooden T-61 (Scheibe Falke) motor-gliders for the ATC was filled.

As a result of a bargain between British Aerospace and the Romanian Government, the BAC One-Eleven airliner was to be built under licence by the ICA aircraft factory at Brasov and motor-gliders and sailplanes produced by ICA were to be sold in the UK. Vickers asked Slingsby to undertake this agency. Although the price was low, the IS-28M2 motor-glider, shown at Farnborough, was not easy to handle in a crosswind take-off and Burton was not impressed. The IS-28 and 29 Brasov all-metal sailplanes proved quite popular and, coming from a state subsidised factory, were offered at a good price on the British market.

The Vega, it seemed, was in danger of being squeezed out of the Slingsby works altogether. In March 1978 there was still only one complete, with a few pre-production fuselage shells waiting for wings and tails. Derek Piggott flew the prototype a few times briefly and reported favourably though cautiously.

The World Championships, held every two years, are important occasions for sailplane manufacturers to demonstrate their wares and to have them thoroughly tested under severe conditions. On the ground, quick rigging and de-rigging after outlandings are necessary, and aerial racing goes on in all the variety of weather conditions that can appear during a couple of weeks.

In July 1978 the great meeting was at Châteauroux in France. The Racing Class contest was won by Helmut Reichmann, flying a very special aircraft from the Brunswick Akaflieg. The SB 11 had huge flaps which not only changed the camber but also increased the total wing area for soaring and retracted entirely for high-speed flight. It was an expensive, heavy aircraft and not easy to fly. It looked as if the rulemakers had once again created a monster. Reichmann himself wrote afterwards that the CIVV needed to think yet again.

The Vega was at last said to be ready, but not for contest flying, and the British team could not use it. The second off the production line was brought to Châteauroux only for demonstration. There were signs of hasty preparation. Unlike the other sailplanes, which had the usual moulded gelcoat exterior, the Vega had an acrylic spray-painted finish. In places there were paint runs that had not been rubbed down, which, whether or not they had any important effect on the boundary layer, did not impress those who inspected the aircraft. The ailerons hinge gap was unsealed. The Vega was flown by a good many people and was well liked on the whole, though the rate of roll was rather less than desirable, the unsealed ailerons feeling rather spongy. It was difficult to assess all-round performance while the competing aircraft were far away on task, but as one of those who tried it remarked, 'with the proverbial ha'porth of tar it should be a very good ship'. For much of the fortnight the Vega was left tied down outside. It was hard to avoid concluding that the Vickers-Slingsby company was not very interested in what happened to it. The Vega was now well over a year late in reaching production and the market was melting away.

Meanwhile, George Burton had taken the first prototype to important competitions at Hahnweide in Germany, and in June, at the invitation of Slingsby's American agent Duane Sprague, he agreed to fly at the US Nationals. Delays in preparing his Vega for this event were such that the sailplane had to be air-freighted to San Francisco. From there, arrangements for Sprague to crew for him having fallen apart, Burton by himself was obliged to tow the glider in its trailer to Ephrata in Washington State. He was further delayed for two days by long arguments with his new company chairman over the transatlantic telephone. Too late for the start of the competition and without a proper crew, he nevertheless flew some of the tasks against the latest German aircraft. On one occasion he beat George Moffatt, the eventual winner in an ASW 20, round a 300km triangle, so the Vega was obviously a good performer, but there was criticism from the knowledgeable Americans of the smoothness and finish of the wings. The good results were attributed to Burton's well recognised skill, not to the Vega.

After these experiences Burton was forced to admit that the Vega was about 3 per cent worse in the glide than the ASW-20 and LS-3. Standards of wing profile accuracy at Kirbymoorside were not yet good enough.

There was no other explanation for the apparent disadvantage in performance, for, as he had said before, there was little difference on paper between any of the Racing Class sailplanes at this time.

Soon after his return to Kirbymoorside, Burton presented the works manager with a copy of the German specification for the waviness of sailplane wing surfaces. His staff apparently knew something that he had not yet been told. The manager bluntly remarked that there was no intention of trying to meet such standards. It was clear that Burton's time at Slingsby was at an end. On 13 September 1978, after a final very brief interview with the chairman, he left the company. Nobody in the gliding movement was very surprised. Burton felt he had been made a scapegoat for production delays and defects in the Vega for which he was not responsible. His position was filled by Jim Tucker, a graduate aeronautical engineer who had joined Slingsby's in 1967, and had been technical director and lately marketing director of the offshore engineering division.

Outstanding orders for the Vega had not been met, but full production began at last and faithful promises of delivery in 1979 seemed likely to be kept. Late in April an open day was held at Slingsby, 'designed to repair the company's reputation with the UK soaring movement, which had become somewhat tattered during the three years of delays and disappointments from when the Vega was first announced'. Three Vegas were made available for flying and 17 had already been delivered to buyers, five of these in the USA. They were coming off the line at the rate of one a week. But, with rather ominous implications, Tucker said: 'as long as our aerospace activities continue to be profitable, there is no cause for winding them up'.

On the same occasion it was announced that there was to be a simplified, cheaper version, the Sport Vega, with flaps deleted and fixed undercarriage. Production capacity for 48 Racing Class and 12 Sport Class Vegas per year existed. A self-launching Vega was also projected. Interest revived, but in mid-1979 there came yet another change of ownership. Vickers at this time had an overdraft of more than £11 million and was under pressure from corporate shareholders to reduce it. Interest in acquiring the Kirbymoorside factory was shown by a company providing diving services to the North Sea oil industry, for whom Slingsby had made submarine equipment. The development costs of the Vega were set off against taxation and the company was sold, to be renamed Slingsby Engineering Ltd.

During 1979 there were competitions in Europe and the USA in which the Vega was able to show its paces. The reports coming from the pilots were not especially enthusiastic. Wally Scott, a former American champion, said he found that the Vega would climb well but lost to the German aircraft in the faster glides, which Burton had admitted a year before. Scott admired many of the smaller features, and it was agreed that the aircraft handled well and was comfortable and very pleasant to fly. Scott concluded: 'The Vega may prove to be the most costly 15m ship of the lot, but . . . it may be well worth it'. It was not at all clear what benefits the customer would gain by paying more. The contemporary German Racing Class sailplanes were also comfortable, handled well and performed slightly better. Scott welcomed the news that more ballast would be permitted in the Vega, which might produce the extra performance needed at high speed, but the fundamental problem of the wing surface accuracy was not addressed.

Very bad news came in August. Baar Selen, a Dutch pilot who had won the Standard Class championship at Châteauroux, entered his new Vega in competitions at Rieti in Italy. Flying at 120kt in moderately calm air, the Vega broke up. Selen used his parachute and escaped unhurt. There followed an intense technical investigation. The stressing calculations were checked and rechecked and Vega wings were subjected to renewed mechanical testing up to the ultimate negative and positive bending and under torsional loads equivalent to flight at 150kt. The first distressing discovery was that a batch of the steel wing root spigots, supplied to Slingsby by a subcontractor, had not been correctly heat treated, and these failed during the tests. All Vegas were grounded until those with faulty steel were found. The spigots were replaced at the expense of the contractor, who admitted liability.

But the spigots were not the cause of Selen's accident. The port wing had broken off about a metre outboard of the fuselage; the carbon spar itself had failed. More testing was done, and many spars were made and loaded without failures. Photographs were taken and eventually published showing a Vega wing on test bent like an archer's bow at full draw without breaking. At the end of all this it was still not entirely clear why the accident happened, although there was a suspicion that the aircraft had been overstressed during earlier stages of the day's racing, flying too fast in rough air. George Burton himself subsequently wondered if the the cause was, after all, wing flutter. The combination of a very stiff carbon spar with more elastic glass skins, as on the Kestrel 22, might have been responsible. More computing at last suggested that some slight reinforcement of the mainspar was sufficient. All existing Vegas were so modified and there was no further trouble.

Such a series of events coming after years of frustrations and delays did not help the Vega's reputation. It was not a cheap sailplane, and it had no measurable advantage, indeed some small deficiency, in performance. Production continued on a very limited scale to satisfy those few orders that had not been cancelled.

The Sport Vega prototype made its first flight in the spring of 1980, and was warmly praised by Derek Piggott after he had flown it. It was, he said, the best thing for many years, a relatively simple aircraft with excellent handling and robust construction, low maintenance costs and with a satisfactory performance for club flying and minor competitions, but there were plenty of rivals in the market for this type of aircraft.

The total of all Vegas and Sport Vegas built was 70. From an accountant's viewpoint, a minimum of 100 might have represented the break-even point. The company now was taking another direction. A further order for 25 T-61E Venture powered gliders came from the ATC, and an agreement was reached for building, under licence, the Fournier RF 6, a French two-seat light aeroplane. This entered production in 1981. Soon it was completely redesigned for fibre-reinforced plastic materials, and as the T-67 Firefly became an out-standingly successful product, in its latest form still in production in 1995 and exported widely. Slingsby Aircraft Ltd, after yet another name change, at last reaped the rewards of the experience gained with the new materials.

In 1982 it was announced that Slingsby was ceasing all glider production. It was not surprising news, although it was very sad. The gliding side of the business had made no profits since the late 1960s. The home market was said to be too small to support a local company in this very specialised business. An influx of cheap gliders from state-owned factories in Eastern Europe was also blamed, but it was not Romanian, Polish or Czechoslovakian manufacturers who captured the international market for high-perfor-mance sailplanes. In the affluent west there were plenty of pilots willing to pay high prices for per-formance gains of one or two percent. It was German factories and young men trained in the Akafliegs of German universities who prevailed, and in 1996 they still do so.

T-65 Vega data

Dimensions

Wingspan	15.00m (49.2ft)
Wing area	10.05m² (108.2ft²)
Aspect ratio	22.4
Length o.a.	6.72m (22ft)
Wing sections	
Root	Wortmann FX 67-K-15 (15 per cent flap)
Tip	Wortmann FX 67-K-15 (15 per cent flap)

Weights

Tare	236kg (520lb)
Flying	331kg (730lb)
Ballasted	508kg (1,120lb)
Wing loading	30.5kg/m² (6.2lb/ft²) to 50.5kg/m² (10.35lb/ft²)

Flap movement: up max. 8°, down (normal) 8°.

Sport Vega

Dimensions
As for Vega but no flaps, no water ballast, non-retract-ing wheel.

Weights

Tare	236kg (520lb)
Flying	354kg (780lb)
Wing loading	35.2kg/m² (7.2lb/ft²)

The Sport Vega cockpit. (*M. Simons*)

Apart from the lively paintwork, representing the constella-tion Lyra, with Vega its brightest member, this photograph shows the lifting handle and non-retracting tailwheel of the Sport Vega. (*M. Simons*)

The Vega prototype in flight. The fuselage was particularly clean, with both main and tailwheels retracted. (*Vickers-Slingsby*)

The Vega at Châteauroux in 1978. (*M. Simons*)

A Sport Vega at Lasham in 1992. (*M. Simons*)

The Vega prototype flown by Derek Piggott

References

Books

Airborne Forces Experimental Establishment Report G48, Departmental Note N. 37

Ash, A., **Gliding in Australia** (Hudson, Melbourne, 1990)

Ashwell Cooke, J. R., **Motorless Flight** (J. Hamilton, London, 1932)

B.G.A. No. 1 Test group, **Handling tests of a Kite 2 glider 10.11.51**

Butler, P., **British Gliders** (Merseyside Aviation Society, 1970, second ed. 1975)

Cumming, M., **The Powerless Ones** (Muller, London, 1966)

Devlin, Gerald M. **Silent Wings** (W. H. Allen, London, 1985)

Ellison, N., **British Gliders and Sailplanes 1922–1970** (A & C. Black, London, 1971)

Flanders, L. H. & Carr, C. F., **Gliding and Motorless Flight** (Pitman, London, 1930)

Geen, F., **The ABC of Gliding** (Allen & Unwin, London, 1952)

Goodyear, H. R. R., **Gliding 1931 Yearbook** (Dorset Gliding Club, 1931)

Heydon, G. A. M., **Flights in NSW with Slingsby Gull** (typescript), 1945.

Lippisch, A., **Ein Dreieck Fliegt** (Motorbuch Verlag, Stuttgart, 1976)

Ministry of Aircraft Production Ref. Non. Res/Acft. 7771/RDT2(d) Specification No. TX8/45

Ministry of Supply **AFEE Report T-65**

Mrazek, J. E., **Fighting Gliders of World War II** (Robert Hale Ltd., London, 1977)

OSTIV **The World's Sailplanes** Vol. 1 1958, Vol. 2 1963

Piggott, Derek, **Delta Papa** (Pelham Books, London, 1977)

Riedel, P. **Über Sonnige Weiten** (Motorbuch, Stuttgart, 1985)

Schweizer, Paul, **Wings Like Eagles,** (Smithsonian Inst. Press, 1988)

Scott, Peter, **The Eye of the Wind** (Hodder & Stoughton, London, 1961)

Simons, M. **The World's Vintage Sailplanes** (Kookaburra, Melbourne, 1986)

Slingsby, F. N. in **The Gliding Book** (Eds Serjeant & Watson, Kaye, London, 1965)

Stamer, F. & Lippisch, A., **Gliding and Sailplaning** (Lane, London, 1930)

Thetford, O, **Aircraft of the Fighting Powers** Vol. VII, Harborough, Leicester, 1946)

Wills, P. A., **On Being a Bird** (Max Parrish, London, 1953)

Welch, Ann, **Happy to Fly** (Murray, London, 1983)

Wood, Alan, **History of the World's Glider Forces** (Patrick Stephens, Northants, 1990)

Wright, L. **The Wooden Sword** (Elek Books, London, 1967)

Periodicals

Aeroplane Monthly
The Aeroplane
Aircraft Engineering
Australian Gliding
Flight
Flight International
Gliding 1950–55, thereafter *Sailplane and Gliding*
Gliding Kiwi
OSTIV Publications
Sailplane and Glider 1931–1955 thereafter *Sailplane and Gliding*
Sailplane and Gliding
Soaring (USA)
Journal of the Royal Aeronautical Society
VGC News

Personal communications

Harry Bache, Geoff Bailey-Woods, G. Bromley, R. Burns, George Burton, D. Carswell, Chris Coxon, Michael Eacock, Anthony Edwards, Peter J. V. Elliott, Norman Ellison, Alan Giles, Ron W. Helm, Harold Holdsworth, Frank G. Irving, Brennig James, R. C. M. King (Ministry of Defence), Peter Layne (NZ GSA), Eoin MacDonald, Ross Macintyre, Robert J. Martin, B. A. Meulbrouck, Alec O'Connor, Derek Piggott, R. Read, Barry Rolfe (BGA), Harry Schneider, the late John Stanley Sproule, G. Terry, Mervyn Waghorn, Peter M. Warren, John Williamson, Christopher Wills.

—